Garrie L. Tufford

PHYSICAL ASPECTS OF
AERIAL
PHOTOGRAPHY

by
G. C. BROCK
M.Sc., F.R.P.S.

DOVER PUBLICATIONS, INC.
NEW YORK

This Dover edition, first published in 1967, is an
unabridged republication wtih minor corrections of
the work first published in 1952 by Longmans,
Green and Co. under the title *Physical Aspects of
Air Photography*. It contains a new Preface by the
author.

Library of Congress Catalog Card Number: 67-18855

Manufactured in the United States of America
Dover Publications, Inc.
180 Varick Street
New York, N. Y. 10014

PREFACE TO THE DOVER EDITION

IT is indeed rewarding that in spite of great advances in the field of aerial photography in recent years, continuing interest in this book, originally published fifteen years ago, should justify its reissue. The original text, which is unchanged apart from the correction of typographical errors, remains valid, though it is necessarily an incomplete account of today's knowledge. Today, when so much stress is laid on micro-image quality, one sees right away that the book lacks an account of the modulation transfer function and associated techniques, which are now widely used in system design and analysis. These concepts were, of course, in their infancy when the book was written, though they are implicit in the account of Selwyn's work on resolving power. The more recent studies of physical evaluation techniques have stressed that resolving power is still valuable (apart from its simplicity) for its inclusion of all components of the photo-optical system, including the human observer. This, of course, gives it both the virtue of significance and the defect of inaccuracy. I venture the rash prophecy that resolving power will remain in use, though less and less as a lens test, long after the newer methods have been developed to their full potential.

Even in the original edition the half-tone illustrations did not always reproduce important subtleties of detail. Since the original photographs are no longer available, the present reproductions have been under a very great handicap. I believe the results are serviceable, however, and still feel that photographic examples are essential to this kind of book.

G. C. BROCK.

Lexington, Massachusetts
January, 1967

PREFACE TO THE FIRST EDITION

THIS book is not an instruction manual; it does not explain how to take air photographs, nor what to do with them when taken. Its aim is to improve their quality by interesting air photographers in the physical aspects of their technique.

The reader will soon discover that I have not set out to write a complete and balanced account of the subject. What I have tried to do is to fill in some of the gaps which my own experience and much discussion with others have shown to be left by the usual instructional courses. Intelligent people who make a serious study of air photography find only too often that the orthodox sources of information tend to dry up just as the problems become interesting in a physical or photochemical sense, and I have tried to keep the flow going at these points, with no more of the readily available knowledge included than is necessary to show what I am talking about. This accounts both for the wide scope of the book and its brief treatment of purely photographic matters.

In serious air photography the value of the result to the user depends on the amount of ground detail it shows, and this often means that the standard of resolution has to be much higher than in ground photography under far more difficult conditions of operation. The use of a miniature camera in ground photography is generally considered to call for a high standard of technique, but in large-scale high-altitude photography the level of resolving power is some ten times higher, and there is small margin for error. The problems encountered in this kind of photography are mostly physical in nature and require to be tackled on physical lines. The results of physical researches have to be put into practice in engineering forms, but this book is not concerned with apparatus as such, and no space is devoted to descriptions of particular pieces of equipment.

The photogrammetric aspects of air photography have been intensively studied over many years and are covered in a very adequate literature; indeed, the newcomer to the subject might be pardoned for thinking that geometry is all-important and that the photography as such calls for little skill or understanding. By dealing with the physical and photographic aspects only, I hope this book will do something to redress the balance.

During the past few years much valuable investigation has been done on the physical aspects of air photography, but it has been published in isolated papers in scientific journals and receives little attention from the general body of those who take and use air photographs. Indeed, much of this work appears to be unknown, or at least uncomprehended, even in the technical circles where it is of the most immediate interest. This book is partly an attempt to make these advances in knowledge more widely known by bringing them together in one volume written from a definite point of view. In doing this I have contributed little or nothing original, but I believe that the information is much more likely to be read and to have some influence on practice if it is all in one place rather than scattered through the literature.

Since the book is primarily aimed at photographers I have devoted some space to relevant parts of elementary physics, but many readers will take this chapter as read. Scientific workers in the field of air photography may also find some interest in the book because it summarises a good deal of the present knowledge of the subject, and references to original papers are included for those who wish to read further. Because this book is written in a semi-popular style I should perhaps explain that I am well aware of the dubious value of some of the technical information published in the more popular photographic press, and I have only used information based on the work of well-known and responsible investigators, or which I know to be correct from personal experience.

Under present conditions there are unavoidable delays in the production of technical books, and an author may well be out of date when his words appear in print. This manuscript was completed in 1949, and certain chapters would have benefited had it been possible to make use of work published since then, but the general approach and conclusions remain unaffected.

With regard to the illustrations, I anticipate that many subtle differences of tone and detail, highly significant in the originals, will be less apparent in the reproductions. Even with these limitations of the half-tone process, however, I feel that photographic examples are essential to a book of this kind.

I should like to make grateful acknowledgment of the work of those investigators whose results I have used, and to acknowledge my great indebtedness to the colleagues with whom I have the good fortune to work at the Royal Aircraft Establishment. My thanks are also due to Professor C. A. Hart, of University College, London; Dr Duncan MacDonald, of Boston University, U.S.A.; and Dr L. E. Howlett, of the National Research Council, Canada, who have made constructive criticisms of various parts of the text.

It should be emphasised that nothing in this book can be taken as expressing or implying official policies or attitudes of the Air Ministry, Ministry of Supply, or any other British Government Department, and that opinions expressed are my own, except where otherwise indicated.

In conclusion, I should like to thank the Chief Scientist, Ministry of Supply, with whose permission publication of this work was possible.

G. C. BROCK.

1952.

CONTENTS

PLATES

(between pages 148 and 149)

1. (A) and (B) Enlargement from typical lens-test negatives, showing Cobb test-objects. (C) Infra-red photograph of typical haze layer with well-marked " top."

2. Comparative photographs showing improvement in lens performance.

3. (A) An extreme example of directional scatter from haze. (B) Low altitude photograph.

4, 5. Comparative photographs on fast and slow panchromatic films.

6, 7. Difference in effective graininess due primarily to differences of subject contrast.

8, 9. Effect of image movement on resolution.

10. Comparative photographs taken over (A) city and (B) country areas.

11. Effect of aircraft altitude on brightness-characteristics of a scene.

12, 13. Haze penetration by different wavelengths of visible light—moderate haze.

14, 15. Haze penetration by different wavelengths of visible light—heavy industrial haze.

16. Comparison of infra-red and panchromatic emulsions.

17. Infra-red reflectance of grass and water.

18, 19. Comparative panchromatic and infra-red photographs.

20, 21. Comparative panchromatic and infra-red photographs.

22, 23. Comparative panchromatic and infra-red photographs.

24, 25. Comparative panchromatic and infra-red photographs.

26, 27. Comparative panchromatic and infra-red photographs.

28, 29. Comparative panchromatic and infra-red photographs.

30, 31, and 32. Laboratory simulation of effects of haze and graininess.

Plate 3 (B) is reproduced by permission of Air Survey Co., London. All other photographs are reproduced by the permission of the Controller of H.M. Stationery Office. Crown Copyright Reserved.

Chapter One

SOME INTRODUCTORY IDEAS

PHOTOGRAPHY has always been distinguished from the older graphic arts by its capacity for a more faithful reproduction of Nature. We speak here of faithful reproduction in the physical sense and not in the artist's sense of creating, by his power of imaginative interpretation, some pattern of tone or colour which is faithful to the general subjective impression conveyed by the original. In the æsthetic sense a good painting can be faithful to its subject without looking particularly like it, but a close physical correspondence with the original is of the very essence of photographic reproduction. Even without colour a good photograph captures more of the essential physical features of a scene than the finest craftsman can record in hours of patient work with the older media. Photography is valuable for the machine-like precision of its drawing, the unbroken continuity of its tonal relationships, and its meticulous rendering of detail. We must admit that the desirability of these attributes and sometimes even their reality are contested by some artists and pictorial photographers, but there are many fields of application for photography as a pure recording medium, and for such purposes the qualities we have mentioned are valuable indeed. We may accept as a legitimate aim for photography the development towards perfection of these powers which mark it off from the older graphic arts. Some such idea has always been accepted by those who have studied the fundamentals of the photographic process. The aim has not always been stated explicitly, but the ideal of better, *i.e.*, more faithful, reproduction has undoubtedly been the underlying stimulus to the major photographic researches of the last hundred years.

A good monochrome photograph has to achieve a certain standard in the accuracy of its geometrical and tonal relationships with the original, and must record details of the smallest size perceptible from the camera station. The study of the geometry of photographs belongs to the sphere of photogrammetry and forms no part of this book, which deals with the factors affecting the reproduction of tone and detail in air photography.

Superficial consideration might suggest that a definition of " perfect " photographic reproduction could readily be formulated, but fuller understanding reveals unexpected obstacles. While it can be seen in a general way that the perfect reproduction should evoke the same stimuli as the original subject, this implies that all such stimuli can be defined and measured, and that for any subject there is a unique combination of them applicable to all observers. Neither of these assumptions is invariably true.

In a limited physical sense we can say that the reproduction is perfect if the ratio of brightness of any two areas of the original scene is the same as in the corresponding areas of the reproduction, and if the relationship

1

holds good down to the smallest areas visible in the original. In other words, tone reproduction must be correct and resolving power good enough to ensure that the tone reproduction is maintained down to the smallest visible details. In much photographic work these requirements can be met fairly well. Correct physical tone reproduction is obtainable over a limited range of brightness which is sufficient for the important details of most subjects, and given a lens of not less than about 4 in. focal length, common photographic materials can record practically all the detail seen by the eye from the position of the camera.

In a physical sense photographic reproduction, therefore, achieves a reasonably high standard, but in the wider sense a perfect physical reproduction is not always adequate, for it does not invariably recreate the stimuli excited by the original scene. Unless the scene is under uniform illumination the eye does not see objects in their true relative brightnesses, objects in shadow always looking brighter than they really are, so that shadows will look too dark in the physically perfect reproduction. Beyond a certain point the conception of photography as a mechanical process automatically turning out perfect tone reproduction has to be abandoned, since human response to brightness stimuli does not follow any simple law. In the reproduction of detail, also, the capacity of the photographic medium is not unlimited. When photographs are viewed under magnification a point is soon reached at which further magnification reveals nothing more ; the limit of resolution has been reached.

The photographic process, therefore, has definite limitations even in the very characteristics which make it so valuable. Success in photography depends to a great extent on the realisation that such limitations exist and that knowledge and care are required by the photographer if the full potentialities of his medium are to be realised. Particular limitations receive a different emphasis according to the nature of the photographic task. In general pictorial and record work none of the special qualities of photography takes precedence, a reasonable balance is required and is generally attained without difficulty. In photogrammetry correct representation of spatial relationships is paramount, good reproduction of detail is desirable, but tone reproduction need be no better than is demanded by the need for recognising important objects. In air photography, although the results are very often used for photogrammetric purposes, there is much to be said for regarding good resolution of detail as the primary if not the most important aim. The absolute level of resolution is nearly always higher, and sometimes very much higher, than in ground photography, but the conditions of operation in the air are directly opposed to the production of clear, sharp photographs, and without constant emphasis on the need for the best possible resolution under all circumstances it will not often be obtained. Tone reproduction as such is relatively unimportant, but the factors which affect it in air photography have highly important if indirect effects on resolving power, and no study of air photography can ignore it. The air photographer should understand the influence of the factors which limit resolution under different conditions of operation, so that his technique can be suited to all types of work. This book is mainly concerned to assist such an understanding; the photogrammetric aspects of air photography are already well covered in other textbooks, and the present volume deals mainly with the physical problems which have to be overcome in obtaining the clearest and sharpest photographs which conditions will allow.

Air photographs in general are characterised by the very small scale on which even the most important objects are reproduced. It is true that large-scale photographs are occasionally taken for special purposes, but we are mainly concerned with the medium or high altitude photographs taken for mapping or military purposes, and which form the overwhelming majority of the total output. Many air photographs are taken from relatively low altitudes for pictorial, record, or news interest, but relatively normal types of equipment and photographic technique will cope adequately with work of this type, and it will not be regarded as air photography for the purposes of this book.

The scale is generally small in air photographs for very good reasons. The use of air photography for economic or military purposes is only justifiable because it can record essential information about a very large area of ground in a very short time, and make the information available for general study on relatively small and convenient pieces of paper. The primary purpose being the recording of as much information as possible at each exposure, and the picture size being limited, it is clearly desirable to photograph at the smallest practicable scale. The scale must not be too small, however, or the limited resolution of the photographic process will interfere with the recognition of important details, and some compromise is always necessary. When there is a conflict between the opposed requirements of a large scale to show ground details as clearly as possible, the need for economy in flying time, and the number of prints to be handled, etc., it is inevitable that the economic factors should win. Scales are always smaller than would be desirable on purely photographic grounds, and the pictures are always viewed under magnification. For example, a common scale in air photographs for topographic mapping is 1 : 30,000; on this scale a road 30 ft. wide is reproduced as a line of nominal width 0·01 in. For military reconnaissance a scale of 1 : 10,000 is often employed. This at once brings out an essential difference between air photography and ground photography. In ground photography we can think in terms of a few principal objects occupying an appreciable area of the picture and containing within themselves many smaller details which are not studied with close attention. In air photography the details *are* the principal objects and they are examined with a magnifier. Under such conditions it is all-important to obtain the highest possible resolving power. The higher the resolution, the smaller the scale at which the photographs will be satisfactory to the mapmaker, the interpreter, the geologist, or whoever has to extract information from them.

Good resolution in air photography is dependent on a large number of factors, and careless work at any stage can jeopardise the success of the complete chain of operations which culminates in the print. A well-designed camera with good optical equipment is obviously the first essential; this has to be properly mounted in the aircraft and well insulated from vibration, and the aircraft must be flown steadily on its course. The exposure must be correct within narrow limits, and the shutter speed adequate to arrest the various movements which might spoil the sharpness of the image. The negative must be properly developed and the print made with care so that as little detail as possible is lost. Above all, the significance of all the interlocking factors involved must be understood, so that the technique can be properly balanced for each of the different tasks that may have to be undertaken.

The equipment used for air photography has to stand up to much more exacting conditions of use than in general ground photography. In the first place, the sheer output of exposures is much greater, typical air cameras turning out five hundred or more exposures per flight, so that the stresses on moving parts are considerable. Vibration, always an enemy to delicate equipment, may sometimes be severe. Air cameras are generally mounted in the floor of the aircraft and receive the full benefit of whatever dirt may be present, besides inevitable knocks and bumps. Temperatures may be very high when the aircraft is parked under a tropical sun, or very low when flying high over cold parts of the world. Under all these difficult conditions the mechanism must suffer no derangement and continue to function satisfactorily for long periods, turning over at the rate of some hundreds of exposures per hour.

The noise, vibration, and physical discomfort at high altitudes are not without effect on the camera operator, and everything possible should be done to ease his task when designing equipment and techniques. Those inclined to minimise this factor might well study an amusing but very realistic account by J. M. Waldram of the difficulties of carrying out technical tasks in aircraft at high altitudes. (1)

All this means that in designing air cameras and training operators the emphasis has been overwhelmingly on the engineering aspects. Flights are expensive, good weather is rare, and the prime requirement is reliability of operation. Nevertheless, on a long view the standard of air photography will only be raised as the physical fundamentals also become widely appreciated and applied, both in designing equipment and in using it.

REFERENCE

1. WALDRAM, J. M. *Discovery*, April 1946.

Chapter Two

LIGHT AND IMAGES

PHOTOGRAPHY is literally " drawing (or writing) with light," and throughout the photographic process there is interaction between light and matter. In the production of a photograph we can broadly distinguish three stages, the emission of light from objects, the collection and focusing of a fraction of this light by the camera lens, and the permanent recording of the image by the sensitive emulsion. This book is primarily concerned with the last stage, but constant reference to the others cannot be avoided. For this reason the present chapter is devoted to a brief and introductory review of some aspects of light and optics which are indispensable for the proper study of photography. For a more detailed study of light in general, of optics, and of colorimetry reference may be made to the standard textbooks. (1, 2)

NATURE AND QUALITIES OF LIGHT

What is light ? Fifty years ago a straightforward answer could probably have been given ; light was a wave motion in the ether. Modern physics would hesitate to say that light *is* anything whatever, but our present purpose will fortunately be satisfied by a non-committal and pragmatic answer. It is sufficient to realise that matter in certain thermal and electrical states emits radiation which can affect other matter at a distance. Some of the properties of such radiant energy can best be described in terms of wave motions, the propagation of different kinds of energy being associated with different wavelengths. The particular wavelengths that interact with our eyes we call light, but otherwise there is no hard and fast distinction between visible light, ultra-violet or infra-red light, or any other kind of radiant energy. The chart in Fig. 1 shows the wavelengths associated with visible light and adjacent regions of the electro-magnetic spectrum, visible radiation lying between the approximate limits of 0·4 and 0·75 microns (1 micron equals 0·001 mm.). White light such as daylight is a mixture of all visible wavelengths in approximately equal proportions, and by passage through a prism or by other suitable optical means it can be dispersed into a spectrum showing all the components in order of wavelength. Such a spectrum exhibits a continuous colour change from violet at the short-wave end through shades of blue, green, yellow, and orange to deep red. The association of colour names with particular bands of wavelengths, as in Fig. 1, is somewhat arbitrary, but gives convenient reference points when precision is unnecessary. Strictly speaking, the colour is associated with the frequency of vibration rather than the wavelength, for the latter is slightly different in different media such as air and glass, but the distinction is not important for our purpose.

5

Natural objects appear coloured because they reflect different wavelengths to a different extent, though white, black, or grey objects reflect all wavelengths equally. A leaf appears green because it reflects green light more

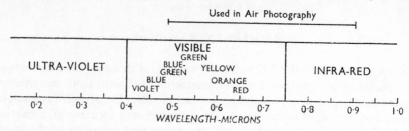

Fig. 1.—Wavelengths in microns of visible and near-visible light.

strongly than blue or red, and although it reflects deep red much more strongly than green the eye is so little sensitive at this end of the spectrum that the predominant colour is green.

The eye is not equally sensitive to all wavelengths of the visible spectrum and requires much less light energy for a given visual response in the green than in the red or violet. The "standard visibility curve" shown in

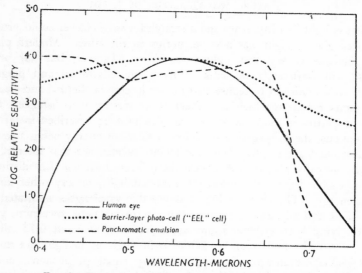

Fig. 2.—Spectral sensitivities of some light-sensitive systems.

Fig. 2 is an expression of the relative sensitivity of the eye at different wavelengths, the ordinates being relative visibility and the abcissæ wavelengths. (Relative visibility is defined as the reciprocal of the relative amount of energy which has to be supplied for a given visual response.) Since the curve tails off gradually at each end, the limits of visibility are bound to be somewhat arbitrary. Spectral sensitivity curves for a panchromatic film of the type used in air photography and for a "barrier layer" photoelectric cell of the type used in exposure meters are also shown in Fig. 2.

Daylight and the light from incandescent artificial sources of radiation, such as tungsten filament lamps, contain all visible wavelengths and are said to have *continuous* spectra. Other artificial light sources such as mercury lamps emit their energy at isolated wavelengths or wave bands. The energy radiated at different wavelengths by continuous-spectrum illuminants is not the same in every case, the whiter sources such as daylight containing approximately equal proportions of all wavelengths, while the yellower, such as electric filament lamps, are deficient in the shorter wavelengths, hence their yellower or more orange colour. The balance of wavelengths in the illuminant is very important in photography on account of the different colour sensitivity of the eye and the sensitive film.

There is a source of radiation known to physicists as a " black body radiator," which has the property of giving a continuous spectrum whose energy distribution depends only on the temperature of the black body, and can be calculated for any temperature. With increasing temperature the total radiation increases and the wavelength of maximum radiation becomes shorter. The energy distribution in daylight and tungsten light approximately follows the laws for black body radiation, and the colour can be matched with great accuracy to that of a black body at some definite temperature. The temperature of the black body which appears to have the same colour as the source under examination is defined as the " colour temperature " of the source. Such temperatures are expressed on the " Absolute " or " Kelvin " Scale of temperatures ; the figures may be converted to degrees centigrade by subtracting 273. Average sunlight has a colour temperature of about 5000° K., average daylight 6500° K., a 100-watt gas-filled tungsten filament lamp 2850° K., and a low-power filament lamp, vacuum type, about 2400° K. The spectral-energy distribution in the visible radiation from a black body at 5400° K., noon sunlight at Washington, D.C., and the light of a tungsten filament lamp at 2360° K., are shown in Fig. 3. The curves have been adjusted so that the relative energies are equal at 0·56 micron, the wavelength of maximum eye sensitivity. It will be seen that the energy is approximately uniform throughout the visible spectrum for the sunlight and the black body radiator at 5000° K., but the electric lamp at 2360° K. radiates most of its energy at the longer wavelengths. About nine-tenths of all the radiation from a tungsten filament lamp is, in fact, in the invisible infra-red region.

The energy distribution in light used for photography may be modified almost at will by use of *light filters* of different colours. Light filters are pieces of transparent coloured glass, dyed gelatine, or other material which absorb some wavelengths more than others ; the flatness and parallelism of the surfaces has to be of a very high standard if no deviation of the transmitted rays is to be caused. White light passing through such a filter emerges deficient in some wavelengths and so acquires a characteristic colour. Thus a yellow filter absorbs blue and violet light, so that the transmitted light is white minus blue-violet, which is a shade of yellow. Similarly a green filter absorbs blue and red light. The total energy is naturally reduced when a beam of light passes through a filter, and the change of energy distribution is not obtained without some loss, *e.g.*, in photography the exposure has to be increased.

The terms " blue," " green," etc., give only a vague idea of the properties of any filter, and to be able to predict their effects we must know the precise fraction of light transmitted at any wavelength. This can be determined with an instrument known as a *spectrophotometer*, and the information is presented concisely in a " spectral transmission curve."

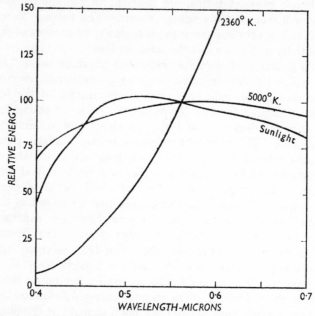

FIG. 3.—Relative energy-distribution in spectra of sunlight: a black body at 5000° K., and tungsten light (2360° K.).

Suppose that the intensity of light incident on a filter at any wavelength is I_0, and that after transmission it is reduced to I. Then the transmission T is defined as

$$T = \frac{I}{I_0}.$$

The *opacity* O is the reciprocal of the transmission, and the *optical density* D is the common logarithm of the opacity.

$$D = \log O = \log \frac{I_0}{I}.$$

The spectral transmission of filters for photography is generally expressed in density units. Curves plotted on a density scale give a clearer picture of the effect of a filter in photographic reproduction, and have the convenient property that the performance of two or more filters in combination can be seen by simply adding the density ordinates at every wavelength.

Transmission or density curves naturally vary a great deal in shape, but can be broadly classified into those with sharp cuts and those which show a gradual change in absorption from wavelength to wavelength. In sharply cutting filters the transition from complete transmission to complete absorption is made as abrupt as possible. Sharpness of cut, if accompanied by complete transmission, is characterised by brilliance of colour. Sharp-cut yellow or red filters are used in air photography to pass as much as possible of the longer wavelengths while excluding the shorter wavelengths completely. Filters of the gradually changing absorption type are used for a variety of purposes, *e.g.*, to convert light at one colour temperature to light at some other colour temperature, to convert the spectral sensitivity of a photo cell effectively to that of the eye, or to counteract the excessive blue-violet response of photographic emulsions. Filters without sharp cuts are pale or degraded in colour. A special case of this is the *neutral density filter*, which is made

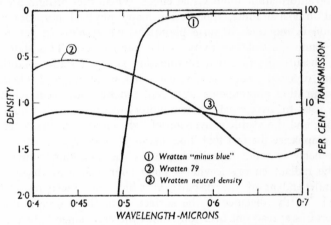

FIG. 4.—Spectral transmission of different kinds of light filters.

from a balanced mixture of dyes or by other means to give a transmission curve having the same density for all wavelengths. Neutral Densities in different depths are used to vary the quantity of light entering an optical system without noticeably affecting its quality. Fig. 4 shows a sharp-cut yellow filter as used in air photography (Wratten Minus Blue), a photometric colour-matching filter (Wratten 79), and a Neutral Density of approximately 1·0. The Minus Blue is clearly a very good approximation to the ideal of complete transmission of the desired wavelengths with a sharp transition to complete exclusion of those not wanted. The Wratten 79 is used to convert tungsten light of 2500° K to approximately the same energy distribution as average sunlight, and hence shows a gradual increase of density towards the longer visible wavelengths. The rise in the deep red is not theoretically correct, and is due to the difficulty of finding dyestuffs which have a suitable absorption of deep red and infra-red while meeting other requirements. The Neutral Density does not give exactly equal absorption for all wavelengths, but the unavoidable deviations from the theoretical straight line have been well balanced out over the spectrum, and the overall colour is substantially neutral.

QUANTITY OF LIGHT

The study of photographic reproduction demands some knowledge of *photometry*, *i.e.*, the science which deals with the measurement of quantity of light. The derivation of photometric units has been handicapped by the fact that although light is a transference of energy and should logically be measured in terms of power, its practical evaluation is nearly always required in terms of the visual stimulus. The fundamental unit of light would express illumination as so many watts per square metre, but the practical system is conceived in terms of standard light sources at specified distances. There is no way of avoiding this difficulty, because the eye does not respond equally to all wavelengths, and a mere specification of power conveys no information about visual effect. Quantities of light are therefore expressed in visual units, though for many physical purposes additional information is required, because photosensitive systems in general do not have the same spectral sensitivity as the human eye. This state of affairs tends to obscure the fact that illumination is not a static condition but a continuing process. For instructional purposes it might be better if the usual illumination photometers were replaced by photo cells whose output could be used to drive small electric motors directly. This would be quite practicable, and the visible conversion of light into mechanical energy would possibly emphasise the fact that illumination is an energy transfer.

Photometry is fundamentally based on the well-known inverse square law. The radiant energy leaving a point source in a given solid angle is clearly independent of the distance at which any receiving surface may be placed. If the distance of the surface from the source is doubled the same energy is spread out over four times the area, since light travels along straight lines. In general the intensity of the illumination, or the flux per unit area, varies inversely as the square of the distance. This is strictly true only for point sources, but if the dimensions of the source are less than one-twentieth of the distance it behaves as a point with sufficient accuracy.

The illumination also depends on the inclination of the receiving surface. In Fig. 5 a pencil of light travelling from a source to the left of the diagram is incident normally on a surface XY on which AB is one side of an elementary area. If the surface is now inclined to X^1Y^1 so that an angle θ is made between the direction of the light and the normal to the surface, it is evident that the amount of radiation originally distributed along AB has now to cover AC, and the new illumination is proportional to AB/AC, *i.e.*, to cos θ. The illumination is at a maximum for normal incidence, and zero for grazing incidence, when cos $\theta = 0$. The full expression of the inverse square law is thus

$$J = \frac{I \cos \theta}{d^2}$$

where J is the illumination, I is the intensity of the source, d its distance and θ the angle between the light rays and the normal to the surface.

There are numerous photometric units, and their relationships and nomenclature are somewhat confusing, but only a few are commonly used in photographic studies. The fundamental unit of luminous flux is the *lumen*, but it is easier to understand the system from the basis of the *candle*

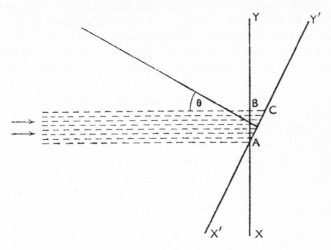

Fig. 5.—The Cosine factor in illumination.

because the concept of luminous intensity is more familiar and easier to grasp than that of total luminous flux.

The *candle*, the unit of luminous intensity, *i.e.*, of flux per unit solid angle, is used to express the relative strengths of light sources. It was originally a literal candle of specified form, but the standard is now maintained by electric lamps or other means. From these, by use of the inverse square law, it is a straightforward matter to obtain convenient levels of luminous intensity in "candle power" and to establish standards of illumination in *foot candles*. The illogically named *foot candle* is the illumination on a surface 1 ft. from a hypothetical point source of one candle power in the direction of the surface. (In some countries the *metre candle* or

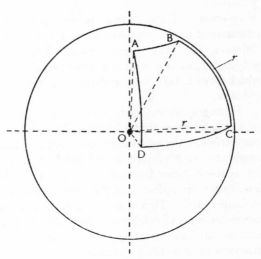

Fig. 6.—Illumination and luminous flux.

lux is the equivalent unit. One foot candle equals 10·76 lux.) The relationship between the candle, foot candle, and lumen can be seen from Fig. 6. A point source O, which radiates uniformly in all directions with a luminous intensity of one candle, is imagined to be at the centre of a sphere of radius r, equal to 1 ft.   Consider the square ABCD, of side 1 ft., on the surface of the sphere.   Every part of ABCD is at the same distance from O, and the light falls normally on every part.   The illumination is therefore uniform all over ABCD at one foot candle.   The total flux incident on ABCD is defined as one lumen, and the total flux from the unit candle at O, *i.e.*, the total flux over the whole surface of the sphere, is therefore 4π lumens.   The foot candle can thus be defined in an alternative way as one lumen per square foot.

Actual light sources never radiate uniformly in all directions, and candle power has to be specified as in a given direction.

The concept of brightness is generally familiar as expressing the amount of light reflected more or less diffusely by a surface exposed to illumination. Brightness can be measured in many different units, but the most commonly used is the *equivalent foot candle*, or *foot lambert*.   This is the brightness of a perfectly white and perfectly diffusing surface exposed to an illumination of one foot candle.   Brightness evidently depends on the reflecting power

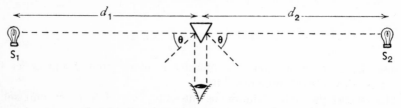

FIG. 7.—Comparison of light sources on the bench.

or *reflectance* of the surface as well as the illumination.   Surfaces such as magnesium oxide are almost perfectly white and are also almost perfect diffusers, *i.e.*, they appear equally bright from any direction.   Ground pot opal glass and white blotting paper are examples of common surfaces which have a very high reflectance (*circa* 80 per cent.), and are also good diffusers.

Photographic exposure meters intended to read the average brightness of scenes are sometimes calibrated in *candles per square foot*; this unit is convertible to the equivalent foot candle by multiplying by π.   The apparent brightness of a surface is independent of its distance from the observer, for as the distance increases the area of the image cast by the eye or other lens system is reduced in the same proportion as the flux arriving at the entrance pupil.   This is not, of course, true for stars or other point sources below the limit of resolution, where all the flux received falls on one element only of the eye or other receiving instrument; here the source becomes fainter with increasing distance.

Measurement of Illumination.—Precise measurements of quantity of light can only be done in the laboratory on an optical bench several feet long, so that the inverse square law can be applied with the requisite accuracy. When the candle power of a source is to be measured, it is set up on the bench and compared with a standard lamp.   Fig. 7 shows the principles of the method.   The two sources are placed on the axis of the bench to right and left on the photometer head, which may be a prism-shaped block of diffusely reflecting material such as plaster of Paris. If I is the candle power of the standard lamp S, it will produce an illumination J_1 on the left-hand face of the photometer head, given by

$$J_1 = \frac{I_1 \cos \theta}{d_1{}^2}.$$

Similarly the unknown lamp S_2 will produce an illumination J_2, given by

$$J_2 = \frac{I_2 \cos \theta}{d_2{}^2}.$$

The unknown lamp is moved along the bench until the eye can detect no difference in brightness between the two halves of the photometer head, indicating that $J_1 = J_2$. It then follows that

$$I_2 = I_1 \cdot \frac{d_2{}^2}{d_1{}^2}.$$

Precise photometry calls for elaborate precautions and is a highly skilled and very lengthy business. In practice the simple type of head shown in Fig. 7 would not be used, as it gives a dark dividing line between the two halves of the field, which greatly reduces accuracy of matching. Details of the accurate procedures of photometry are given in the standard works on the subject (1, 2), and are outside the scope of this book.

It will be clear that the accuracy of visual photometry is ultimately limited by the sensitivity of the eye to small differences of brightness. This *contrast sensitivity* may be approximately defined as the least brightness difference which can be appreciated by the eye, but since this depends on the experimental details of the method of measurement, *e.g.*, the average or " adapting " brightness of the field of view, precise and yet general definition is not possible.

If two adjacent small areas are just distinguishably different when the brightness of one is B and of the other is $B + \triangle B$, the contrast sensitivity, $\triangle B/B$, is approximately 0·02 over a wide range of absolute values of B. For example, if the two areas are located in a uniformly bright field of a brightness of about 100 e.f.c., $\triangle B/B$ is approximately 0·02 for values of B between 25 and 400 e.f.c. This constancy of contrast sensitivity is not merely useful in photometry ; it is also of fundamental importance in photographic tone reproduction. (3) The contrast sensitivity of the photographic emulsion can in principle be made very much greater than that of the eye, but the permissible increase is limited in actual photography by various practical considerations. If the detail of importance is not large relative to the grainy structure of the developed emulsion, however, the photographic contrast sensitivity may become less than that of the eye.

Portable Photometers.—It is often necessary to measure illumination outside the laboratory, *e.g.*, to determine the level of illumination given by lighting installations in photographic studios. For such purposes portable photometers are used. These instruments may be photo-electric or visual in principle. The photo-electric meter consists of a rectifier or self-generating type of photo cell coupled to a micro-ammeter. The cell is laid on the surface where the illumination is to be measured and the scale reading noted. The scales of these instruments are calibrated in visual foot candles against standard lamps on the optical bench; their accuracy is necessarily rather low by laboratory standards, and the British Standard specification for portable photometers allows a tolerance of ± 10 per cent. When using portable visual photometers the illumination is found by measuring the brightness of a surface of known reflecting power placed in the required position.

Measurement of Brightness.—Portable *brightness meters* or telephotometers are used to measure the brightness of surfaces, and inasmuch as the surface is necessarily viewed in a telescopic system of some kind, remoteness or inaccessibility does not constitute a difficulty. These meters can take

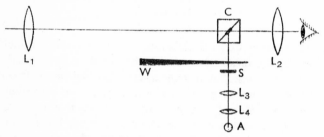

FIG. 8.—Telephotometer optical system.

various forms, but the general principle is always that of matching the brightness of the surface with a small test patch of variable brightness projected into the field of the telescope. The optical system of a typical telephotometer is shown in simplified form in Fig. 8. The lenses L_1 L_2 make up the telescope system, L_1 forming an image of the object at the middle of the photometric cube C, where it is seen inverted on looking through the eye lens L_2. The cube consists of two right-angled glass prisms cemented together along their hypotenuse faces after one of these faces has been silvered over a very small area. This small silvered patch reflects light from the diffusing screen S, which is illuminated by the lamp A and condenser system L_3 and L_4, the rest of the cube transmitting light as though it were a solid block of glass. The patch is in the same plane as the image given by lens L_1, and hence is seen in focus and can be brought into juxtaposition with any part of the subject by moving the whole photo-meter. The brightness of the patch can be matched to that of the surface being measured by moving the neutral density wedge W. (A neutral wedge is a neutral density filter which varies in density at a uniform rate from one end to the other. It can be made by casting a thin wedge-shaped piece of grey gelatine, or by grinding a piece of black glass to a wedge. Neutral wedges are normally long and narrow, but for portable photometers they are often cast in an annular form.) Means are provided for keeping the light output from the lamp constant. In typical commercial photometers, brightness can be measured to an accuracy of ± 10 per cent. on surfaces subtending as little as half a degree at the eye.

Brightness measurement of small areas of the subject is theoretically the most rational basis for estimating photographic exposures, but has not so far been used to any great extent, partly because suitable equipment is expensive and has not been available until fairly recently, and partly for other reasons.

Typical Figures of Illumination and Brightness.—The highest levels of illumination and brightness are ordinarily encountered out-of-doors, though the values naturally vary over an enormous range. The highest level of illumination in full sunshine is of the order of 10,000 foot candles. Observations at Teddington showed that at noon the illumination was above 1000 foot candles on 272 days in the year, and below 500 foot candles on thirty-three days. (4) Indoors the illumination is much lower, being of the order of 20 foot candles in daylight, while 12 foot candles represents a relatively high level for artificial illumination as recommended for work in drawing offices, etc. (4)

The brightness of the earth's surface as seen vertically from aircraft is of the order of 500 equivalent foot candles under full sunshine, but the figure naturally varies according to the nature of the terrain as well as the illumination.

FORMATION OF IMAGES

A point source of light may be regarded as the origin of a system of spherical waves, travelling out into space in all directions. It is a convention in optics to isolate particular portions of the wave fronts and to represent the directions in which they are travelling by straight lines known as *rays*. A group of rays deviating from a point is known as a *pencil*. In practice true point sources do not exist, and light coming from a source of finite size is regarded as a group of pencils, known as a *beam*. The pencils of light emanating from points on an illuminated surface can be converged again to points by passage through a lens, thus forming an image of the surface.

Although the reader will be familiar with the conception of image formation by lenses and with other aspects of photographic optics, it is worth reviewing some basic ideas which will be referred to again in later chapters, and whose significance in air photography and in general photographic practice is rather different. In air photography, if we exclude photogrammetry as a subject in itself, the geometrical aspects of the optics are relatively simple, since questions of depth of focus do not arise, while the aberrational defects of lenses assume unusual importance. The photographic lens is often extolled as a near-perfect instrument whose defects can be ignored. While this outlook has some justification in general photography, the air photographer should always remember that the resolving power of his negative is limited among other things by the lens. The defects of lens and film are in general of the same order of importance, though in wide-angle survey work the lens is often the most serious factor.

The suitability of a lens for a particular task in air photography is judged initially from the three characteristic constants, viz., focal length, relative aperture, and angle of view. The first two of these are always engraved on the lens mount by the manufacturer, but the third, oddly enough, is never specified on the lens itself.

Focal Length.—In optical terminology, *focal length* is primarily defined for the ideal case of a *thin lens*, *i.e.*, a lens giving perfect definition and thin enough for its thickness to be neglected, so that measurements can be made from the plane of symmetry passing through the optical centre and intersecting the axis at right angles. In Fig. 9 a bundle of parallel rays B_1, proceeding from an infinitely distant source, strikes the front surface of the thin lens L and after refraction all the rays pass through one point on

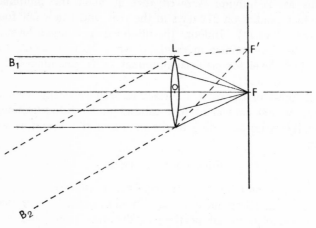

FIG. 9.—Focal length of lens.

the axis. The distance of this point F from the optical centre O of the lens is the focal length, F being one of the *principal foci*. (The other principal focus is situated on the opposite side of the lens, and represents the point of convergence of parallel rays proceeding from right to left of the diagram.) Other bundles of rays, parallel to each other but not to the axis, as at B_2 in the figure, converge to points such as F_1 in the plane containing F and at right angles to the axis. Because of the reversibility of optical paths, light originating at points such as F and F_1 gives rise to bundles of parallel rays which are imaged at infinity. It should be noted that only *point sources* can give *parallel beams*, finite sources give diverging beams even when the source lies in the principal focal plane, though every point of the source gives a bundle of parallel rays.

This conception of focal length cannot be applied directly to actual photographic lenses. A typical lens used for air photography has several components separated in a mount excluding any possibility of measurement in the simple way just described. The focal length of complex lenses can, in fact, be measured directly, as for a thin lens, but it is necessary to take the measurements from certain points known as *Gauss* or *Nodal points*.

These points may be located at any point inside or outside the lens, depending on its construction. The position of the nodal points can be determined without difficulty by use of suitable optical equipment, but in air photography it is more usual to determine the focal length by an indirect method relating intimately to the use which is made of the quantity and which does not require any measurements from the lens itself. The air photographer is chiefly interested in the focal length of his lens because it tells him the scale at which the ground will appear in his negatives, *i.e.*, the ratio of the length of any object in the negative to the length of the original object. The relation between scale and focal length can be appreciated by reference to Fig. 10. The camera, with its axis vertical, is at a height h above the ground,

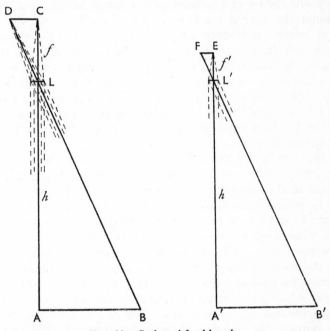

FIG. 10.—Scale and focal length.

h being so great that rays reaching the lens from the ground are effectively parallel. The figure cannot be drawn to a true scale, and the lines LA and LB are broken to suggest the relatively great distance of the object AB. Parallel bundles of rays from A and B converge to a focus at C and D, as suggested by the faint lines, but the geometry is more readily followed by concentrating on the *principal rays* AC and BD which pass undeviated through the centre of the lens. (The principal rays may be regarded as the hypothetical central rays of the bundles.) It is clear from the geometry of the figure that if f is the focal length of the lens in the left-hand diagram, the scale of reproduction is given by $CD/AB = f/H$. Similarly the scale is f/h for the shorter focal length lens shown in the right-hand diagram, and is obviously smaller in this case. The figure has been drawn with A on the optical axis, and unless the lens is free from distortion the simple geometrical relation is only true for rays close to the axis. Focal length can therefore be found without making any measurements from the lens itself, by determining the size of the image of an object of known length, lying in the plane at right angles to the optical axis at a known and considerable distance. It is much more convenient, however, to be able to determine focal lengths in the laboratory, and the method of doing so also follows from Fig. 10. If A is on the optical axis, and AB subtends an angle θ at the lens, then it follows from the figure that $f = CD/\tan \theta$. There is no need to have the distant object if we can replace it by two bundles of parallel rays, one arriving along the lens axis and the other from a direction at a known small angle to the axis. Parallel rays are readily produced in the laboratory with the aid of a *collimator*, *i.e.*, a device having a test target such as an illuminated cross at the focus of a good quality lens. The target is imaged at infinity, and hence will be in sharp focus when photographed with an aircraft camera which is also focused on infinity. To determine focal length, the lens in its camera, focused for infinity, is set up in front of the collimator on an accurate turntable, one photograph is taken with the image of the cross on axis, and a second after the camera has been turned through a known small angle. The length of the image is measured after the negative has been developed, and the focal length is then found from the relation already given.

The focal length of a lens determined in this way, without measurement from any part of the mount, is known as the *equivalent focal length*, *i.e.*, the focal length of the thin lens which from this point of view is equivalent. When very precise measurements have to be made, as in air survey, the lens cannot be assumed to be free from distortion, and the equivalent focal length as determined for rays deviating very little from the axis cannot be used without appreciable error in the outer parts of the field. For survey purposes the lens is calibrated by taking the angular measurements at several points across the field and choosing a mean value, known as the *calibrated focal length*, which gives the best averaged distribution of the errors. The camera designer may require to know the *back focal distance*, *i.e.*, the distance from the vertex of the rear glass of the lens to the focal plane, or the *flange focal distance*, which is the corresponding distance from the mounting flange. Since the nodal points of some lenses, *e.g.*, telephoto types, are outside the mountings, the back and flange focal distances are sometimes very different from the equivalent focal length.

Relative Aperture.—The illumination in the image, which is a matter of great importance in photography, clearly depends on the fraction of the luminous flux emanating from the object point which enters the lens and is finally concentrated in the image point. This flux is the product of the illumination at the lens, which is determined by the subject, and the effective area of the lens aperture, which can be varied at will up to its maximum value by an Iris diaphragm or a series of stops. Although the area of the lens aperture is the factor governing image illumination, apertures are invariably marked in a series of values based on the ratio of the focal length to the diameter of the stop. Thus where f is the focal length and D the stop diameter, the aperture is expressed as f/D, the quotient being defined as the *relative aperture*. A lens of 8 in. focal length and having a stop 1 in. in diameter works at $f/8$. Relative aperture as a guide to exposure is only correct when the lens is focused at infinity, a different relation being required for nearer objects. (5) Since the area of the aperture is proportional to the square of its diameter, and it is desirable for the image illumination to be varied in powers of two, the scale of stops is arranged to increase by square root-of-two steps. Different scales are in use, the two principal being the Continental and that used by Great Britain and America. The two series are given below :—

$f/$No Systems

Continental series . 2·2, 3·2, 4·5, 6·3, 9, 12·5, 18, 25, etc.

British series . . 2, 2·8, 4, 5·6, 8, 11, 16, 22, etc.

Neither system is fully logical, for it is common for lenses to have a maximum aperture in one of the series and all the smaller apertures to be in the other series, *e.g.*, English lenses with a maximum aperture of $f/4·5$ continue with the series 5·6, 8, etc. Indeed the whole system of stop markings is due for overhaul, because the relative aperture is only one of the factors determining image illumination. The situation is complicated in ground photography by the importance of relative aperture in determining depth of focus, but in air photography no such difficulty arises, and there is a clear case for a system which would give a more accurate specification of the real light-gathering power of lenses. Work is in progress to this end.

An accurate determination of the relative aperture of a lens obviously requires an accurate knowledge of the focal length in the first instance. Given this, the effective diameter of the aperture has next to be found. For a simple lens this is the diameter of the stop, but in the case of a complex photographic lens the front glass may well be of greater diameter than the nominal relative aperture would indicate, and the stop diameter may be less. This applies particularly to wide-angle survey lenses, where the designer has provided extra-large diameter front and rear glasses in the effort to avoid vignetting of the aperture by the lens barrel for the extreme off-axis rays.

The effective stop diameter is most readily found by putting a minute point source of light on the axis of the lens at its principal focus, and receiving the emergent beam on a photographic plate. The diameter of the resultant patch of density can be measured, and it will be clear that this is the diameter of the beam of parallel rays from a distant object which just passes through the stop and is effective in image formation.

Angle of View.—A lens will give satisfactory definition and illumination at its focal plane within a circle of definite and limited diameter ; outside that circle the image is not of acceptable quality. The angle subtended at the rear nodal point of the lens by the diameter of this circle is the *angle of view*. The same angle is subtended at the front nodal point by the diameter of the circle of useful coverage on the ground. The angle of view of a camera is the angle subtended in similar fashion by the diagonal of the picture frame, and hence is known if the equivalent focal length of the lens is available. Lenses are generally computed to cover the angle of view determined by the camera with which they are to be used.

The commonest picture size for air cameras used in English-speaking countries is 9×9 in., with 5×5 in. the next most popular. It is common for focal lengths to be in multiples or submultiples of 1 ft., for ease in calculating scales, but this custom is not universal. Six inches is the shortest focal length which is practicable for use with the 9×9 in. camera, the angle of view being just over 90 degrees. Very wide angles such as this are mainly used in topographic surveying, where it is desirable to cover the greatest possible amount of ground at each exposure, but the wide cover is only obtained at the expense of detail resolved, and where detail is all-important, as in military reconnaissance, much narrower angles of view and longer focal lengths are required.

Defects of the Optical Image.—So far we have assumed that the images formed by simple lenses are geometrically perfect, and that the rays diverging

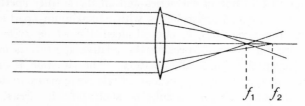

Fig. 11.—Spherical aberration.

from a luminous point can be converged again to a point image. As is well known, simple lenses do not give perfect imagery, except in monochromatic light, over exceedingly small angles of view and at limitingly small apertures. In terms of the wave theory of light, the form of the spherical wave is distorted during refraction by the lens. On the more usual convention, rays diverging from the luminous point do not all converge to a single image point, but to a number of points, depending amongst other things on the position at which they strike the lens. These departures of the rays from their ideal paths are said to be due to the existence of *aberrations* literally " straying from the path." The path in question is, of course, the hypothetical and somewhat arbitrary one prescribed by the requirements for perfect definition ; strictly speaking the aberrant rays are not straying but merely following the only path possible for them in the given circumstances.

Some aberrations are a natural consequence of the spherical form in which lenses have to be made, whilst others arise from the different refractive indices of glass for different wavelengths. The simplest aberration, *spherical aberration*, is illustrated in an exaggerated fashion in Fig. 11. Rays striking the lens close to the axis are focused at a greater distance than those which arrive in the outer zones. It is obvious that there will be no position of sharp focus, a screen placed at f_1 or f_2 receiving a concentrated spot surrounded by a diffuse halo. If the aperture of the lens is limited to a narrow zone around the axis, or a narrow annular zone, sharp focus can be obtained at the expense of illumination in the image. The lens designer can reduce spherical aberration to a relatively small amount, but the fault is always present to some extent, and is more difficult to eliminate in lenses of large aperture, for obvious reasons. Unless spherical aberration is negligible, it follows that there is no unique focus position for a lens. Similar effects arise from other aberrations, and in general the " focus " is a somewhat arbitrary compromise rather than a definite point along the axis.

Chromatic aberration, another of the more elementary aberrations, is due to the fact that a simple lens acts as a prism and deviates light of different wavelengths to a different extent. Thus in Fig. 12 a pencil of white light striking a narrow zone of the simple lens is dispersed, during refraction, into its component wavelengths, which come to a focus at different points along the axis, in order from violet to red, forming a miniature spectrum. Such an image would not give sharp visual or photographic impressions unless the effective range of wavelengths was reduced by use of a very

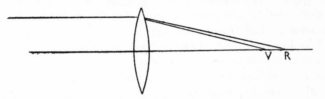

Fig. 12.—Chromatic aberration.

narrow-cut filter, which again would cause serious loss of light. Stopping-down the lens to a very small aperture does not in principle affect this aberration, but in practice the increased depth of focus reduces its effect. The worst effects of chromatic aberration can be avoided by *achromatising* the lens by the combination of positive and negative elements of different glasses. If the negative element is made of a more highly dispersing glass than the positive, it can neutralise the dispersion of the latter while still leaving the combination as a positive lens. This achromatisation can only be fully accomplished for two wavelengths, in the more usual types of lens. In the earliest days of photography it was correctly concluded that blue and yellow-green light should be brought to the same focus, since the eye is most sensitive in the middle region of the spectrum, and the photographic emulsions of those days were only sensitive to blue-violet. There is less justification for this procedure nowadays, because panchromatic emulsions sensitive to all wavelengths are quite generally used. In air photography panchromatic emulsions have been used, in conjunction with strong yellow filters, since 1916 at least, yet such is the influence of tradition that it is only within quite recent years that achromatisation of air camera lenses for blue and yellow has been superseded. The newer lenses are designed to bring green and red light to the same focus, though in fairness to lens designers it must be admitted that imperfect achromatising is only one of many factors which affect the performance of a photographic lens.

The detailed study of the numerous different aberrations and their cure forms part of the science of geometrical optics, and is quite beyond the scope of this book. Lens computation is a highly complicated subject, and the production of a new type of photographic lens requires some months of calculation before any glass is worked. Unfortunately there are limits to what the designer can achieve by use of normal mathematical techniques, spherical surfaces, and glasses of available types. Moreover, excessive complication in the construction of a lens is undesirable, for every additional component means greater expense in production and adds to the loss of light by surface reflections. It is not usually possible to eliminate any of the aberrations; all that can be done is to reduce them and balance them until the patch of light that represents a point is small enough to satisfy the designer's idea of what he is aiming for. Until quite recently there has been little or no information on the effective size of the aberrational patches, the energy distribution within them, and the relation of these things to the kind of definition given in the photograph. Thus photographic lens development has tended to lack precision at certain vital points, in spite of mathematical and manufacturing skill which excites the admiration of the onlooker. The reasons for this state of affairs will be clearer when Chapter Five has been read. Lens designers have achieved quite remarkable results in the face of quite extraordinary difficulties, yet the majority of the lenses used in aircraft cameras are very far from perfect. In general terms, really good definition can only be achieved over relatively narrow angles of view. A telescope lens covering only a degree or so can be made quite free of aberration, a long-focus air camera covering about ten degrees has enough aberration to limit the resolving power even on a fast emulsion, while a wide-angle air survey lens covering some ninety degrees can only be made with very imperfect corrections, and the aberrational blurring of the image is obvious in photographs even under moderate magnification. At any angle of view the sharpness of the image is impaired as the aperture is increased, and for a given design of lens the size of the aberration patches is more or less proportional to the focal length. Since air-camera lenses are usually of much greater focal length than those commonly used on the ground, the effects of imperfect correction are the more obvious. This is emphasised by the fact that the details of air photographs are invariably studied under magnification.

The lens is, of course, only one of the factors affecting photographic definition or resolving power. The optical image has to be received and recorded, and at both of these stages the sensitive emulsion introduces its own defects into the final result. In the past the emulsion has too often been unjustly blamed and regarded as the main drag on photographic resolving power. Modern researches have enabled a juster assessment to be made, and an account of some of this work will be found in Chapter Five.

Illumination in the Image.—From the photographic standpoint, the varying brightnesses in the subject are converted by the camera lens into corresponding levels of illumination at the focal plane. The relation between object brightness and image illumination is in general complex, but is easily derived for the simplest case of an object on the axis of the lens and at a distance very large in comparison with the focal length. In Fig. 13 a small square area of side S is on the optical axis at a distance l from the lens.

FIG. 13.—Illumination in the image.

Since l is taken to be very large in comparison with the focal length f, the image of side s is formed at f from the lens, and its area is given by

$$s^2 = S^2 \frac{f^2}{l^2}.$$

Now the square area may be regarded as a source of light, its candle-power being BS^2 if we measure the brightness B in candles per square foot. The illumination at the front face of the lens must therefore be BS^2/l^2, assuming that S is small relative to l. If the diameter of the circular lens aperture is D, the total flux of light passing through it is

$$\frac{BS^2}{l^2} = \cdot \frac{\pi D^2}{4}.$$

This flux is then distributed over the image area so that the illumination J in the image in foot candles becomes

$$J = \frac{\pi D^2}{4} \cdot \frac{l^2}{f^2 S^2} \cdot \frac{BS^2}{l^2} = \frac{\pi D^2 \cdot B}{4f^2}.$$

Now the relative aperture of the lens is defined as f/D, this being usually written as f/No, so that

$$J = \frac{\pi B}{4f/\text{No}^2}.$$

For ease of illustration we have expressed the brightness in candles per square foot, but where equivalent foot candles (foot lamberts) are used the image illumination is given by

$$J = \frac{B}{4f/\text{No}^2}.$$

So far we have neglected any losses of light due to absorption in the glasses of the lens and reflection at the air-glass interfaces. A single thin lens absorbs very little light, but the complex lenses used in photography, especially in air photography, where the glass elements are often relatively thick, can have quite appreciable absorption. The greatest loss, however, is generally due to the reflections. A single air-glass surface causes a loss by reflection of some 4 per cent. of the incident light, so that the transmission of a single lens is not greater than $(0\cdot96)^2$. A complex lens with, say, eight air-glass surfaces transmits only $(0 \cdot 96)^8$, *i.e.*, just over 72 per cent., of the incident flux, neglecting any absorption. When absorption losses are added the effective transmission will be of the order of $0 \cdot 66$, and the formula must be modified accordingly. Reduction of surface reflections by " coating " the lens elements can eliminate the greater part of this loss. Applying the modified formula to a lens at $f/8$, we find that the illumination in the image is approximately 1/300 of the object brightness in foot lamberts. Thus a ground brightness of 600 foot lamberts, which is typical for the ground seen from above on a sunny day, gives an image illumination of 2 foot candles (about 22 lux) in an air camera used at $f/8$. When the object is not on the lens axis the illumination in the image is reduced. If in Fig. 13 the area S is located at an angle θ to the axis, but is in the same plane as before, its distance from the lens is $1/\cos \theta$ and the illumination at the lens is then correspondingly less. The effective aperture of the lens is reduced by its inclination to the direction of the incident light, and the image illumination is further reduced by the fact that the light strikes the focal plane at the angle θ. It can be shown by a rigorous analysis that for a simple lens, if I is the axial illumination in the image of a uniformly bright area of indefinite extent, then the illumination at any angle is given by $I \cos^4 \theta$. Actual photographic lenses always show a more rapid fall-off in illumination than is indicated by this. In some cases this additional loss is due to *vignetting*, *i.e.*, masking of the lens aperture by the mount, but even a wide-angle lens can be almost free from this trouble if well designed. Even with complete freedom from vignetting, however, the illumination off-axis is usually slightly less than is given by the $\cos^4 \theta$ relationship. The fact that coated lenses approximate more closely to the theoretical relation suggests that the departure may be due to increasing reflections for off-axis rays. It has also been shown that departures from the $\cos^4 \theta$ law can be due to aberrational distortion of the effective aperture of the lens in the outer parts of the field. (6) Fig. 41, page 103, shows the variation in off-axis illumination for lenses of different types. Special measures have to be taken with wide-angle lenses to counteract this fall-off in illumination, but even with lenses of normal angle the unevenness of exposure across the field must be regarded as one of the first obstacles to satisfactorily accurate reproduction of the brightnesses of the subject. Indeed, where very accurate reproduction is essential, it is usual to employ lenses of very narrow angle.

Flare Light.—The light which affects the sensitive film in the camera is made up of two components, the focused rays which form the image, and the rays which arrive at the focal plane from all directions after one or more reflections from the surfaces of the lens components, the blades of the shutter, or the sides of the camera body in a badly designed instrument. This generally reflected or scattered light is sometimes known as "flare light," though originally this term referred to the formation of local concentrations of non-focused light by a faulty lens. Some authorities prefer the term " glare," while others use " non-image-forming light." The latter term is rather clumsy, however, and as "flare" is more widely accepted than "glare," we shall use the former to denote light which is not focused and is more or less uniformly distributed over the focal plane. The light which forms the image proper can most conveniently be called *focused light*.

Until fairly recently it was usual to pay little attention to the flare light ; indeed, its existence was often ignored. As so often happens in photography, the fault can be present to a relatively marked extent before the photographs become useless, and small amounts which cause a minor loss of quality pass unnoticed unless comparative tests are made. In air photography flare is equivalent to an increase in the haziness of the atmosphere, and contributes to the loss of shadow detail, hence it should be kept as low as possible.

There are two main sources of flare light, the first being the lens. Lens flare may arise from reflections and inter-reflections at the glass-air interfaces, from imperfectly blacked parts of the mount or diaphragm leaves, etc., and, above all, from dirty glasses or glass surfaces which have become " ground " by over-zealous cleaning. Surface reflections can, of course, be reduced by anti-reflection coating, but the effects of the best coating are entirely reversed by a thin film of dirt. The second main source of flare is the camera body. This is especially likely if the lens covers a much wider angle of view than is being used, so that the inside of the body or lens cone becomes flooded with light. The trouble can be avoided by making the cone wide enough to give ample clearance to the rays forming the image. Cones which closely follow the path of the focused rays and only just provide clearance at the corners are a fruitful source of flare. Some air survey cameras and some of the more expensive miniature cameras are exceptionally bad offenders in this respect. While a badly designed cone can be improved by fitting baffles or diaphragms to intercept part of the scattered light, the aim should always be to arrange the design so that no light ever falls on a surface whence it can be reflected towards the focal plane.

The evaluation of flare light is not a simple matter, because its effect varies according to the brightness distribution in the subject. Goldberg (7) who seems to have made the first investigations on the problem, was primarily concerned with lenses, and introduced the term " specific brilliance " as a numerical expression for the flare characteristic. His figures were based on measurements of the amount of light scattered into the image of a perfectly black body, *e.g.*, a small hole in a blackened enclosure, surrounded by a uniformly illuminated field of effectively indefinite extent. Using a similar method, Chilton (8) found that some lenses new from the manufacturer and in a perfect state of cleanliness and polish can scatter enough light to give the black body an apparent brightness of 5 per cent. of the surrounding field brightness. Jones and Condit (9) consider that this method of expressing flare is of limited value, since it only gives the magnitude of the flare light for the somewhat artificial conditions of the test. In practical photography subjects are not of uniform brightness, and the effect of the flare light depends on what is being photographed. Nevertheless, some such method as that of Goldberg provides the only means of specifying the flare characteristics of lenses or cameras in such a way that different instruments can be compared on a level basis. K. M. Baird (10) has measured the flare light in a number of aircraft cameras by a method essentially the same as Goldberg's. He finds values ranging between 7 per cent. for a well-designed reconnaissance camera to 23 per cent. for a survey camera with a badly designed cone. In another survey camera with a 6 in. wide-angle lens the flare was reduced from 35 per cent. to 11 per cent. by coating the lens. In general, the flare was greater on axis than at the edge of the picture area.

The effects of flare light on the reproduction of tone and detail will be considered in later chapters.

REFERENCES

1. Hardy and Perrin's "Principles of Optics" (McGraw-Hill) is one of the best general textbooks for the present purpose.
2. "Photometry," by J. T. Walsh (Constable), is the standard British work on its subject.
3. A good account of contrast sensitivity in relation to photography is given in Mees' "Theory of the Photographic Process" (Macmillan), chapter XX. See also "An Introduction to Colour," by R. M. Evans (Wiley, 1948).
4. "The Lighting of Buildings." H.M. Stationery Office, London, 1944, p. 77.
5. A fuller account of the determination of focal length is given in British Standard Specification, No. 1019.
6. GARDNER, IRVINE G. "Validity of the Cosine-power Law of Illumination," *Journ. Research National Bureau Standards (U.S.A.)*, **39**, 213, 1947.
7. GOLDBERG, E. "Der Aufbau des photographischen Bildes" (W. Knapp, Halle, 1922), **81**.
8. CHILTON, L. V. "Light-scatter from Photographic Lenses," *Phot. Journ.*, 1937, p. 381.
9. JONES, L. A., and CONDIT, H. R. "The Brightness Scale of Exterior Scenes and the Computation of Photographic Exposure," *Journ. Opt. Soc. Amer.*, **31**, 651, 1941.
10. BAIRD, K. M. "Veiling Glare in Aerial Photography," *Can. Journ. Res.*, **27**, 4, July 1949.

Chapter Three

PROPERTIES OF NEGATIVE EMULSIONS

THERE are many light-sensitive compounds which can be used to take pictures, but the sensitivity of the silver halide processes, embodying the development of a " latent image " after exposure, is greatly superior to that of all others and they are almost universally used for present-day photography. For air photography in particular, where brief exposures must be given, nothing but the silver bromide emulsion can be used.

The term " emulsion " is a misnomer, according to strict physico-chemical nomenclature, for photographic emulsions are dispersions of silver halide crystals in gelatine. In a fast emulsion as used for taking air photographs the crystals are of the order of one micron in size, and the sensitive film appears opalescent or turbid. In consequence of this opalescence or turbidity, and the presence of the sensitive material of the layer in discrete particles, the developed photographic image has a granular structure which imposes very definite limitations on the size of detail which can be recorded. The size of the silver halide crystals can be varied in manufacture, but in general the sensitivity depends on the size, and fast emulsions cannot be made without relatively large grains of the size just mentioned. Emulsions having grains so small that they appear transparent require about one thousand times as much exposure as the fastest types made.

The fast emulsions used for air photography contain silver bromide with traces of silver iodide and other compounds to enhance their sensitivity. Their high speed, and indeed the speed of all silver emulsions, is intimately connected with the formation of a latent image and the reactions which take place when this is revealed by development. Latent image and development theory is quite outside the scope of this book and should be studied in the standard photographic works of reference. (1)

Most air photographs are made by the negative-positive sequence of operations, mainly on account of the need for turning out numerous copy prints. Negative-positive also offers greater tolerance for errors in exposure than the reversal-to-positive process. This latitude in exposure extends also to processing, and is not an unmixed blessing, for it allows results of a kind to be obtained with careless work. Throughout the photographic process the transition from the best possible result through the merely passable to the unsatisfactory can be very gradual, and it is fatally easy to turn out results which may be usable but fall below the highest quality the process will give. This can be avoided if the photographer is constantly aware of the characteristics and limitations of his materials and uses them to the best advantage.

In air photography the negative is of more than usual importance, for in it are contained the fruits of careful planning and expensive flying hours, and no effort to improve its quality can be too great. It is true that this quality is not always fully utilised, since no print will reveal all the detail present in a good negative, but if the detail is there it can be made available by making two or more prints or by using diapositives, and the best possible negative should always be aimed at.

The negative materials used in air photography have somewhat different properties from those used in most ground photography, and they are handled in very different ways. This chapter discusses the more familiar sensitometric properties of negative emulsions from the standpoint of air photography ; Chapter Four deals with developing technique, and Chapters Five and Six are concerned with the ability of negative emulsions to record fine detail, a matter of paramount importance.

Although the processing of negative emulsions is discussed as a separate subject, it should always be remembered that their properties do not appear until they have been developed, and depend very much on the development technique employed. Whenever emulsions are being compared in this book, it should be understood that they have been processed in precisely the same way, unless otherwise stated.

Intelligent discussion of many of the important properties of negative materials is only possible in sensitometric terms, and the first sections of this chapter are devoted to a short exposition of sensitometric methods. Fuller accounts are given in the larger photographic textbooks, *e.g.*, Reference 1.

PHOTOGRAPHIC SENSITOMETRY

Like so many of the terms used in photography, " sensitometry " lacks precision. Literally it means the measurement of sensitivity, but sensitometric studies give much more information than this, and the subject is best regarded quite broadly as the quantitative study of the reaction of photographic materials to light. A knowledge of sensitometric methods is of vital importance to the technical photographer, because it enables him to substitute some measure of precision for sheer guesswork. There may be no need for sensitometry in pictorial photography, but in a technical application such as air photography the operator who cannot use sensitometric methods, or at the least measure densities, is in much the same position as an engineer who cannot measure lengths.

Units of Exposure and Response.—The first object of sensitometry is to establish the behaviour of the sensitive emulsion on exposure to light, for which it is necessary to have units of exposure and response. " Exposure " is a word used very loosely by photographers, but in the precise sense it is defined as the product of the intensity I of the illumination and the time t for which it acts.

$$E = It.$$

The unit of illumination in sensitometric laboratories has always been the *metre-candle*, even in English-speaking countries where the foot-candle is used in general photometry and illuminating engineering. The actual light sources used as standards evolved via the candle, pentane and acetylene lamps to the familiar tungsten-filament lamp. Since different photographic materials have different spectral sensitivities, however, sensitometry by tungsten light would not be a true guide to the relative exposures required in daylight, which is the illuminant for the majority of photographs. An emulsion sensitive to blue only might need the same exposure in daylight as one sensitive to blue, green, and red, yet the latter would be relatively more sensitive in a comparison made by unfiltered tungsten light. The colour temperature of the standard lamp is therefore raised by use of the so-called " Davis and Gibson " filter, which consists of solutions of copper and nickel salts and is fairly stable and very reproducible. The Seventh International Congress of Photography in 1928 accepted as the standard light source for sensitometry a tungsten lamp calibrated and run at a colour temperature of 2360° K. and screened by a Davis-Gibson filter converting

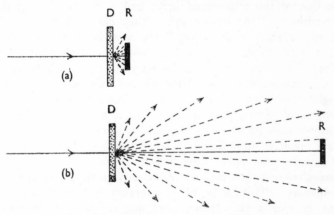

FIG. 14.—(*a*) Diffuse density ; (*b*) specular density.

the radiation to the approximate energy distribution of average noon sunlight at Washington, U.S.A. (2) The colour temperature of this average sunlight is 5400° K. (2) Lamps of other colour temperatures can be used by modifying the composition of the filter. The lamps are calibrated without the filter, and the calibrated candle-power multiplied by the transmission of the filter.

The unit of exposure is therefore the *metre-candle second* of artificial sunlight produced in this standardised way.

The response of the emulsion to sunlight, *i.e.*, the blackening produced after exposure and development, is measured in density units. *Density* has already been defined as the common logarithm of the reciprocal of the transmission ; a density of 0·3 transmits 50 per cent. of the incident light, while a density of 2·0 corresponds to a 1 per cent. transmission. This definition is straightforward for a perfectly transparent substance, but the developed photographic image is a granular deposit which scatters a proportion of the incident light, and the density therefore depends on the geometrical arrangement of the device used to measure the transmission. This will be clear from Fig. 14, where a beam of light incident normally on the photographic material D is scattered during transmission ; at (*a*) the receiver, a photo cell having a plane sensitive surface, collects practically all the light transmitted, but at (*b*) only a part of the scattered light is effective. Whatever means are adopted to measure the ratio of the incident to transmitted light it is clear that arrangement (*b*) will always give a higher density than (*a*). Where most of the transmitted light is effective the density is said to be *diffuse*, and where little or none is effective the density is *specular*. Another difficulty arises from the fact that photographic deposits are not always perfectly neutral in spectral transmission, while the spectral sensitivity of the positive materials on which the negatives are printed is different from that of the eye or the photo cell used for the density measurement. It has been found necessary to issue precisely worded specifications of the different types of density. (3) The type now accepted as standard in Great Britain is " British Standard Diffuse Density," which is based on collimated incident light, total collection of the transmitted light, and a receiver having the same spectral sensitivity as the human eye. Most densities, however, are still measured as " contact opal density," the negative being illuminated by more or less parallel light and opal glass being placed between the negative and receiver ; alternately the negative may be placed on an illuminated opal and the receiver mounted a short distance above it to collect parallel light or light from a cone of small angle. When a heavy opal glass is used these arrangements give almost the same figures as in the standard method, which is only suitable for use in a standardising laboratory, and the differences are of little practical importance. The densities given in this book were measured on a " contact opal " type of densitometer.

Sensitometers.—Sensitometric testing starts with the giving of a graduated series of exposures. This can be done by varying the time while the intensity is constant, or vice versa. If time and intensity were reciprocally interchangeable both methods would give the same result, but all photographic emulsions suffer more or less from *reciprocity failure*, and in general time scales give different results from intensity scales. In most practical photography reciprocity failure has a negligible effect, but it cannot be overlooked in sensitometric testing. Since the emulsion in the camera is exposed for a constant time to a series of different intensities, the sensitometer should do the same, and the time of exposure should be the same in the sensitometer as in the camera. The latter condition cannot always be fulfilled, since the production of accurately reproducible artificial daylight at the requisite intensity of illumination is not easy. In industrial photographic laboratories the testing is arranged to suit the exposure conditions most likely to be encountered in the use of the product, and fast negative materials are usually tested on an intensity scale instrument at an exposure time of about 1/25 sec. Air-film emulsions are often tested at the same time of exposure, but the practice is not altogether logical, for the reciprocity failure between 1/25 and 1/300 sec., which is a common exposure time in air photography, is equivalent to a difference of sensitivity of about 50 per cent. in certain cases. Since the reciprocity failure is not necessarily the same for all fast emulsions there is a possibility that emulsions graded in one order of sensitivity by sensitometric test might be in a different order in practical air photography. No trouble of this kind seems to have been encountered so far, due no doubt to the fact that there is a general similarity between the reciprocity characteristics of the faster emulsions.

The scale of intensities in a sensitometer is usually obtained by means of a *step wedge*, which is a series of strips of neutral density filter arranged in ascending order of density, the density increment from each step to the next commonly being 0·15, so that the exposure is varied by a factor of $\sqrt{2}$. The step wedge is not entirely satisfactory, since the filter material is never perfectly neutral and even the most generally satisfactory type, the photographic silver deposit, is not absolutely stable. For precise work the density actually effective in exposing on the type of emulsion being tested has to be determined by calibration on the optical bench. In some sensitometers the intensity scale is made to vary continuously instead of by steps, using a continuous wedge.

If sensitometric results are to be related to some practical condition the exposed strips must be developed in the same type of developer as will be used for the practical operation. The time, temperature, and degree of agitation of the solution must be very carefully controlled, or the results will not be reproducible. The precision required varies with the nature of the experiments, but the temperature should not normally be allowed to vary by more than 0·2 of a degree Fahrenheit.

Densitometers.—Densitometers have been made in various forms, ranging from the simple visual types to very complex electronic constructions. Those in common use do not give an absolute density measurement, all referring the density of the sample to a sub-standard such as a wedge or relying on some characteristic of the amplifier in electronic types. In some models a beam of light is made to pass alternately through the sample and through a part of a continuous wedge ; the wedge is moved until equality of density is obtained as judged by the equality of the currents given by a photo cell. In others the light passes successively through the comparison wedge and the sample ; with no sample in position the dense end of the wedge is in use and the instrument is balanced so that the light transmitted is equal to a standard reference brightness ; the sample is then inserted and the wedge moved until balance is restored, when the change in density of the wedge gives the density of the sample. Either visual or electronic means may be used to determine the balance point in this case. More elaborate electronic densitometers eliminate the rather unsatisfactory wedge and pass the output from a photo cell to an amplifier having a logarithmic response, or to a linear amplifier followed by a galvanometer with a logarithmic response. In such.devices, however, the onus for permanency and accuracy is merely transferred from the wedge to the amplifier.

The most generally useful densitometer for air photography, where relatively few readings have to be taken, is the " Capstaff Purdy," a simple visual instrument of the subtracting density type made by the Kodak Company. It has the advantage of measuring a small circle, some half millimetre in diameter, so that the density of individual image areas of the negative can be measured. Visual densitometers are very tiring, however, when numerous readings have to be made in succession, and photo-electric types are always used in testing laboratories where much sensitometry is done.

The Characteristic Curve.—When a photographic emulsion is exposed in a sensitometer and the densities obtained after development are plotted against the logarithms of the exposure, a curve of the general form shown in Fig. 15 is produced. This is the so-called " characteristic curve," which is strictly speaking " characteristic " only for that piece of coated film exposed under the precise test conditions and developed in the particular way of the experiment. The use of the curve to represent the behaviour of the emulsion under other conditions of exposure and development, even when these are nominally the same, or to represent the behaviour of different batches of the same brand of emulsion, is an approximation which must always be made with caution. With this reservation, the characteristic curve is a complete statement of the behaviour of the emulsion, and its value to the photographer can hardly be over-estimated.

Different characteristic curves are given by different emulsions and by the same emulsion under different processing conditions, but certain similarities appear in all of them and can be discussed by reference to a typical curve such as that in Fig. 15. Starting from the left-hand side, the curve continues for a short distance parallel to the log exposure axis at a small density known as the " fog." This is the region in which the exposing light has been too weak to produce any effect, and the fog is of chemical origin. Fog should not exceed a density of 0·3 in fast air-film emulsions which have been fully developed but not over-developed. The transparent film base also has a slight density, but this is usually about 0·02, except in the case of anti-halation backed films, when it will be of the order of 0·3. Base density is not usually shown, as it has no effect on reproduction.

With increasing exposure the curve begins to rise and the slope increases, eventually reaching a maximum value at which it remains constant during a further substantial increase in the exposure. Eventually the slope begins to decrease again and finally reaches zero once more. The lower and upper curved parts of the characteristic are known respectively as the " toe " and " shoulder." It was formerly thought desirable to have all the negative densities on the straight line, thus maintaining a linear relationship between the logs of the image brightness and the corresponding densities, and for this reason the straight line was called the " region of correct exposure " and the toe was known as the " region of under exposure." It is now recognised that for most photographic purposes there is no special need for " straight-line " negatives, perfectly satisfactory pictures being obtained by working partly on the toe. In some specialised applications, however, high-altitude air photography being one, it is desirable to work on the straight line as far as reasonably possible.

The chief value of the characteristic curve, as already pointed out, lies in the fact that it is a complete statement of the performance of the emulsion under the test conditions, but it is often convenient to have numerical data to express certain aspects of this performance in a more concise way. The most frequently used constants derived from the characteristic curve are speed, gamma, latitude, and fog.

Speed.—The use of the word " speed " to express the sensitivity of an emulsion to light is particularly unfortunate in connection with air photography, where the same word has at least two other meanings in common use. Nevertheless it is so firmly entrenched in the general photographic literature that its use must be continued ; the meaning should always be clear from the context.

Speed can be defined in a general way as the reciprocal of the exposure required to bring the emulsion to some chosen point on the characteristic curve, such that an acceptable photograph is obtained when the darkest tone of the subject is reproduced at that point. There has been very great difficulty in agreeing on a suitable point, mainly because of the fact that good reproduction can be obtained without all the tones of the subject lying on the straight line. If all emulsions gave the same shape of characteristic curve this would be no obstacle, and a simple statement of the exposure required to reach some small density above the fog level would suffice. Unfortunately, emulsions vary greatly in contrast, in the shape of the toe part of the characteristic curve, and in the ratio of the length of the toe to the length of the straight line, thus making any simple definition of speed extremely difficult. One thing is certain, however, namely that from a tone reproduction point of view speed has nothing to do with density as such, but must be closely related to *gradient*, and there must be a point of minimum useful gradient somewhere on the toe of the curve. Moreover, since negatives are printed on papers of different contrasts, the minimum useful gradient cannot be a constant figure but may be expected rather to be a constant fraction of the average gradient of the portion of the characteristic curve used to record the brightness range of the subject. From such considerations Jones (4) developed the " fractional gradient " criterion of speed, which is now widely accepted for general photographic use. Readers interested in this subject are advised to study in the original papers the lengthy and painstaking investigations which led to the adoption of this method of defining speed.

The fractional gradient criterion defines speed as the reciprocal exposure required to produce a certain gradient G which is $0 \cdot 3$ of the average gradient $\bar{G}$ of the characteristic curve between the point where G is measured and a second point which has received an exposure greater by $1 \cdot 5$ log units. Thus the minimum gradient used in recording a subject whose brightness range is 32 to 1 is not less than $0 \cdot 3$ of the average gradient over the whole subject range. This criterion is essentially a statement in sensitometric terms of the statistically determined result that if negatives are exposed to points on their characteristic curves defined in this way they yield prints (on suitable papers) which most people will accept as satisfactory. The 32 to 1 brightness range is a fairly representative figure for the types of subject encountered in ground photography, but it is much greater than the range of high-altitude views, and on that account the fractional gradient criterion is not necessarily the best for air photography.

In Fig. 15 the point on the toe of the characteristic curve where the speed is measured on the fractional gradient criterion has been marked as $0 \cdot 3\overline{G}$; the density at this point is 0·04 above fog and the gradient is 0·3, while the average gradient over a subject range of 32 to 1 is 1·0, which is fairly satisfactory for low-altitude air photography. In high-altitude photography, however, the average brightness range is about 5·5 to 1 ; if this is recorded on the curve in Fig. 15 at a minimum density of 0·04 above fog the average gradient is only 0·65, and the contrast is inadequate. While a sufficiently contrasty print could probably be obtained by use of a suitable printing paper, there is no reserve of contrast to cope with very hazy conditions,

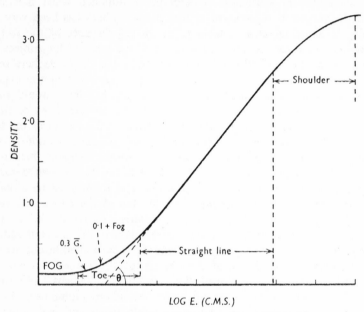

LOG E. (C.M.S.)

Fig. 15.—Typical characteristic curve of negative emulsion.

and it is much better to expose so that most or all of the negative densities lie on the straight line. For this reason the Jones fractional gradient speed criterion is not ideal for use in air photography. It might be possible to derive a more satisfactory criterion based on the average brightness range of high-altitude views, but there is little point in pursuing this because a more logical criterion has been suggested. Jones derived his speed criterion from the consideration that the aim of photography is to produce good prints, i.e., prints which are tonally satisfactory. Howlett (5) with equal logic, points out that the aim of air photography is to record the maximum amount of fine detail, and that the " speeds " of negative emulsions should be expressed on a scale where they are proportional to the reciprocal exposures required to give maximum resolving power. This has the advantage that the speed is then a unique characteristic of the negative, for it is one of the fundamentals of photographic resolving power that the

negative resolution cannot be increased in printing. Satisfactory prints can
be obtained, on printing papers of suitable contrast, from portions of negative
characteristic curves of widely differing gradients, but nothing that can
be done in printing will make any substantial increase in the negative
resolution. There is thus a very good case for measuring speed at the point
where the emulsion reaches its maximum resolving power.

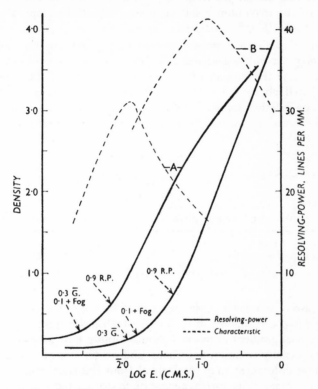

Fig. 16.—Characteristic and resolving power curves for
two different emulsions.

Although the principle of measuring speed at a fixed density, *e.g.*, at 0·1
above the fog density, as proposed in the original German Din system,
is theoretically unsound, it is the easiest of all methods to use, and can be
quite satisfactory when comparing emulsions whose characteristic curves
are of basically similar shape, and particularly in any manufacturing or
production application when the control of speed in different batches of
the same emulsion is required. For these reasons it is very widely applied
as a working measure of speed, while the fractional gradient or resolving
power criterion is recognised as the true standard.

The use of the resolving power speed criterion and some contrasts with
other criteria can be illustrated by reference to Fig. 16, where characteristic
curves are given for two emulsions A and B, of which A is obviously the
faster on any criterion. The broken lines are the curves for resolving power

against log exposure. They were determined by making series of exposures on to the emulsions through a contact test object with a contrast ratio of about 2 to 1, and plotting the resolving powers found after development against the logs of the mean exposures given through the light and dark parts of the test object. The point of maximum resolving power on curves such as these is not always easy to locate with precision, and Howlett suggests that the speed should for preference be measured at the exposure corresponding to 0·9 of the maximum resolving power, where the slope of the curve is much steeper. The characteristic curves have been marked at the points corresponding to 0·9 of maximum resolving power, $0.3\overline{G}$, and density of 0·1 plus fog. It will be seen that the maximum resolving power is obtained at a density near the bottom of the straight line part of the characteristic curve, and well above the points where speed is measured on the other criteria. The relative speeds of the two emulsions on the three criteria, expressed in terms of emulsion A as 100 per cent. on each criterion, are given in Table 1.

TABLE 1

Emulsion.	Relative Speed.		
	0·1 + Fog.	Fractional Gradient.	0·9 Maximum Resolving Power.
A	100	100	100
B	19	25	16

In the case of emulsion A the point of $0.3\overline{G}$ coincides with the density of 0·1 above fog, but this is not so for B, which has a relatively longer toe. On the fractional gradient criterion B would require four times the exposure of A, on the density criterion five times, and on the resolution criterion six times. These differences may seem small from the standpoint of practical photography, where it is rarely necessary to vary exposure by a smaller factor than two to one, but sensitometric figures should have the greatest possible significance as well as the highest precision, and there can be no doubt that the resolution criterion of speed is highly desirable, even on the limited evidence which has just been presented. In general, the maximum resolving power for any emulsion is reached near the bottom of the straight line, which means that from the point of view of air photography the fractional gradient criterion gives artificially high speeds to " long-toe " emulsions ; this is avoided by the use of the resolution criterion.

At the time of writing there is no internationally agreed standard method of specifying the speeds of emulsions for use in air photography, though speeds are often specified on the Weston scale. The high-speed panchromatic emulsions most commonly used have a Weston speed of 100 ; in terms of physical units they require an exposure of the order of 0·01 metre candle second to yield a density of about 1·0 above fog, which is usually the density of maximum resolving power and hence the mean density in correctly exposed high-altitude negatives. In terms of the "British Standard Specification for the speed and exposure index of a snapshot material," their speed is about twenty-nine degrees, but air negatives are usually developed much more fully than a snapshot material and the effective speed is accordingly greater, approximately thirty-three degrees on the same scale.

Latitude.—In broad terms *latitude* is the range of exposures which can be given while still retaining an acceptable standard of reproduction. Latitude therefore depends on the brightness scale of the subject and standard of acceptability adopted. In ground photography a photograph is judged primarily on the quality of its tone reproduction, and is accepted or rejected on somewhat arbitrary standards, which nevertheless command a reasonable measure of agreement among different observers. Reproduction which is generally agreed to be good can be obtained by working on the toe of the characteristic curve down to the point fixed by the "fractional gradient" criterion of speed determination, and from this point over the whole length of the characteristic curve up to an analogous point on the shoulder the reproduction can in principle be equally good. The difference in log exposure between the upper and lower limiting points is the "useful exposure scale." The difference between the useful exposure scale and the log brightness scale of the subject is the exposure latitude. In emulsions of good quality, developed to a low gamma as in ground photography, the useful exposure scale is not usually less than 2·5, and the log brightness scale as imaged in the camera is of the order of 1·5, so that the exposure latitude is of the order of 10 to 1, *i.e.*, up to ten times the minimum exposure can be given without loss of quality. Many negative emulsions have even greater latitude, but this refers to tone reproduction quality only, and when the graininess of the image is an important factor the effective latitude is much less than these figures would suggest.

In air photography the resolution of fine detail is of paramount importance, and this imposes a greater restriction on exposure latitude than any considerations of tone reproduction quality. In Fig. 17 the characteristic curve of an emulsion used for air photography has been drawn, while the curve above it shows the variation of resolving power with log exposure. Since the latter curve passes through a maximum it follows that, strictly speaking, there can be no latitude for any subject however short its brightness scale, while the resolving power must vary throughout the tones of any subject with a brightness scale of appreciable length. In these circumstances any definition of exposure latitude must be somewhat arbitrary, because no two people are likely to have the same ideas on the tolerable departure from maximum resolving power. One possible standard is to assume that the levels of resolving power in the negative must not fall below 80 per cent. of the maximum at any point; in Fig. 17 the useful exposure scale for the negative emulsion defined in this way is about 1·25, and since the average log brightness scale for high-altitude views is 0·75, the exposure latitude is about 0·5, say, three to one. In spite of the shorter brightness scale of aerial views, the exposure latitude is therefore less than in ground photography.

It should perhaps be emphasised that exposure latitude is determined by the shape of the characteristic and resolving power curves and by nothing mysterious in the " quality " of the emulsion. Given a characteristic curve having a long enough straight-line portion, or curved portions of adequate gradient, there is no limit to exposure latitude for satisfactory tone reproduction other than the inconvenience of using very high negative densities. This leads to the point that good latitude is incompatible with a high gamma, for with gammas much greater than unity density builds up very rapidly

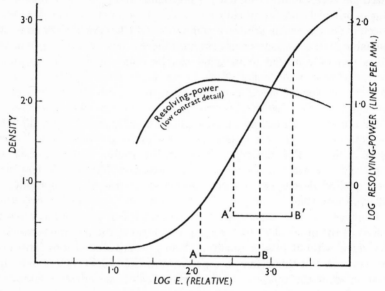

Fig. 17.—Exposure latitude in relation to characteristic and resolving power curves.

with relatively slight errors of over-exposure. For this reason alone the exposure latitude would be small in air photography, but the need for good resolving power makes it smaller still.

Gamma.—The contrast-rendering power of an emulsion, usually called its " contrast," is measured by the *gamma,* or slope (tan θ in Fig. 15) of the straight-line part of the characteristic curve. This is a matter of convenience, since the straight line is the only part of the curve where the slope can be defined by a simple number. · It often happens, however, that the shape of the characteristic curve is such that part or most of the negative density range lies on the curved toe portion. In such cases gamma is obviously not a reliable guide to contrast, and all that can be done is to specify the mean slope of the curve between the limiting densities in the negative. This may seem obvious, but it is not at all unusual to find contrast defined by gamma in negatives where none of the densities are on the straight line.

The optimum gamma for negative emulsions to be used in high-altitude air photography is about 1·3, but at low altitudes a gamma of unity or rather less, as in ground photography, is preferable.

Fog.—A small fog density is unavoidable in fast emulsions, especially when they are fully developed as in air photography. The effect of excessive fog is to raise the general density and hence the graininess of the image, and to reduce the contrast in the darker tones of the subject. The limits of tolerable fog are difficult to define with any precision, because there is no sharp boundary between good and bad results where fog is correspondingly low or high. Excluding fog due to stale or badly stored emulsions, accidental exposure to light, faulty chemicals, etc., the fog density will vary with the degree of development. The fast emulsions now generally used in air photography only reach their maximum speed if developed to a point where fog is of the order of 0·2. This is only a rough guide, but it can be a very useful one. If a negative has a fog between 0·1 and 0·2 the development has been correct for maximum speed, if below 0·1 the negative is under-developed, and if above 0·3 the fog is excessive. It will be observed that these fog values are greater than is considered tolerable for ground photography.

Colour Sensitivity.—The silver halides used in all negative emulsions are basically sensitive only to blue, violet, and ultra-violet light, the precise limits of sensitivity depending on the particular halides and the exposure which can be given. Fast emulsions made up with gelatine and silver halides only are sensitive from the violet to the edge of the blue-green in the visible spectrum. The general sensitisers such as sulphur compounds added to raise the white-light speed do not affect the spectral sensitivity, but sensitivity to the longer visible wavelengths is conferred by adding small proportions of certain rather fugitive dyes. The dyes are not in solution and acting as light filters, but are adsorbed to, or loosely combined with, the silver salts. Their colours are roughly complementary to the spectral region for which the emulsion is made sensitive, so that a red sensitiser absorbs red light and looks green. In some way the emulsion is able to make use of the energy absorbed by the dyestuff in a region where it does not itself absorb, and so its sensitivity is effectively extended to longer wavelengths. Emulsions sensitised to the green and yellow are known as " orthochromatic," while the term " panchromatic " is applied to emulsions which are continuously sensitive from the violet end to the orange-red or further. Few if any panchromatic emulsions now in use have any appreciable sensitivity to the deep-red end of the spectrum ; it is quite possible to sensitise for this region, but there would be little point in doing so for ordinary photography, where the broad aim is to give the emulsion the same spectral sensitivity as the eye. Outstanding advances in colour sensitising have been made by emulsion manufacturers over the last twenty years or so, and although red-sensitive plates were available for air photography as far back as 1914 they were greatly inferior to the modern emulsions in the ratio of the added sensitivity to the total sensitivity.

The panchromatic emulsions now used for air photography are sensitive with remarkable uniformity from the violet end of the visible spectrum to the red at about 0·65 micron. The " sensitivity " here referred to is the true sensitivity as measured on an equal-energy spectrum. Wedge

spectrograms made to tungsten light can give a misleading impression of
sensitivity to the longer visible wavelengths, since the light source radiates
so much more energy at the red end of the spectrum than at the blue end.
Artificial daylight gives a closer approximation to the true sensitivity, but
it is still necessary to correct for non-neutrality in the absorbing wedge.
Expression of the true sensitivity is further complicated by the fact that
most emulsions give differently shaped characteristic curves at different
wavelengths, so that any statement of spectral sensitivity must be to a
certain extent based on arbitrary definitions. Some manufacturers publish
true spectral-sensitivity curves for their products, with a statement of the
exact method of defining the sensitivity ; a curve of this kind relating to
Kodak " Aerographic Super XX " is reproduced in Fig. 18. The spectral

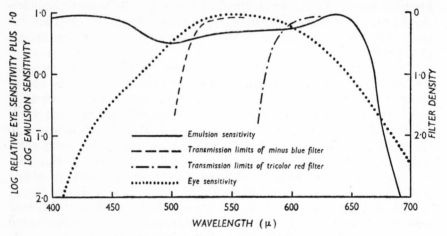

FIG. 18.—Spectral sensitivity of " Super XX Aero " film.

sensitivity in this case is defined as the reciprocal exposure in ergs per
square centimetre required to produce a density of 1·0 on development for
five minutes at 18° C. in D19b. Considering the spectrum as divided into
three parts, the red and blue sensitivities are about equal while the green
sensitivity is lower, nearly twice as much exposure being required at
0·5 micron as at 0·64 micron to produce the constant density of 1·0.

The spectral sensitivity of the panchromatic emulsion shown in Fig. 18
is obviously very different from that of the human eye. In general
photography it is usually desirable to have approximately the same visual
and photographic sensitivities, and panchromatic emulsions for general
use are therefore given a lower red sensitivity than that shown here, so that
by weakening the effective blue sensitivity with a pale yellow filter on the
lens the greatest response is obtained somewhere in the middle of the
spectrum. In air photography there is no *a priori* reason why the eye and
the emulsion should see colours in the same relative brightness, and it is
a more important requirement to obtain the highest possible speed behind
the deep-yellow filter customarily used to reduce the effects of atmospheric
haze. Density curves for two standard filters used in air photography, the

" Minus Blue " and " Tricolour Red," are also shown in Fig. 18, the parts of high and low density being omitted for clarity. The Minus Blue is about the best compromise between using light of the longest possible wavelengths and allowing enough light energy to pass so that sufficient impression is made on the film with short exposures. It requires about two and a half times increase of exposure in average daylight, which is a greater increase than would be expected from the relative areas under the full curve and the part enclosed by the filter density curve in Fig. 18. No doubt some of the difference is made up by reflection losses at the filter surface and the rest by the small amount of near ultra-violet light to which the unfiltered emulsion would respond, and by the relatively greater proportion of blue-violet light in daylight than in an equal-energy spectrum. The red filter is not very often used with panchromatic emulsions ; it requires about five times increase of exposure.

Modern panchromatic emulsions, especially the highly red-sensitive types used for air photography, owe a high proportion of their total white-light sensitivity to their dye sensitising, though their sensitivity does not necessarily extend any further into the red than it did with the older types. This far-red sensitivity of the older emulsions, however, was very low in relation to the blue sensitivity, and very deep filters would have been necessary to make any effective use of it. The relatively poor response of the older emulsions to the longer wavelengths can be deduced from the greater multiplying factors quoted for yellow filters, and from the fact that in the early days of air photography a large range of filters of different depths was used. Nowadays there is little point in having a range of yellows of different depths, because the increase of exposure is only two and a half times with the Minus Blue, and if anything useful is to be gained in exposure by letting through some blue light it would be necessary to omit the filter altogether, as is sometimes done in low-altitude photography.

The improvements in panchromatic sensitisings, which have been of the utmost importance for the advancement of air photography, are found in the products of all the leading makers. The special films for air photography marketed by Ilford, Kodak, Agfa, etc., are all characterised by high red sensitivity and small multiplying factors for yellow and red filters. There are differences in the spectral sensitivity curves of different makes, but these are of little practical significance. There are also slight variations in filter factors among the different makes and different batches of any one make, and since a filter is always used these are equivalent to a variation in speed. The speed without a filter has no great significance, and it would seem logical for the speeds of such emulsions to be determined behind some agreed standard filter such as the Wratten Minus Blue.

The limit of sensitivity at the red end of the spectrum in emulsions made for air photography is somewhat arbitrary, and one suspects that manufacturers have made use of the best sensitisers available out of a range developed primarily for other purposes. In air photography there are potential advantages in using the range 0·6 to 0·8 micron rather than the 0·5 to 0·64 micron range used at present, and this point is further discussed in Chapter Fourteen.

RESOLVING POWER AND GRAININESS

The developed photographic image is not homogeneous, but consists of clumps of silver grains with interstitial spaces. When viewed under high magnification the individual clumps and grains which cause this *granularity* can be seen, but at much lower magnifications, too low to resolve the individual clumps, the image shows a definite lack of " smoothness " known as the " graininess." Graininess may be regarded as an irregular fluctuation of density on a scale comparable with that of the finer details of the image ; it is significant in air photography because it spoils the perception of fine details, especially those of low contrast.

Although the effects of graininess are obvious enough, its very nature makes specification and measurement difficult, and although much work has been done on this subject there is as yet no agreed standard method for expressing the graininess of emulsions on a numerical scale. Jones (6) has given a review of proposed methods and he points out the confused state of the nomenclature. From the present point of view the chief significance of graininess is its obscuration of detail, and in this sense it increases with the density of the negative, though on older methods of measurement in which the magnified image of the developed emulsion was studied under constant illumination the graininess apparently reached a maximum at the low density of 0·3. Graininess is sometimes measured in a relative way by comparison of high-magnification enlargements, but Romer and Selwyn have developed a method which seems to be very closely in line with the actual effect of graininess in air photography. In their method (7) a highly magnified image of the uniformly exposed and developed emulsion is projected on to a series of low-contrast Cobb test objects (see Chapter Five) printed on bromide paper, the graininess being measured from the size of the smallest test object which can be seen. This is exactly parallel to the effect of graininess in breaking-up and obscuring the detail in images.

In general photography graininess as such is quite important, but in air photography the graininess is less important than its effect in obscuring detail. Other factors than graininess also cause a loss of detail, and a measure of the emulsion *resolving power* is of more direct value than any figure for graininess. It also has the advantage of being easy to define and relatively straightforward to measure. Photographic resolving power is discussed in more detail in Chapter Five, where the influence of the lens as well as the emulsion is considered. For the moment we are interested in the emulsion only ; its resolving power can be determined either by using a contact test object made on a very fine-grained plate, or by photographing a test object with a lens of very good correction. The former method is preferable, since it avoids any ambiguity due to imperfections of the lens, but contact test objects are difficult to make and do not have a very long life.

Emulsion resolving power depends on many factors, *e.g.*, the contrast of the test object and its shape, the kind of development, the level of exposure, the colour of the light, etc., but most of these can be standardised and resolution measurements repeated with a reasonable accuracy. Further details on resolving power and its measurement are given in Chapters Four, Five, and Six.

Graininess and resolving power are closely related to emulsion speed, fast emulsions in general being more grainy and having lower resolving power than slow emulsions. In Fig. 19 log speed has been plotted against log resolving power for a number of Kodak panchromatic emulsions, using data published by the manufacturer. The resolving power figures refer

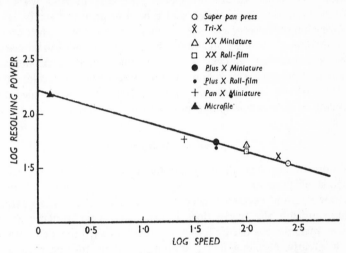

FIG. 19.—Speed and resolving power for panchromatic emulsions.

to a test object contrast of 30 to 1 and recommended development for each emulsion (usually D76). Although the data are scanty, it is interesting to note that the points do not scatter very far from a straight line. It can be seen that heavy sacrifices of speed are required for small increases in resolving power. The slope of the line indicates that emulsions having twice the resolving power of the fast panchromatic types commonly used for air photography would require about ten to twelve times as much exposure. Those in the same speed class as " Panatomic X " requiring about four times as much exposure only give some 40 per cent. greater resolving power.

HARDNESS AND WATER ABSORPTION

The user of photographic emulsions does not have much occasion to consider their hardness or water absorption, because these properties are fixed by the manufacturer in such a way that no trouble is experienced under the usual conditions of processing in temperate climates. So long as the gelatine does not frill or blister and the film dries at a reasonable speed, the subject may almost be forgotten. The subject is worth mentioning, however, if only to emphasise that these good qualities of modern emulsions have been developed by careful work on the part of the manufacturers and need not necessarily be regarded as unchangeable. Within limits the manufacturer can vary the hardness of the emulsion, which largely determines the amount of water taken up by a given weight of gelatine, and also the ratio of gelatine to silver salts, which affects the weight of water absorbed by a given weight of emulsion. There are obvious restrictions on the variations possible in either of these cases, but within reasonable limits it is desirable for the emulsions used in air photography to have the smallest possible water absorption and the greatest possible hardness. The conditions under which air negatives are processed, especially in field work, expose them to risk of mechanical damage, and a hard gelatine surface is less likely to suffer abrasion than a very soft one. This is especially true when processing at high temperatures, where an emulsion needing no additional hardening treatment is a great advantage. Moreover, the drying of air negatives is always a lengthy matter on account of the large area of wet film involved, and anything which reduces the amount of water taken up by the emulsion and requiring subsequent evaporation is well worth while.

KEEPING QUALITY

It is unfortunate that all photographic materials change in properties over periods of time of the order of a year or more, even when stored carefully away from excessive heat or moisture. Broadly speaking, the faster the emulsion the worse does it keep, and panchromatic emulsions keep worse than unsensitised types. Needless to say, the deterioration in storage is greatly accelerated by undue exposure to moisture or high temperatures, or to chemical fumes, and every effort should be made to keep unexposed film cool and dry. There seems to be little advantage, however, in storage at temperatures below 50° F.

Without wishing to disparage the great achievements of film manufacturers, it is necessary to emphasise that the age of the emulsion cannot be ignored, and much more attention has to be paid to it in air photography than in ground photography. In most ground photography it is comparatively rare for the maximum speed of the emulsion to be required, and if the speed has fallen in storage it is nearly always possible to give double the exposure or whatever increase may be needed without detriment to the quality of the result. In air photography the need for giving a brief exposure in order to arrest movement and for using the smallest possible lens aperture in the interests of good resolving power make it desirable to have the highest possible emulsion speed available at all times. In some cases, e.g., in wide-angle surveys, where there is a considerable loss of light in the lens, a fall of emulsion speed to half may make photography impossible at early and late hours of the day.

There seems to be no generally agreed figure for the rate of speed loss on storage, and indeed it would be very remarkable if the behaviour of different samples of so complicated a system as the photographic emulsion could be predicted with any great accuracy. One estimate states that speed falls away by 0·1 log units for each six months' storage at normal temperatures, thus after eighteen months the speed will have fallen to half the initial figure. This may be taken as a rough guide, but it is much more to the point to ensure that film is used quickly than to seek for accurate prediction of its speed loss on storage. In general there seems to be no great prospect of improvements in keeping quality of negative emulsions, though according to a paper by Calhoun (8) Eastman aerographic films, now coated on " safety " (acetate-butyrate) base, lose speed less rapidly than older coatings on nitrate base. Emulsions coated before 1942 fell to half the initial speed in five months if on nitrate base, and in nine months if on safety base. Improved emulsions coated after 1943 on safety base fell only to 90 per cent. of initial speed in six months and about 70 per cent. in twelve months. It is only fair to add, however, that not all authorities are agreed that emulsions in general keep better on safety base.

CHOICE OF A NEGATIVE EMULSION FOR AIR PHOTOGRAPHY (9)

The negative emulsion for air photography must have the highest possible speed behind a yellow filter to allow the brief exposure times required to arrest image movements ; its graininess must be as low as possible to give good reproduction of fine details of low contrast ; its gamma should be high to overcome the flattening effects of haze. Unfortunately high speed cannot be had without graininess, and undue contrast means impracticably small latitude in exposure and difficulties in printing. The slowest emulsions which could be considered at all for modern air photography are the Kodak " Panatomic X," Agfa " Aeropan," and similar types having a speed of about 30 Weston and slightly finer grain than the types having a speed of 100 Weston. On the other hand, there are faster emulsions such as the Kodak " Tri X " type, having a speed of about 200 Weston but more pronounced graininess than " Super XX " and similar types. A detailed consideration of the various conflicting requirements, as given in other chapters, leads to the conclusion that the emulsions with speed of about 100 Weston give about the best balance between speed and graininess, at least for modern aircraft flying faster than, say, 150 m.p.h. The choice is not a very critical one, however, and in practice there is very little difference in the amount of ground detail which can be recorded. On balance the advantage lies with the faster emulsion, and in view of the facility it offers of working in weaker light it is undoubtedly the best choice. The very fastest emulsions are undesirably grainy, will not always give sufficient contrast, and do not keep quite so well.

The desirable gamma, as determined by the need for printing the average high-altitude negative on paper of medium contrast, is about 1·3, and the fast emulsions sold for air photography mostly give this gamma when developed for maximum speed in D19b developer.

Writers in the Continental literature on air photography (10) (11) advocate emulsion characteristics rather different from those just put forward, suggesting a gamma of 2·0 or more and a speed of the order of 30 Weston ;

Agfa "Aeropan," in fact, meets their specification. The choice appears to be based on the rather obvious need for high contrast to offset the low contrast of the subject and fine grain for the reproduction of fine detail, but this ignores the effects of image movements. If the slower type of emulsion is used, and the time of exposure is short enough to arrest image movements, then for much of the time it will be worked on the toe portion of its characteristic curve; on the toe the slope is effectively the same as on the straight line of a faster emulsion, and if the high gamma is not used there seems to be no good reason for having it.

REFERENCES

1. MEES, C. E. K. "The Theory of the Photographic Process" (Macmillan) is the standard reference work for photographic theory.
2. "Eighth International Congress of Photography." (Heffer & Sons, Cambridge). London, 1928.
3. British Standard Specification, No. 1384 (1947), "Diffuse Transmission Density."
4. JONES, L. A. "The Evaluation of Negative Film Speeds in Terms of Print Quality," *Journ. Frank. Inst.*, pp. 227, 297, and 497, 1939.
5. HOWLETT, L. E. "A New Criterion for the Speed of Aerial Photographic Emulsions," *Canadian Journ. Res.*, 24, 4, 1946.
6. JONES, L. A., and HIGGINS, G. C. *Journ. Opt. Soc. Amer.*, 35, No. 7, 435.
7. ROMER, W., and SELWYN, E. W. H. *Photo. Journ.*, 83, January 1943.
8. CALHOUN, J. M. "The Physical Properties of Safety Aerographic Film," *Photogrammetric Engineering*, July 1947.
9. HOWLETT, L. E. "Choosing a Negative Emulsion and Development for Daylight Aerial Photography," *Canadian Journ. Res.*, March 1948.
10. SCHMIECHEK, U. *Jahrbuch der deutschen Luftfahrtforschung*, 3, 84-92, 1937.
11. KUJAWA, G. VON. "Erfordernisse des Fliegerfilms," *Veröffentlichungen des Wissenschaftlichen Zentral-Laboratoriums der photographischen Abteilung Agfa*, 4, 128.

Chapter Four

PROCESSING OF NEGATIVE EMULSIONS

THE sensitive emulsion shows no visible change after exposure and apparently bears no record of the optical image which was formed upon it in the camera. Under ordinary microscopic examination the silver halide crystals look the same as before exposure, but a change has taken place, and if the emulsion is immersed in a suitable reducing solution, the *developer*, a reaction starts at definite points on some of the crystals, and if allowed to continue the whole of each developing crystal is reduced to metallic silver. This process of complete reduction initiated by the sub-microscopic particles of the latent image enormously increases the effect of the original exposure and is the reason for the remarkable light sensitivity of the photographic process.

In any area of emulsion subjected to a uniform exposure only a fraction of the total number of crystals will have enough sensitivity to acquire a latent image, and the number ultimately reduced to metallic silver will depend on the composition of the developer and the time for which it is allowed to act. The conditions of development are therefore of great importance in the relation between exposure and density ; indeed, the emulsion can hardly be said to have any photographic properties at all until it has been developed. From this point of view the French word for " developer," viz., *révélateur*, is undoubtedly very precise and logical. When development has been stopped the densities are not very greatly altered by any variations in the subsequent operations, and exposure and development may thus be regarded as the sole determinants of the negative density.

After development there will in general be some unreduced silver halide remaining, and this must be dissolved out in the operation of *fixation*, since it slowly darkens on continued exposure to strong light. After fixation the film must be washed in plain water to remove the fixing solution which otherwise would crystallise on the surface of the emulsion and would also impair its permanence. The washed negative is finally dried to moisture equilibrium with the air.

Each of these stages in the processing operation presents intriguing physico-chemical problems on which a great deal of research has been carried out, but full accounts of these matters must be sought in the larger photographic textbooks. (1) The purpose of this chapter is to select and stress those aspects of processing which are of particular importance in air photography.

DEVELOPMENT

All developing solutions conform in their fundamental make-up to a more or less standard pattern, though the detail variations may be

47

considerable. The primary constituent is the *reducing agent*, usually an organic compound derived from benzene. The reducing agent is inhibited from reaction with atmospheric oxygen by the *preservative*, sodium sulphite. The reducing agent will not work efficiently unless the solution is at the correct pH,* which is normally on the alkaline side and is maintained by adding a proportion of an alkaline salt, known as the *accelerator*. A *restrainer*, which is normally an alkaline halide, is added to keep chemical fog at a minimum, but also has some effect on the shape of the characteristic curve. Thus there are five essential constituents in a developer, if we include the water required to hold the chemicals in solution and to provide the correct environment for the chemical reaction. In any particular developer, however, there may be more than one chemical of each type, and in some cases the number may be reduced by allowing the preservative to provide the necessary alkalinity.

Only three reducing agents are widely used in air photography, viz., metol (also sold as " Elon " by the Kodak Company), which is the compound mono-methyl-para-aminophenol sulphate ; hydroquinone, which is para-dihydroxy benzene ; and pyrogallol, which is trihydroxy benzene. Metol and hydroquinone are used, generally together, for developing both negative and positive emulsions ; pyrogallol is used for negative emulsions only on account of its tendency to give a yellow stain. Other things being equal, metol gives negatives of lower contrast than hydroquinone. Other organic agents are used for development in general photography, but they have no advantages for air photography and need not be considered here.

Sodium carbonate is the commonest accelerator, but the particular alkali is of small importance, the pH, rather than the means employed to produce it, being the factor which determines the rate of development. When very rapid development is required the alkaline hydroxides are employed, while for slow action very weak alkalis such as borax can be used. Sodium sulphite itself is feebly alkaline, and in some metol developers it is the only source of alkalinity.

Sodium sulphite is the only compound commonly used as a preservative, and it is a constituent of all developers used in air photography. Apart from its preservative functions, sulphite enters into the complex chemical reactions of development and has a slight solvent action on silver halides.

Potassium or sodium bromides are the common restrainers, and are equivalent if used in molecularly equivalent proportions. No other inorganic salts are commonly used as restrainers, but organic anti-foggants may be used in addition under certain conditions, such as development at high temperatures when fog is liable to become excessive.

A very large number of organic and inorganic compounds will act as developers, they can be used together in different proportions, with alkaline salts of various types as accelerators ; the concentration of the sulphite and restrainer can be varied within wide limits, and other chemicals can be

---

* The pH of a solution is a number expressing its acidity or alkalinity. The number is the log of the reciprocal of the hydrogen-ion concentration. Strong alkalis have a pH of about 11, pure water is about 7, and strong acids 2 to 3 on this scale.

added for special purposes such as " fine-grain " development. It is possible to devise an almost infinite number of formulæ, all of which will work in the sense that they will develop an image on exposed film, but as a rule they differ from the well-tried standard formulæ only in the time they take to produce the same result. Two or three of the standard formulæ worked out by the emulsion manufacturers will meet all the requirements of air photography, and there is little to be gained by amateur experimentation ; it is much more important to understand the use of existing formulæ than to seek for new ones.

SENSITOMETRIC STUDY OF DEVELOPMENT

This section is a sensitometric study of the behaviour of standard types of fast panchromatic film sold for air photography when developed in the recommended standard formulæ. It should be understood that while this discussion is representative of the general behaviour of such emulsions, the examples should not be expected to correspond exactly with results quoted elsewhere. Photographic emulsions are complex chemical systems, and different brands of the same nominal type of film, and even different batches of the same brand, do not necessarily behave in quite the same way. Moreover, the conditions of development are not easily standardised, and small differences in purity of chemicals, degree of agitation of the solution, etc., can make appreciable differences to the results. While such effects as the increase of speed and growth of fog with increasing development time are of quite general application, the reader must not expect to repeat the experiments here described and obtain exactly the same figures.

Two standard developer formulæ have been chosen for the study of development; D19*b* and DK20. D19*b* is now fairly standard for high-altitude air photography in England, though in America D19, which is very similar, seems to be preferred. Either of these two formulæ gives good contrast together with high speed, has good keeping qualities, and a good exhaustion life. DK20 is representative of the class of fine-grain developers used in general photography. The two formulæ are given here for easy comparison :—

D19*b*			DK20		
Metol	. . .	2·2 gm.	Metol	. . .	5·0 gm.
Hydroquinone	. .	8·8 ,,	Sodium sulphite (anhy-		
Sodium sulphite (anhy-			drous)	. . .	100·0 ,,
drous)	. . .	72·0 ,,	Kodalk *	. .	2·0 ,,
Sodium carbonate (an-			Potassium thiocyanate	.	1·0 ,,
hydrous)	. .	48·0 ,,	Potassium bromide	.	0·5 ,,
Potassium bromide	.	4·0 ,,	Water up to	. .	1·0 litre
Water up to	. .	1·0 litre	*p*H of fresh bath .	.	8·3 approx.
*p*H of fresh bath .	.	10·2 approx.			

D19*b* will be seen to contain a greater concentration of reducing agents than DK20, a greater proportion of restrainer, and to be much more strongly

---

* " Kodalk " is a proprietary alkali made by Kodak Ltd. It is intermediate in strength between sodium carbonate and borax. It may be replaced by an equal weight of sodium metaborate.

alkaline. The higher alkali concentration makes D19*b* a more rapid-acting developer than DK20, while the absence of hydroquinone in the latter contributes to its softer-working quality. The fine-grain properties of DK20 are due to solvent action of the thiocyanate and the high sulphite concentration preventing the agglomeration of adjacent silver crystals during the progress of development.

Development in D19b.—The developer used in the experiments now to be described was essentially D19*b*, but contained 6 gm. of potassium bromide per litre. This slight modification was made in order to simulate somewhat

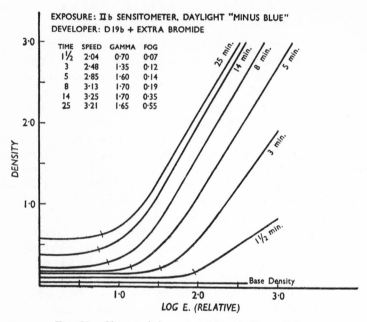

FIG. 20.—Characteristic curves of fast air film at different development times.

more closely the characteristics of a developing bath which has been in use for some time and has accumulated reaction products of development, one of which is alkali bromide. It is better to show sensitometric results in a developer which approximates practice as closely as possible, and in practice much more film is developed in used developer than in perfectly fresh developer. Although the differences from fresh developer are not of major importance, it was thought better to start with a bromide concentration approximating that in a half-exhausted bath.

Six strips of a fast panchromatic air film were exposed in a sensitometer and developed in the modified D19*b* formula for different times at 20° C. (68° F.), the solution being well agitated by brushing the emulsion surface. After processing the densities were measured and characteristic curves plotted ; these curves are reproduced as Fig. 20. The table in Fig. 20 gives the values of fog, gamma, and relative speed measured at a density of 0·1 above fog, for each time of development.

The most obvious feature of Fig. 20 is the movement of the characteristic curves to the left with increasing time of development. This clearly means an increase of speed with development time on whatever criterion speed may be measured. With increasing time of development fog rises, at first comparatively slowly, then more rapidly. Contrast, measured as gamma, also increases rapidly in the early stages of development, but reaches an almost constant value after five minutes. The variation of these characteristics with time is plotted in Fig. 21, time being plotted on a log scale since equal progress in developing action takes place in equal multiples of time. The log of the speed is seen to increase linearly with the log of the time for

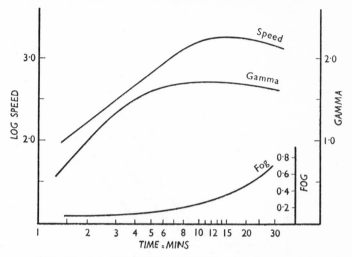

FIG. 21.—Fast film developed in D19*b* : variation of speed, gamma and fog with time.

times up to eight minutes, but thereafter the rate of increase falls off, the speed reaches a maximum and then declines again. The decreasing slope of the speed-time curve corresponds approximately with an increasing slope of the fog-time curve, and when the speed begins to fall the fog is rising rapidly. The gamma-time curve flattens out and reaches a maximum earlier than the speed-time curve.

The first conclusion to be drawn from the study of these curves is that speed, fog, and development time are intimately related. If we are interested in obtaining the maximum emulsion speed, as we nearly always are in air photography, we must develop long enough. In this case the time to stop development for absolute maximum speed is about fourteen minutes, but at this point the fog is high and rising very rapidly. High fog is undesirable, and for most purposes it would be better to stop at about eight minutes, where fog is 0·2 and speed is about 80 per cent. of the maximum. This relation between speed and fog is a fairly general one. When using fast emulsions with developers such as D19*b* it will normally be found that maximum speed is reached by developing to a fog of about 0·2 whatever the temperature between the limits 60° to 75° F.

The next conclusion is that maximum speed is associated with maximum contrast; we cannot have one without the other. Conversely we cannot vary contrast by varying the development time unless we are prepared to accept a variation in speed. To take a rather extreme example, if we require a gamma of 0·8 with this film and developer we should have to accept a speed only one-twenty-fifth of the maximum. D19*b* is not, in fact, suitable for low-contrast development.

In speaking of contrast we have been referring to the characteristic curve and in particular to its gamma. In actual photography the contrast

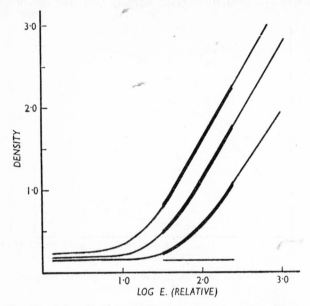

Fig. 22.—Effect of varying development time at constant exposure.

of the *negative*, *i.e.*, its density range, will not vary in the same way as the gamma, assuming that we give a constant exposure and develop for different times. The course of events is illustrated by Fig. 22, where the characteristic curves for three, five, and eight minutes are re-drawn from Fig. 20, and a line of length 0·9 log exposure units, corresponding to the brightness scale of a medium altitude view, has been drawn above the log E axis. As we are assuming a constant camera exposure, the position of the latter line does not change, but with increasing development time the corresponding densities fall on the parts of the characteristic curves indicated by the thicker lines.

Clearly the *negative contrast* increases with development time, not so much because of any difference of gamma as because the subject is recorded on different parts of characteristic curves which are all very similar. It may incidentally be noted that the tone reproduction is different in the three cases, due to the use of different relative proportions of the straight line and toe. At eight minutes the densities are nearly all on the straight line, while at three minutes they are mostly on the toe, and in the latter case gamma is meaningless as a measure of contrast. If it is essential to give a numerical expression for contrast, the simplest course is to quote the mean slope over the relevant part of the curve, *i.e.*, the density difference divided by the log brightness difference of the subject.

This example shows that the effect of developing time on contrast is less straightforward than might appear. Increased time of development does in general increase the contrast of the negative, but not necessarily by way of an increased gamma ; the increased speed due to the extra development may in effect move the subject further up a curve of the same shape and the same gamma, thus giving the increased contrast in a less obvious way. These points are emphasised because the usual treatment of development in photographic textbooks suggests that the change of gamma is the most important factor, and the change of speed is often ignored. This may not be unreasonable in ground photography, where the development is not usually carried so far as in air photography and where the change of speed, in developers containing less bromide than D19*b*, is not so marked. Since the final result of increased development time is a negative of greater contrast, the precise mechanism by which this is obtained may not appear to matter, but experience shows that confusion is caused by attempts to apply gamma figures in circumstances where gamma is quite inappropriate as a measure of contrast. In such cases an intelligent use of the full characteristic curve is the only way in which sensitometry can be helpful.

Fine-grain Developers.—During the past few years great interest has been taken in fine-grain development, mainly in connection with the use of small cameras for general ground photography, and numerous formulæ have been published. Excluding the more exotic types not based on responsible investigations, these formulæ can be broadly classified into two groups, the first of which employs conventional reducing agents such as metol and hydroquinone in association with a silver halide solvent such as potassium thiocyanate and/or a high sulphite concentration, while the second class employs special reducing agents such as paraphenylene-diamine or its derivatives. The fine-grain properties of the first group are believed to be due to the solvent action preventing the fusion of adjacent clumps of silver halide crystals during development, while the second group probably also acts by a solvent action, but of a more complicated nature. Since fast emulsions of different make are likely to contain different proportions of bromide and iodide, one would not expect them to react in quite the same way to solvent developers, and this seems to be borne out by experiments of Loveland. (2) Nevertheless, fine-grain developers have a definite value for ground photography and the standard formulæ give a genuine reduction in graininess. Much of the improvement, however, is associated with development to a low gamma, which can be done with these developers without excessive loss of speed. If a fine-grain developer such as DK20 is used to produce maximum speed and contrast by prolonging its action, the graininess is not much less than would be produced by a more active formula such as D19*b*.

Graininess is so obviously a factor limiting the perception of detail in many air photographs, and so many air photographers use fine-grain developers in their private photographic pursuits, that the use of these formulæ for developing air negatives is a perennial source of argument. In fact, they offer no advantage and some disadvantages compared with D19*b*, but belief in their value is so widespread that the subject merits full discussion. It should be pointed out, however, that many other things besides the type of development can affect the graininess of air negatives, and this section should be read in conjunction with the relevant parts of Chapters Five and Six.

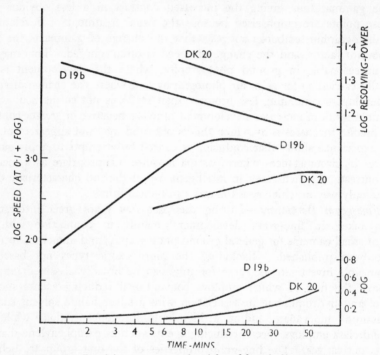

FIG. 23.—Resolving power, speed and fog of fast air film developed in D19*b* and DK20.

Development in DK20.—In comparing DK20 with D19*b* for air photography we have to decide whether it offers any advantage in graininess when development is carried far enough to give the speed and contrast required. The data presented in Fig. 23 enable this comparison to be made. They were obtained by exposing strips of a fast panchromatic emulsion, as used for air photography, in a sensitometer and developing in the two developers for a range of times at 20° C.; the characteristic curves were then plotted and the speed and contrast figures derived. The resolving power, which depends on the graininess but is a measurement of greater practical importance, was also determined for each step of each sensitometric strip by exposing behind a contact test object of the low-contrast Cobb type (see Chapter Five). Resolving power curves were drawn for each time of development and the maximum resolving power obtained at each time was derived. In Fig. 23 the upper pair of curves gives the resolving power for the two developers over the range of developing times, the middle pair gives speed and the lower pair fog.

As we would expect from its greater activity, D19b develops more rapidly than DK20, reaching maximum speed at fourteen minutes, with a fog of 0·3; at this time DK20 is far from its maximum speed, which is reached at about fifty minutes, at a fog of 0·4. Even at the impracticably long development time of fifty minutes the maximum speed with DK20 is only half that with D19b. In the early stages of development, however, DK20 gives higher speed; for a gamma of 1·0 it gave twice the speed of D19b, with this batch of film.

Resolving power falls off with increasing time of development in both developers, and the rate of fall-off is about the same in each case. At any given time of development the resolution is some 25 per cent. higher in DK20, but at times which give equal speed the difference is only a few per cent. At ten minutes development in D19b and thirty minutes in DK20 the fog is just over 0·2 in both cases and the speed is close to the maximum, so that these are reasonable conditions for comparison; under these conditions DK20 gave 7 per cent. greater resolving power than D19b, but less than half its speed.

The gamma-time curves have been omitted from Fig. 23 for clarity; with the make and batch of emulsion used in these tests practically the same maximum gamma was reached with both developers, but this is unusual and in general DK20 gives lower contrast than D19b however far development is carried.

We may therefore sum up in the following way :—

(a) D19b gives more than twice the maximum speed obtainable with DK20.

(b) DK20 in general gives higher resolving power than D19b, but when development is carried out for maximum speed in both developers the difference is less than 10 per cent.

The resolution of ground detail in air photographs depends on the image quality of the lens and on the image movements as well as the resolving power of the emulsion. As a rule the shutter speed is fixed at some value which is just adequate to arrest image movement, so that if DK20 were substituted for D19b the lens aperture would have to be opened up by one or more stops, and with most lenses the image quality would deteriorate by more than 10 per cent. It would then be problematical if we should see any difference in ground detail resolved, although the image would look less grainy. We should therefore have gone to an inconveniently long development time with no positive advantage, and it must be concluded that fine-grain developers such as DK20 are not worth considering any further for air photography. The ultra fine-grain types such as paraphenylene-diamine are even less worthy of attention, because they give lower contrast than DK20 and a greater loss of speed.

Similar arguments can be used to answer other questions which might be raised about development, *e.g.*, it might be suggested that development in D19*b* should be stopped at less than maximum speed to obtain the benefit of slightly higher resolution. The answer is that if all factors involved in obtaining the highest resolution of ground detail are taken into account, development for maximum speed in D19*b* gives about the best balance between speed and resolving power. These conclusions are only valid so long as the image movements and the characteristics of lenses place a premium on working at the shortest possible exposure times and smallest possible lens apertures. When image movements and lens aberrations are not the dominating factors, fine-grain development may have a place in air photography ; but as yet there are no signs that this is likely to happen.

DEVELOPMENT IN PRACTICE

The discussion in the previous section was based on data obtained under laboratory conditions, where developer exhaustion is not a factor, the temperature was accurately controlled, and the solutions had free access to the developing emulsion. It is now necessary to give some attention to problems encountered in practical development of air negatives.

Time and Temperature Relationship.—Development being essentially a chemical reaction, its rate varies with temperature. Very low temperatures, say below 16° C., are ruled out by the impracticably long times involved, and very high temperatures by the softening of the emulsion, but within these limits similar results can be obtained at any temperature by giving an appropriate time of development. The results will not be exactly the same at different temperatures, however, even when the correct times are given. In general, high temperatures give more fog and less contrast, and it is highly desirable to keep within the range 18° to 24° C. on all occasions and to develop always at 20° C. if possible. Time-temperature graphs are commonly used to give the equivalent times for different temperatures, but it should be understood that their basis is somewhat arbitrary, depending on the particular characteristic for which equality is sought. In general photography times are usually quoted for equal gammas at the different temperatures, but this is not strictly possible when development is carried out to maximum gamma, for the maximum will be lower at the higher temperatures. For air photography it is more logical to quote the times for maximum speed, which is substantially the same thing as the times for a constant fog. If we take the fog for maximum speed at the best temperature, 20° C., and give appropriate times for producing the same fog at other temperatures, then the same speed will be obtained at all temperatures, but the gamma will be lower above 20° C. and higher below 20° C. The time-temperature relationship for D19*b* requires the time to be halved for each 5° C. increase of temperature above 20° C., or doubled for 5° C. below 20° C., at least within the range 18° to 30° C. This holds good either for fresh developer or for developer which has been used to develop a considerable area of film up to 100 sq. ft. per gal. at least.

Development in Spool Tanks.—The method of developing long rolls of air film in spool tanks seems to have been used first in the Royal Air Force, and is now in use by air photographers all over the world. Various ingenious mechanisms have been produced, in more recent years, for winding the film automatically from one spool to the other, and this has extended the scope of the spool-tank method.

The spool-tank principle has certain very definite advantages. The arrangement of carrying the film closely rolled on two spools immersed in the developer and winding from one to the other continuously leads to a small portable apparatus which is nevertheless capable of handling relatively long rolls and is extremely economical of solution. From a photo-chemical point of view, however, this is a most drastic treatment to apply, for the film is alternately exposed in the developer for brief periods and rolled tightly on itself for longer periods. Apart from the apparent danger of mechanical damage to the tender gelatine surface, which is presumably avoided by the lubricating action of the solution, troubles would be anticipated from uneven development, " neighbourhood effects," distorted characteristic curves, etc., yet in practice the method works very well. The reason for its success in the face of apparently insuperable difficulties is undoubtedly the very full development given to negatives exposed in aircraft cameras. The troubles referred to are all manifestations of different degrees of development due to some parts of the film receiving less active treatment than others. If the negative is withdrawn from the developer at a stage when density is still increasing rapidly, such effects are much more likely than when development is carried as far as it will go. Neighbourhood effects such as the production of a light line alongside the boundary of a heavily exposed area are due to a local high concentration of development products, including alkali bromides, which diffuse out from the high-density areas where development is proceeding vigorously and retard the development of adjacent less-exposed areas. The influence of such reaction products is less if the developer already contains a high proportion of bromide, as is the case with D19b and similar formulæ. Distortion of the characteristic curve by depression of the higher densities might be expected because of exhaustion of the developer in high-density areas during the period when the film is tightly wound on itself and fresh developer has no access. That such effects give little serious trouble must be due to the fact that the swollen film holds sufficient developing agents, in a concentrated solution such as D19b, for the reaction to continue with sufficient energy during the rolled-up period. As more turns of film are wound on to a spool core, the emulsion spends less and less time in free contact with the developer and more time rolled up, and eventually trouble is encountered even with D19b. With spool cores of the order of 3 in. in diameter marked distortion of the characteristic curve appears if lengths of film longer than 60 ft. are developed. Much greater lengths than this are regularly developed in spool tanks, but there is a definite loss of quality, and continuous developing machines are advisable for anything greater than 100 ft. The defects of spool-tank development are minimised by winding the film to and fro as rapidly as possible so that the emulsion comes into contact with fresh developer as often as possible in a given time. In hand-operated apparatus it is usual to wind the spools at the rate of 120 revs. per min. Some of the mechanically operated types work at a higher speed, but any very marked increase of winding rate is precluded by the problems of accelerating and decelerating the film at the ends of the cycles without mechanical damage.

Typical characteristic curves, illustrating the distortion due to spool-tank development as compared with open-dish development, are shown in Fig. 24. Fast panchromatic film, with R.A.F. pyro-metol developer, was used in producing these curves. It will be noticed that approximate equality with

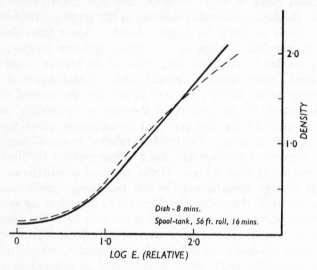

FIG. 24.—Characteristic curves for dish and spool-tank development.

dish development was given by developing for twice as long in the spool tank at the same temperature and in the same developer. The need for additional time is due to the restricted access of developer and the lack of agitation during most of the development. During brief periods, however, the agitation in spool-tank development is very good, and with a very short length of film the characteristic curves are similar to those obtained with brush development or other forms giving equivalent turbulence of the solution. If the time of development is kept constant with increasing lengths of film, the emulsion speed at first changes very little, but contrast falls off more rapidly due to slowing up of development in the high-density regions, as exemplified by the spool-tank curve in Fig. 24. Some compensation can be had by increasing the development time, but exact equality for different lengths is never possible. If the increase of time is adjusted for equal contrast in the middle and upper densities, speed and fog increase with increasing length of film, while if the times are arranged to give equal speed at all lengths, contrast progressively diminishes. With lengths greater than about 150 ft. the increase of time required to maintain a useful degree of contrast is so great that fog becomes prohibitive. (It can already be seen to be higher than in the dish development in Fig. 24.) In general it will be clear that the relation between film length and development time will depend on the rate of winding, the composition of the developer, and the particular criterion of " equality " in development which has been chosen.

When using D19*b* developer in most of the commercially available spool tanks, and winding at 120 revs. per min., the ratios of time in Table 2 are suggested as giving about the best compromise between speed, fog, and contrast for different lengths of film. The choice is inevitably somewhat arbitrary, however, and subject to personal opinion.

TABLE 2

Time-length Relations for Spool-tank Development

Film Length.	Time of Development, D19*b*, 20° C.
Feet.	Minutes.
Up to 25	12
,, 50	15
,, 100	21
,, 150	26

As would be expected from what has already been said about the general characteristics of spool-tank development, serious troubles are encountered if attempts are made to develop to a gamma much below the maximum for the material in use, especially if the developer contains little or no bromide. For example, if air negatives are duplicated on standard cine positive emulsion, the master positives and duplicate negatives cannot be developed successfully in spool tanks. This is because cine-positive emulsion has a maximum gamma greater than 2·0, and for duplication it must be developed to a gamma of unity or less in a developer such as D76, which is slow working and contains no bromide and very little alkali. Any attempt to develop it in this way gives serious trouble with uneven densities and neighbourhood effects ; this can be avoided by using a material such as yellow-dyed cine positive, which has a much lower maximum gamma and has to be developed nearly to finality in order to reach a gamma of unity.

Development in Continuous Processing Machines.—Air negatives are not always available in sufficient quantities at one time and place to justify the design and installation of a really satisfactory continuous processing plant. When the turnover justifies continuous machinery, however, the outlay is well repaid by the greater convenience of working and the improvement in uniformity of output. One of the greatest practical advantages of continuous processing is that it makes the individual treatment of negatives by over-zealous operators a very difficult matter ; the vast majority of negatives are best given a standardised uniform development, and this is what is achieved by continuously operating plant, which blocks the desire of the unskilled to " have a look."

The continuous machinery which has been developed up to date, or at least those models which have been described in unclassified literature, appears to be a compromise between size, rate of output, and a satisfactory quality of processing. The main difficulty in the design of such equipment is to find space and time for thorough washing and for slow drying in air of controlled humidity. Detailed discussion of these problems is, however, outside the scope of this book.

Fear is often expressed that the tensions to which the film is exposed during development in continuous processing machines may cause distortion of the base, so rendering the negatives unsuitable for survey work. No one seems to have produced any evidence of this, however, and as Calhoun points out (3), tension sufficient to strain the film beyond its elastic limit could hardly be produced in any well-designed machine.

Developer Exhaustion and Sensitometric Control.—Accounts of development usually discuss the subject in sensitometric terms by reference to the performance of fresh solutions. This is reasonable enough in relation to amateur photography or other branches where it is feasible to use developer once only, but the discussion becomes somewhat academic where the same solution remains in use for a considerable period and is used for processing a great deal of film. The justification for the usual practice is that a developing solution is a complex chemical system, which is quite difficult enough to standardise when fresh ; the variations which may occur during its working life, as a result of developing different amounts of film exposed to different degrees, with indeterminate conditions of replenishment and exposure to air, make it almost impossible to fix on any definite state as typical of " used " developer and hence more suitable for descriptive purposes. In principle it is possible to carry out chemical analysis of the solution at any stage and determine what changes are required to restore the original performance ; the analytical technique is continually being improved and will no doubt become more widely used, but at present the equipment is too expensive and complex for all but the largest users, such as the motion picture industry. In any case, some of the changes which take place are such that it is not practicable to return to the original composition of the developer.

It is, of course, well known that any developing solution can be used successfully for the development of a much greater area of exposed film than is necessary to produce an easily detected change in its performance, and in practice the gradual change in activity over the working life is combated by various means such as change of time and the addition of " replenisher " solutions.

One of the simpler yet important changes which take place in the working life of a developer is the accumulation of soluble bromide as a product of the developing action. Since the volume of developer is continually being reduced by the amount carried out in the emulsion, which enters dry, it is possible to offset the increase of bromide concentration by adding a replenisher solution of similar basic composition to the developer itself, but without bromide. Thus the D19b replenisher contains no bromide, while the concentration of developing agents is increased and caustic alkali is present in addition to the alkali carbonate, as an additional means of restoring the waning activity of the used developer. A common practice is to add replenisher solution in sufficient quantity to keep the developer volume constant. This is replenishment in the rough sense only, since the volume removed by the film does not necessarily bear a constant ratio to the increase of bromide concentration, but it is better than no replenishment at all. A more precise method is to develop sensitometric strips on a standard batch of film at intervals in the life of the developer and to add replenisher in amounts judged from past experience to be correct for restoring the activity. This may, of course, require the withdrawal of some used solution each time. Full control of replenishment requires chemical analysis in addition to sensitometry.

Although the composition of a developer varies continuously during its working life, and the composition can never be predicted accurately, it is generally possible to distinguish three phases in the life of the bath. These are not precisely defined or differentiated but in continuous machines where average types of air negative are developed in D19b, keeping the volume constant with D19bR, the following sequence is broadly discernible. In the first stage, when the developer is fresh, it will be found that a development time of, say, four minutes at 75° F. gives about 90 per cent. of maximum speed and contrast at a fog of approximately 0·2. As film is developed, the fog level at a constant time of development rapidly falls, and after some 10 sq. ft. per gal. have been developed the time must be increased to about seven or seven and a half minutes, maximum speed now being obtained at a lower fog, approximately 0·15. The solution is now in a fairly stable state, and the time can be left constant until about 100 sq. ft. per gal. have been developed. During this second phase the fog and speed slowly fall at a constant time of development. It is of interest to note that throughout this period the used developer will actually give some 20 per cent. higher speed than fresh developer, assuming that the time can be sufficiently prolonged. The effect as normally observed, however, is the retention of the original speed at a lower fog. When more than about 100 sq. ft. per gal. have been developed the speed and contrast begin to fall off rapidly and the bath should be discarded. There is thus a period between 10 and 100 sq. ft. per gal. where the developer is in a " matured " and fairly constant state. When it has reached this state its composition differs materially from fresh D19b. At 50 sq. ft. per gal. the bromide concentration has approximately doubled its original value of 4 gm. per litre, and it might be considered worth while to start with the doubled concentration in the effort to avoid the initial maturing period. However, it is not possible to match used developer exactly by adding bromide, or even bromide and iodide, to fresh developer, and the common practice of developing fogged waste film to mature a new bath is probably justified. It is reasonable to hope that with the improvement of methods of chemical analysis and of replenishment it will eventually be possible to keep the developer activity much more constant than can now be done.

When development is carried out in spool tanks and there is no sensitometric control, the following details about developer exhaustion may be found useful. Using a tank holding $1\frac{1}{2}$ gals. of D19b, and keeping the volume constant by addition of D19b, four rolls of film 56 ft. $\times$ 5$\frac{1}{2}$ in. can be developed without serious differences of speed of contrast at a constant time. It may be noted that the first roll carries the bath past the maturing stage, and that a considerable volume of developer is carried out by the spool unit, making the topping-up the more effective. If topped-up with D19bR, up to eight rolls can be developed without changing the initial time and without any very serious loss of speed or contrast.

In some branches of photography, such as the motion picture industry, sensitometric control is regarded as an indispensable adjunct to processing in continuous machinery. It can be useful in air photography also, but not quite in the same way. The chief requirement in motion picture photography is for a constant gamma, which can be readily obtained by varying the development time or by altering the chemical composition of the bath according to the indications of sensitometric strips exposed on a standard emulsion. This is possible because cine film is not normally developed to its maximum contrast. In air photography, however, the emulsion is usually developed for maximum speed and hence maximum contrast also is obtained. Any attempt to keep to a constant gamma would inevitably lead to appreciable speed variations. The situation would be further complicated by the fact that different makes of the same nominal type of film, and even different batches of the same make, by no means give the same maximum gamma under identical development conditions. Attempts to keep a constant gamma with different batches and makes of film in use would therefore involve a sacrifice of speed, since the development would sometimes have to be cut to the point where the most contrasty film gave a gamma which could be reached by the least contrasty on long development. In so far as speed and contrast are to a limited extent interchangeable, some kind of controlled development could be worked out, but it is usually much simpler to give constant development and accept whatever variations are inherent in the speed and contrast of the film batches used, trusting to printing to iron out most of the differences. This is not a desirable state of affairs, but it cannot be avoided when development must be for maximum speed in the interests of maximum resolution. Where a certain loss of resolution can be tolerated in the interests of more uniform negative quality, and especially if one make of film only can be used, development to a constant gamma, or to a gamma which is varied under control to suit the contrast of the subject, would be quite practicable.

With full development of all negatives sensitometric control is used merely to determine the activity of the bath by passing through it sensitometric strips exposed on a standard batch of film of the same type as is used for the air photography. According to the indications of the strips the time of development can be altered to give constant speed on the standard batch, or, what is simpler, a constant fog, which will also ensure fairly constant speed. This is not full sensitometric control, but does ensure that at least one of the many factors which determine the characteristics of the final photograph is kept constant, and to that extent it is better than no control at all.

FIXATION

The developed negative consists of the swollen gelatine film, containing the metallic silver image, the residual undeveloped silver salts, and such developer as is carried out of the bath. The primary purpose of fixation is to remove the undeveloped silver salts, but the fixing bath is usually called upon to stop development quickly by neutralising the alkali and to harden the gelatine preparatory to washing and drying. If the emulsion is not exposed to light until fixation is complete, the stop action is not strictly essential, but if it is omitted and no separate stop bath is provided, the developer carried over in the film soon discolours the fixing bath as it oxidises and may cause stains.

The silver halides, being insoluble in water, are dissolved out of the film by treatment with compounds which form soluble salts of a complex nature, these diffusing out into the fixing bath and the wash water. The compound now universally used for this purpose is sodium thiosulphate, commonly called " hypo " because at one time it was believed to be sodium hyposulphite. It is cheap, stable, and non-poisonous, and has no serious solvent action on the developed silver image.

The developing action can be stopped by keeping the fixing bath mildly acid, but since thiosulphates are decomposed even by weak acids a simple addition of acid to the fixing bath is not allowable. In presence of sodium sulphite, however, no decomposition takes place, and the acid fixing bath typically contains a weak acid such as acetic with enough sulphite to protect the hypo. Acid salts such as sodium bisulphite or sodium hydrogen sulphate may be used instead of acetic acid. Weak acids are preferable to strong in acid fixing baths, because they allow the concentration of acid substance to be high enough for neutralisation of a relatively large volume of developer without the pH being inconveniently low. For improvement of this desirable property the bath is often " buffered " by addition of compounds such as boric acid, or borates, or sodium acetate, which keep the acidity fairly constant throughout the useful fixing life. Constant acidity not only maintains the stop qualities of the bath at their initial level, but also ensures that the action of the hardening agent does not fall off.

Potassium alum is the hardening agent usually added to acid fixing baths. Chrome alum baths give rather greater hardening when fresh, but they do not keep very well and soon become inferior to the potash alum types, which are perfectly satisfactory for all normal purposes.

The time of fixation is not critical, since the process goes to completion. It is usual to fix the negative for twice the time taken to clear all visible traces of the undeveloped silver salts, and although this extension of the time is not strictly necessary it is a useful precaution against premature removal from the bath. The negative should not be left in the fixing bath for excessive times, e.g., overnight, or it may be slightly reduced. When hardening fixing baths are used the time of immersion is governed by the necessity for complete action of the hardener. If the alum concentration is about 15 gm. per litre full hardening will require approximately ten minutes, but with higher alum concentrations less time will be needed. The alum and hypo concentrations are therefore adjusted in well-balanced formulæ so that fixation and hardening are completed at about the same time.

Hardening fixing baths are strongly advised, because a hardened negative takes up less water during washing and dries more rapidly. For use in spool tanks the Kodak F5 and F10 formulæ, given on page 74, are recommended. In continuous processing machines the time available for fixing is often limited, and it is desirable to increase the hypo concentration in these formulæ up to the optimum figure of 400 gm. per litre. At 21° C. most emulsions will clear within two and a half minutes in a bath of this concentration, but the hardening will not be so great as with the lower hypo concentration and hence slower fixing of the original formulæ. If greater hardening is required than can be obtained in five minutes, the alum concentration can be increased up to 30 gm. per litre. The " all-dry " formula is a modification, with increased hypo concentration, of a formula given by Woosley and Pankhurst (4) for fixing motion picture positive emulsions ; the hardening is very satisfactory in five minutes, and the formula has the advantage that all the constituents are solid chemicals, thus eliminating the need for transporting liquid acids when processing is done away from base.

When the most rapid possible fixation is essential, ammonium chloride may be added to the bath, or ammonium thiosulphate may be used if available. The Kodak F7 and the ATF5 formulæ both fix four to five times as rapidly as F5, when using Kodak Super XX and similar types of emulsion, but the gain is not necessarily the same for all emulsions. The hardening will, of course, be reduced in proportion to the saving in time, and the ammonium salts are said to cause a reduction in hardening apart from the shorter time. A good account of ammonium thiosulphate and ammonium chloride fixing baths is given by Allnutt, to whom the ATF5 formula is due. (5)

In ground photography it is customary to pass the developed film through an acid stop bath prior to fixation, thus relieving the acid fixing bath of most of the task of neutralising the developer alkali and prolonging its useful life. A weak solution of acetic acid is often used for the purpose. This practice is not without its dangers if applied to air negatives, which after prolonged development in D19b are swollen with a solution containing a high concentration of alkaline carbonate. When the developer and stop bath mix within the emulsion, carbon dioxide gas is evolved, small bubbles are formed and grow, and the emulsion may be ruptured in small blisters. This blistering is particularly liable to occur at high temperatures, and sometimes gives trouble even if the film is transferred direct to a rather acid fixing bath. It is less likely to occur if the fixer is well agitated to prevent the growth of the bubbles. Because of this blistering an acid stop bath is best avoided unless it is of higher pH than an acetic acid solution of the customary 2 or 3 per cent. strength. If a stop bath must be used a 3 per cent. chrome alum solution (formula Kodak SB3) could be tried, but stop baths are usually omitted altogether in air photography, the reduced life of the fixer being a small price to pay for simplicity in processing.

WASHING

A very brief wash after fixation will reduce the salt concentration below the point at which crystallisation will occur on the gelatine, but it is necessary to carry the process much further than this. The fixing bath contains complex silver salts, traces of which if left in the emulsion would slowly decompose and stain the clear gelatine, while traces of hypo slowly interact with the silver image and turn it brown. Given a continuous flow of fresh water over the film the soluble salts will rapidly diffuse out, their concentration within the gelatine diminishing exponentially with time. According to Mees (6), under these ideal conditions the gelatine will contain less than one-thousandth of its original salt concentration after six minutes. In practice washing conditions rarely allow a continuous exposure of the film to a rapid water stream, and the time has to be extended to half an hour or more, when processing average lengths of film in spool tanks. In continous processing machines the film is freely exposed during the washing process, but the space available for tanks does not usually allow adequate time to be given. A well-designed spray washing system, such as has been used for the washing of colour film in the German motion picture industry, appears to have advantages, since it gives very rapid renewal of the water at the film surface and so encourages diffusion outwards of the salts.

Sea water may be used for washing negatives with complete success, in fact the elimination of hypo is about twice as rapid as in fresh water. (7) A final rinse in fresh water is, however, necessary to rid the gelatine of the hygroscopic constituents of sea salt.

Water Supply.—The quality of the water available for photographic solutions is usually taken for granted, and if drinking water is used this is normally a safe assumption. It should perhaps be pointed out that in some localities the water is quite hard enough to justify the installation of a softening system, which will ensure clean and lime-free negatives. In certain overseas localities the water contains a proportion of alkali, which may be high enough to cause trouble by accelerating developer action, especially with the low-energy, fine-grain types. There is no simple remedy for the trouble, and short of finding an alternative source of supply it will be necessary to determine the alkali content by chemical analysis and modify the developer formula accordingly. Sea water, however, may be used safely for making up all developer and fixing baths and the effect of the salt content can be ignored.

FIXATION AND WASHING FOR PERMANENCE

The permanence of developed negatives depends on the thoroughness with which they are fixed and washed and on the subsequent storage conditions. Negatives which have been fixed without special precautions in one of the baths already mentioned, washed for at least ten minutes in running water, and stored in a cool dry place away from chemical fumes (especially sulphuretted hydrogen) will keep in good condition for at least five years and probably longer. When much better permanence than this is required, care must be taken to ensure more complete removal of hypo and silver complexes. The subject has been given very thorough study by Crabtree of the Eastman Kodak Laboratories, (8) who distinguishes two probable requirements :—

(a) General purposes keeping, where it is usually sufficient if the negatives remain in good condition for a few decades.

(b) " Archival " keeping, which implies complete removal of all injurious substances with a view to storing the negatives for a period of the order of a hundred years or as limited by the permanence of the base material.

Photographers wishing to attain either of these standards should preferably study the original paper, because the conditions are very complex, but for convenience the main recommendations are summarised here.

Fixing Process.—Hypo and silver complexes will not be completely removed by washing after potassium alum hardening fixing baths unless the pH of the bath is above the isoelectric point of gelatine ($4\cdot9$). Most acid hardening baths start their life at a lower pH than this, but approach or pass it as they become contaminated with alkaline developer. On the other hand, the Kodak F6 formula starts at $4\cdot9$ and does not change appreciably during its life. F6 is therefore recommended where good keeping is required.

Silver complexes will be retained by the film if the silver concentration in the fixing bath rises above $1\cdot5$ gm. per litre. To avoid a very frequent renewal of the bath it is preferable to use at least two baths in succession, the first being renewed or replaced by the second after a period of use. The object of the two baths is to ensure that the film passes through a bath containing less than $1\cdot5$ gm. silver per litre before it is washed, and care should therefore be taken that the first bath does not become too rich in silver, or the carry-over may raise the silver concentration of the second above the point where it can work efficiently. For general purposes, where only one bath is used, it should be discarded after fixing about 20 ft. of $9\frac{1}{2}$ in. wide film per gal., but if two baths are used the first can be used up to 50 ft. per gal. For archival storage a single bath should only be used to 2 ft. per gal., and the first bath of a pair up to 30 ft. per gal.

Washing Process.—All possible steps should be taken to ensure that the water in contact with the emulsion is rapidly renewed, and the removal of hypo and silver complexes will be accelerated if the temperature is kept up to 65° to 70° F. Under the usual washing conditions at least an hour is required for complete elimination of hypo, but spray washing or good agitation, as by compressed air, will reduce the time required. The film should be tested for residual hypo and silver as described by Crabtree and summarised below.

Testing for Hypo and Silver.—The old permanganate test is of limited sensitivity and does not indicate the amount of hypo held by the film. When it is possible to cut a small test piece from the film the mercuric chloride test may be used. The reagent is a solution containing $2\frac{1}{2}$ per cent. mercuric chloride (poisonous) and potassium bromide per litre. One square inch of washed film is placed in 10 c.c. of the reagent and the development of a turbidity is observed. Complete washing out of hypo, required for archival storage, is indicated by a negative result.

Silver in negatives can be detected by the sodium sulphide spot test. A drop of $0\cdot2$ per cent. sodium sulphide solution containing 10 c.c. of 40 per cent. formalin per litre is placed on a clear part of the negative and allowed to stand for five minutes before blotting-off. The presence of silver complexes is indicated by a brown stain.

DRYING

Air negatives would ideally be dried slowly in air of about 50 per cent. humidity without any use of heat, thus avoiding stresses as far as possible, but the need for rapid output and for keeping up with the speed of continuous processing machinery generally necessitates some heat, applied either as hot air or as radiant heat directed at the film. A methylated spirit bath is sometimes used to speed up drying by replacing the water by a more volatile liquid, but spirit drying is not normally recommended, as it causes serious distortions in the base and renders the negatives useless for mapping. Even when dimensional stability is unimportant there are disadvantages in the use of spirit, because it is liable to give opalescence by dehydrating the gelatine, and is liable to attack and weaken acetate base. (The modern " safety " bases, however, are not seriously affected by spirit, in the sense of being mechanically weakened, though they naturally suffer from the distortions already mentioned.) Chemical accelerators of drying, such as a saturated solution of potassium carbonate, are messy and inconvenient for long lengths of film.

At present the best way of drying air negatives in a reasonable time is to hasten the evaporation of water by blowing air of low relative humidity across it at high velocity. The air is usually dried by heat for simplicity, additional heat being required to make up the latent heat of evaporation of the water. In view of the large areas of the negatives there is a considerable mass of water to be evaporated ; a typical negative material, after washing and removal of surface liquid, contains about 1 kg. of water per 100 ft. run of 9 in. wide film, so that the power required for evaporation alone is far from negligible. Present types of drying equipment consume a power of the order of 5 kw. when drying 9 in. wide film at a rate of 4 ft. per min. but there is some evidence that better performances may be expected, following closer study of dryer design. There would appear to be some scope for improvement in finding the best balance between the power allotted for heat and for raising the air velocity, and in designing the details of the air flow for best efficiency. Calhoun (9) indicates that the drying rate varies as the $0\cdot8$ power of the air velocity, so that within limits it obviously pays to divert a good deal of power to air movement. Modern dryers effect a great economy in heating power by circulating the air in a closed system from which a part of the air is continuously removed while a slow stream of fresh air is continuously passed in, thus keeping the humidity at a reasonable level. Some designs use radiant heat and claim high efficiency, but there is little evidence in favour of this system, and in at least some cases it would appear that the heating lamps operate mainly by raising the temperature of the air.

Special Processing Methods

In air photography, as in all other photography, the processing is only a means to an end ; it should therefore be standardised along well-established lines and not changed without good reason. The special techniques described in the following paragraphs are not therefore recommended for use under any but exceptional circumstances. The account is included to round off the general picture of negative processing and to put the information on record for easy reference and use when justified.

Development for Low Contrast.—Most air photography needs fairly high negative contrast, gammas of 1·0 to 1·5 being usual, and the standard types of emulsion give this order of contrast when developed for maximum speed in D19*b*. In much low-altitude work, however, the subject brightness range is such that a much lower gamma, of the order of 0·8 to 1·0, is desirable. It has already been pointed out that reduction of the development time merely leads to a loss of speed without much drop in gamma, and the loss of speed is particularly serious in low-altitude photography, where the dark shadows require an increased exposure and the image movement often demands a higher shutter speed. At 500 ft. the camera exposure may typically have to be four times that required at 20,000 ft., so that the requirement is really for an increase of emulsion speed coupled with a reduction in contrast.

One solution to the problem is to change the emulsion to a type such as Ilford HP3 or Kodak Tri-X, which are faster than the standard aero types and usually give a lower gamma in D19*b*. If this is not possible, the metol developer, formula ID3, recommended by Moore (10), may be tried. It will usually give a markedly lower contrast than D19*b*, with no loss of speed if development is carried far enough. A suggested time of development for a short length of film in a spool tank is ten minutes at 20° C.

If operating from slow-flying aircraft, there may be emulsion speed in reserve, and the standard low-activity developers, such as D76 or DK20, may be preferred, because they keep better than the metol formula. A suitable time for a gamma of 1·0 would be about eighteen minutes at 20° C. in a spool tank.

Development for Maximum Speed.—The reference to Moore already quoted should be consulted for a useful general survey. Although D19*b* gives about the best compromise between speed and graininess for most air photography, there are occasions when the utmost possible speed is required even at a sacrifice in graininess or other desirable qualities. In such circumstances other developers may be tried.

With some emulsions the R.A.F. pyro-metol developer formula, as used in former times by the Royal Air Force, gives slightly higher speed without increase in graininess. The increase in log speed will probably not be greater than 0·1 with most emulsions, it may be less, or with other emulsions it may be as much as 0·3 ; the only course is to try it with the emulsion available, since all that can be positively said is that there will be no loss of speed compared with D19b. A further slight increase may be had by use of the " staining " version of the same formula, but in this case the graininess will be appreciably worse. It was at one time thought that the stain deposited with the silver image gave a considerable increase of effective speed, but the gain has been shown to be very small by a sensitometric study in which the contact-printing densities of the stained images were evaluated in order to plot the effective characteristic curves. The stain, as such, increases *contrast*, but has very little effect on true speed.

Other developer formulæ are often proposed for obtaining the utmost possible speed, and some of them do give a genuine increase, but as with pyro the amount of the gain cannot be predicted with certainty. All of these special developers, however, cause a large increase in graininess, which is often most troublesome in the fog and low densities where the under-exposed image is naturally found. A Kodak formula quoted by Moore (10) is given in the general formula list as SD19a.

Special treatments before or after development have also been proposed as a means of increasing speed. Hypersensitising with alkaline solutions such as ammonia, triethanolamine, or caustic potash before exposure have been advocated, but such treatments are troublesome to apply and seriously lower the keeping qualities of the emulsion, which must be used within a few hours. Intensification of the latent image by exposure to mercury vapour has had a vogue, but in general is not worth the effort involved. Intensification of the latent image by exposure for a period of the order of an hour to a very weak light after removal from the camera, the so-called " latensification " seemed promising at one time. The method was thoroughly investigated by Moore (11), who showed that although it gave remarkable increases in speed for negatives developed to a low gamma, the increase was much less for negatives developed fully in, for example, R.A.F. pyro-metol. Moreover, the increase is less marked for very fast emulsions than for slower types. The speed increase to be expected with the fast emulsions used for air photography is only about 30 per cent. Nevertheless the method may be considered worth trying, as the film is not wetted and the post-exposure fogging is easily done. The intensity of the fogging light should be adjusted so that with an exposure time of about thirty minutes the total fog is approximately 0·1 greater than the fog which would normally be produced with the time of development used. The hypersensitising action is independent of the colour of the light, so that a masked-down safelight provides a convenient low-intensity source. There is no increase in graininess.

Intensification after development may also be considered as a processing technique for increasing speed, and a genuine improvement in the value of seriously under-exposed negatives is obtainable. The graininess is greatly increased, however, by all intensification procedures. The best intensifiers are either the old uranium formula or the Kodak formula In6, quinone-thiosulphuric acid (12); both these formulæ are given in the formulary. Negatives for intensification should be very thoroughly washed, as traces of hypo will upset the action.

Processing at High Temperatures.—It is sometimes impossible to keep the processing solutions below the recommended upper limit of temperature of 24° C., and special methods have then to be adopted. It should again be emphasised that high temperatures should always be avoided if at all possible, even at the cost of deferred processing, because the photographic quality of the negatives is never so good as when they are developed at normal temperatures. Softening of the emulsion can be countered by suitable hardening baths, but fog rises, even at reduced times of development, and the addition of extra restrainer carries the risk of dichroic fog. The organic anti-fogging agents have some advantages, but clean negatives are only obtained at the expense of speed. High temperatures also lead to a reduction in the maximum contrast obtainable.

The maximum safe temperature for normal processing depends very much on the characteristics of the emulsion in use. Emulsions not described as specially hardened are not normally safe above 75° F., but the hardened types can usually be taken up to 90° F. Depending on the temperatures and the kind of film in use some or all of the measures detailed below may be found useful.

Hardening Fixing Bath.—While a hardening fixing bath is advised under all circumstances, it should be regarded as absolutely essential above 70° F. (21° C.). Care should be taken to see that adequate time is allowed for complete hardening, as the fixing may be very rapid at high temperatures.

Hardening Stop Bath.—The hardening life of the fixing bath will be improved if the film is passed through a stop bath such as SB4 between development and fixation. Immersion should be for at least three minutes with good agitation in the first few seconds to avoid risk of precipitation of chromium hydroxide by the alkaline developer.

Modifications to Developer.—D19b has a fairly high salt content and does not cause serious swelling of the emulsion up to about 75° F. (24° C.). Above this temperature it has been recommended to add sodium sulphate, which is photographically inert but helps to prevent any greater swelling. The development times appropriate at 20° C. should be given for all temperatures up to 90° F. (32° C.); above 90° F. reduce the times by one-third. The proportions of anhydrous sodium sulphate to add are shown in Table 3.

TABLE 3

Temperature.	Grammes of Anhydrous Sodium Sulphate per Litre.
° F.	Grammes.
75 to 80	50
80 ,, 85	75
85 ,, 90	100
90 ,, 95	100

Pre-hardening Bath.—If the specially hardened films are not being used, a hardening bath may be necessary before development when the temperature is 90° F. or more. A suitable formula is given on page 76.

The hardening agent generally used before development is formalin, either in liquid form (solution of formaldehyde) or as the polymerised solid form, paraformaldehyde. Formaldehyde reacts with sodium sulphite, liberating caustic alkali, hence if added to developers (except those already containing caustic alkalis) it accelerates the reaction and causes fog. Even if used as a pre-development bath, fog is caused by traces of formalin left in the emulsion when it enters the developer. This can be avoided by incorporating a buffering agent such as borax or sodium citrate in the pre-hardening bath. As formalin gives effective hardening only in alkaline solution, a stronger alkali such as caustic soda may also be added to give a pH of about 9·0. This pH is high enough to give good hardening, while the buffering action of the borax prevents any further rise when the formalin reacts with the sulphite of the developer. As a further precaution against fog the bath also incorporates a small proportion of anti-fogging compound. The formula given includes Kodak anti-fogging agent, but other similar compounds could probably be substituted. The film should be immersed for three minutes and need not be washed before transferring to the developer. Since the hardening slows up development, the times normally used at the chosen temperatures should be increased by 50 per cent. This pre-hardener will enable the normal unhardened type of film to be developed in the unmodified D19b formula at temperatures up to 100° F.

Rapid Development.—Developers containing caustic alkali, such as the Ilford " RR " X-ray developer, give full emulsion speed and contrast in about one and a half minutes, compared with the ten minutes or more required in D19b. There is a slight but not very serious loss of resolution, but otherwise the rapid developer gives equally satisfactory results. However, rapid development is not advocated for normal use, because it is liable to give trouble with uneven action in view of the very short time involved, and solutions containing caustic alkalis are unpleasant to handle. The mixed developer will not keep for more than a few days even in closed vessels. In practically all air photography a saving of a few minutes in the processing time is of little significance in relation to the hours spent in flight.

References

1. MEES. " Theory of the Photographic Process." Macmillan.
2. MEES. " Theory of the Photographic Process," p. 461. Macmillan.
3. CALHOUN, J. M. " The Physical Properties of Safety Aerographic Film." *Photogrammetric Engineering*, July, 1947.
4. WOOSLEY, D. P., and PANKHURST, K. G. " Sodium Hydrogen Sulphate in Acid Fixing Baths," *Photo. Journ.*, **82**, 12, January 1942.
5. ALLNUTT, D. B. " Some Characteristics of Ammonium Thiosulphate Fixing Baths," *Journ. Soc. Mot. Pic. Eng.*, **41**, 300, October 1943.
6. MEES. " Theory of the Photographic Process," p. 533. Macmillan.
7. CRABTREE, J. I., and EATON, G. T. " Washing Photographic Films and Prints in Sea-water." *Journ. Soc. Mot. Pic. Eng.*, **40**, 380-91, 1943.

8. CRABTREE, J. I., EATON, G. T., and MUEHLER, L. E. " The Removal of Hypo and Silver Salts from Photographic Materials as Affected by the Composition of the Processing Solutions," *Journ. Soc. Mot. Pic. Eng.*, **41,** 9, July 1943.
9. CALHOUN, J. M. " The Physical Properties and Dimensional Stability of Motion Picture Film," *Journ. Soc. Mot. Pic. Eng.*, **43,** 4, October, 1944.
10. MOORE, G. S. " The Last Ounce of Speed," *Photo. Journ.*, **88-A,** 240, 1948.
11. MOORE, G. S. " Hypersensitisation of the Latent Image by a Uniform Low-intensity Light Exposure," *Photo. Journ.*, p. 41, January 1941.
12. MUEHLER, L. E., and CRABTREE, J. I. " A Single-solution Intensifier for Very Weak Negatives," *Photo. Journ.*, **86-B,** 1946.

FORMULARY

DEVELOPERS

D19*b* (standard negative developer)—

Metol	2·2 gm.
Hydroquinone	8·8 ,,
Sodium sulphite (anhydrous) . . .	72·0 ,,
Sodium carbonate (anhydrous) . . .	48·0 ,,
Potassium bromide	4·0 ,,
Water up to	1·0 litre

Ilford ID19 gives similar results.

D19*b*R (replenisher for D19*b*)—

Metol	3·9 gm.
Hydroquinone	15·6 ,,
Sodium sulphite (anhydrous) . . .	72·0 ,,
Sodium carbonate (anhydrous) . . .	48·0 ,,
Sodium hydroxide	8·0 ,,
Water up to	1·0 litre

DK20 (fine-grain developer)—

Metol	5·0 gm.
Sodium sulphite (anhydrous) . . .	100·0 ,,
Kodalk	2·0 ,,
Potassium thiocyanate	2·0 ,,
Potassium bromide	0·5 ,,
Water up to	1·0 litre

D76 (for lower contrast than D19*b*)—

Metol	2·0 gm.
Hydroquinone	5·0 ,,
Sodium sulphite (anhydrous) . . .	100·0 ,,
Borax	2·0 ,,
Water up to	1·0 litre

ID15 (low contrast metol giving full speed)—

Metol	3·0 gm.
Sodium sulphite (anhydrous) . . .	20·0 ,,
Sodium carbonate (anhydrous) . . .	17·0 ,,
Potassium bromide	0·5 ,,
Water up to	1·0 litre

For use dilute with an equal volume of water. Develop for ten to fifteen minutes at 68° F., or to a fog of about 0·2.

R.A.F. pyro-metol (slightly higher speed than D19*b*)—

Metol	4·2 gm.
Potassium metabisulphite	5·1 ,,
Pyrogallol	5·1 ,,
Sodium sulphite (anhydrous) . . .	30·0 ,,
Sodium carbonate (anhydrous) . . .	30·0 ,,
Potassium bromide	2·0 ,,
Water up to	1·0 litre

For a staining developer omit the sodium sulphite.

SD19a (for maximum speed when increased fog and grain can be tolerated)—

Metol	2·2 gm.
Hydroquinone	8·8 ,,
Sodium sulphite (anhydrous)	96·0 ,,
Sodium carbonate (anhydrous)	48·0 ,,
Potassium bromide	5·0 ,,
Hydrazine dihydrochloride	1·6 ,,
Kodak anti-fogging agent	0·04 ,,
Water up to	1·0 litre

The hydrazine dihydrochloride and anti-fogging agent are dissolved in a small quantity of water and added to the mixed developer (which is standard D19 before this addition) just before use. Develop twelve to twenty minutes at 68° F. for a fog of 0·4 to 0·6. Gives two or three times greater speed than D19 or D19b.

Paper Developers

D72 (for chloride or bromide papers)—

Metol	3·1 gm.
Hydroquinone	12·0 ,,
Sodium sulphite (anhydrous)	45·0 ,,
Sodium carbonate (anhydrous)	67·5 ,,
Potassium bromide	1·9 ,,
Water up to	1·0 litre

Fixing Baths

F5 (hardening for negatives)—

Sodium thiosulphate (crystals)	240·0 gm.
Sodium sulphite (anhydrous)	15·0 ,,
Glacial acetic acid	13·0 c.c.
Boric acid (crystals)	7·5 gm.
Potassium alum	15·0 ,,
Water up to	1·0 litre

pH 4·1.

F10 (for negatives : more rapid than F5 and greater hardening)—

Sodium thiosulphate (crystals)	330·0 gm.
Sodium sulphite (anhydrous)	7·5 ,,
Glacial acetic acid	20·0 c.c.
Kodalk	30·0 gm.
Potassium alum	22·5 ,,
Water up to	1·0 litre

pH 4·6.

F7 (for very rapid fixation of negatives)—

Sodium thiosulphate (crystals)	360·0 gm.
Ammonium chloride	50·0 ,,
Sodium sulphite (anhydrous)	15·0 ,,
Glacial acetic acid	13·0 c.c.
Boric acid (crystals)	7·5 gm.
Potassium alum	15·0 ,,
Water up to	1·0 litre

ATF5 (for very rapid fixing of negatives)—

Ammonium thiosulphate	200·0 gm.
Sodium sulphite (anhydrous) . . .	15·0 ,,
Acetic acid, glacial	14·0 c.c.
Boric acid (crystals)	7·5 gm.
Potassium alum ·	15·0 ,,
Water up to	1·0 litre

F6 (high pH, for good permanence of negatives)—

Sodium thiosulphate (crystals) . . .	240·0 gm.
Sodium sulphite (anhydrous) . . .	15·0 ,,
Acetic acid, glacial	13·0 c.c.
Potassium alum	15·0 gm.
Kodalk	15·0 ,,
Water up to	1·0 litre

pH 4·9.

" All-dry " fixing formula

A	Sodium thiosulphate (crystals) . . .	400·0 gm.
	Sodium sulphite (anhydrous) . . .	15·0 ,,
	Sodium acetate	15·0 ,,
	Boric acid (crystals)	10·0 ,,
B	Sodium hydrogen sulphate . . .	15·0 ,,
	Potassium alum	32·0 ,,

Dissolve A in about 60 per cent. of the water at 120° F. (50° C.) and B in about 20 per cent. Mix the two solutions at a temperature not above 70° F. (21° C.) and adjust volume to 1 litre.

F1 (for papers)—

Sodium thiosulphate (crystals) . . .	180·0 gm.
Sodium sulphite (anhydrous) . . .	11·0 ,,
Glacial acetic acid	10·0 c.c.
Potassium alum	11·0 gm.
Water up to	1·0 litre

IF4 (non-hardening acid fixer for papers)—

Sodium thiosulphate (crystals) . . .	200·0 gm.
Potassium metabisulphite (or sodium metabisulphite)	25·0 ,,
Water up to	1·0 litre

STOP BATHS

SB3 (mildly acid hardening)—

Chrome alum	30·0 gm.
Water up to	1·0 litre

SB4 (for tropical development, non-swelling)—

Chrome alum	30·0 gm.
Sodium sulphate (anhydrous) . . .	60·0 ,,
Water up to	1·0 litre

PRE-HARDENING BATH (PRE-DEVELOPMENT, TROPICAL)

Kodalk	20·0 gm.
Paraformaldehyde	2·0 ,,
Kodak anti-fogging agent	0·025 ,,
Boric acid	5·0 ,,
Sodium sulphate (anhydrous) . . .	50·0 ,,
Water up to	1·0 litre

Dissolve the first three chemicals in the order given, using about 750 c.c. of the water at 100° F. Dissolve the remaining chemicals in the rest of the water and mix the solutions.

INTENSIFIERS

Uranium—

A	Uranium nitrate	20·0 gm.
	Glacial acetic acid	10·0 c.c.
	Water up to	500·0 ,,
B	Potassium ferricyanide	20·0 gm.
	Water up to	500·0 c.c.

Mix one part A with one part B and dilute with six parts of water. This solution attacks metal tanks.

Quinone-thiosulphuric acid (Kodak In6)—

A	Water at 70° F.	750·0 c.c.
	Sulphuric acid (concentrated) . .	30·0 ,,
	Potassium dichromate	22·5 gm.
	Water up to	1·0 litre
B	Water at 70° F.	750·0 c.c.
	Sodium bisulphite	3·8 gm.
	Hydroquinone	15·0 ,,
	Kodak wetting agent (10 per cent. solution) .	20·0 c.c.
	Water up to	1·0 litre
C	Sodium thiosulphate (crystals) . .	22·5 gm.
	Water up to	1·0 litre

For use : Add two parts of B to one part of A with stirring, followed by two parts of C. Continue stirring and add one part of A. The order of mixing is important.

Notes.—

1. The wetting agent is not essential but gives even action.
2. The sulphuric acid should be added *slowly* to the water. Never pour water on concentrated acid.
3. Before intensification negatives must be hardened in the alkaline formalin bath SH1 for five minutes, followed by a five-minute wash.
4. The water used for the solutions A, B, and C must either be distilled or be known to contain less than fifteen parts of chloride per million.

HARDENING BATH (KODAK SH1)

Water	500·0 c.c.
Formaldehyde (nominal 40 per cent. solution) .	10·0 ,,
Sodium carbonate (anhydrous) . . .	5·0 gm.
Water up to	1·0 litre

Chapter Five

PHOTOGRAPHIC RESOLVING POWER

THE ability of a camera to record fine detail is generally expressed in terms of resolving power. This is not because the resolution test is necessarily the best or the only possible test, but because it is the simplest way of comparing lens and film combinations on a quantitative basis. It has been found in practice that the intelligence value of air photographs increases with increase of photographic resolving power, and once this essential prime fact has been established the use of a numerical scale adds precision and clarity to discussions of experimental fact or attempts at a unifying theory.

The conception of resolving power is not, of course, peculiar to photography. It originated in astronomy, where it is sometimes difficult to separate the images of two distant points of light such as double stars very close together on a black background. This is a clear-cut case and is resolving power in the true sense, but when applied to photography the term has a different meaning. When referring to emulsions only it is measured by photographing with a high quality lens a series of groups of black and white lines, the width and spacing of the lines being equal but decreasing from group to group in a regular way. The width of a line plus a space in the smallest group recognisable in the developed image is taken as the smallest distance resolvable, and the reciprocal of this is called the resolving power in lines per millimetre. Alternatively a contact test object of similar form may be printed directly on the emulsion. This again is fairly straightforward in relation to some applications of photography, e.g., recording of close spectral lines. The use of resolving power figures in relation to the formation of ordinary photographic images has a less satisfactory logical basis. Nevertheless resolution tests are being widely used to express the performance of lens and emulsion combinations, and it is unlikely that they will be replaced by any other test in the immediate future. While this stressing of the quantitative expression of camera performance is all to the good, it must always be remembered that photographic resolving power and the resolving power of lenses and optical instruments in general are quite different things which must not be confused. It will later be shown that there is no strict connection between the visual and photographic resolving powers of photographic lenses. " Photographic resolving power," as used in this book, means the ability of a camera, i.e., lens plus emulsion, to reproduce fine details of the type of the test object specified. It has no absolute or permanent significance derived from physical optics in the way that true resolving power, as of a telescope, can be derived.

While it is convenient to discuss the visual resolving power of lenses in terms of small point sources on a black ground, the actual measurement is frequently carried out by observing or photographing targets of black and white lines. A typical line target is shown in Fig. 25. It consists of groups of white lines on a black background, the line width being equal to the spacing and diminishing in geometric progression from group to group. (In Fig. 25 and other illustrations of test objects the lines are shown as black on a white ground for convenience in reproduction, but in practice it is usual for the lines to be lighter than the background.) In this type of target the length of the lines is always made considerably greater than their width. In optical theory it is shown that the resolving power of a highly corrected lens depends only on its aperture and the wavelength of the light. Photographic lenses do not rank as highly corrected in this sense, but at moderate and small apertures their visual resolving power measured on axis does approximate to the theoretical value. With a target of black and white lines the measured figure for a typical air camera lens is about two hundred lines per millimetre at $f/8$, which is not far short of the theoretical value for that aperture, and as the lens is stopped down the resolution falls off in accordance with the theoretical prediction. The resolving power of photographic emulsions, measured also by black and white lines but without use of a lens, is approximately fifty lines per millimetre for fast panchromatic emulsions, and two hundred lines for very slow document copying emulsions.

FIG. 25.—Line test object.

In practical photography the user is not particularly concerned with the resolving power of either the lens or the film considered separately ; what he wishes to know is the combined performance of the two. From what has just been said it might appear that the film is the only factor of importance, since the visual resolving power of lenses is much higher than the resolving power of the fast emulsions used in air photography and in photography generally. Until a few years ago it was, in fact, commonly believed that for this reason there was no point in improving the performance of lenses. This is an apparently obvious and unassailable conclusion, but it has been shown to be quite incorrect by more recent researches, especially those of E. W. H. Selwyn and his associates. (1), (2) An account of these more modern developments is given in this chapter, but in anticipation it may be said that a more complete understanding of the subject has shown that the visual resolving power of a lens is no guide to its photographic performance. At some future time it may become possible to predict photographic from visual resolution, but in the present state of our knowledge this cannot be done.

It should perhaps be emphasised that the sketch of the present state of knowledge given in this chapter is based on a relatively limited amount of research, and current views are fairly certain to be modified as knowledge of the subject grows. Nevertheless, so much more is known about the subject now than even ten years ago that an account of recent advances cannot be omitted.

MEASUREMENT OF RESOLVING POWER

Test Objects.—In comparing the resolving power of lenses it is necessary to have some standard form of test object, which should correspond as closely as is reasonably possible to the conditions of actual use. The details of interest in air photography may be of any shape, so that no one form of object will be the most representative. On the other hand, groups of long lines and isolated points of light do not occur with any great frequency in aerial views. Objections can be raised against almost any conceivable

FIG. 26.—Test objects for measurement of lens/film resolving power.

form of test object, but the type known as the " Cobb," which has generally been adopted in England, seems freer from objections than most. The form of the Cobb test object is shown in Fig. 26 ; it consists of two light lines on a darker background, the length of the lines being three times their width, and the separation equal to their width. The length is great enough for the object to have a directional property without a disadvantage associated with the groups of longer lines previously used. In judging the resolution on a grainy photographic image with long-line objects the observer tends to join up scattered grains along the line direction, and thus to see resolution at a point where it would not have been visible in detail of random size and distribution. The usual criterion of resolution with the Cobb object is that the lines shall be seen as separate and that their direction shall be correctly identified. Groups of four objects of each size are generally used, oriented in pairs at right angles so that resolution may be measured in two directions. The size interval is commonly 10 per cent., *i.e.*, each object is 1·1 times bigger than its predecessor in the series. Howlett (3) has proposed the annulus target, also shown in Fig. 26, which has considerable advantages. The proposed criterion of resolution is that the boundary of the ring shall be recognised as unbroken, and this removes any ambiguity as to the interpretation of results when the resolution is very different in different directions. It also shortens the time of reading results, since the one object caters for resolution in all directions. There is so much in favour of the annulus target that it is to be hoped that this form will become universal.

In addition to the shape, the contrast between the light and dark parts of the test object must also be defined, because the contrast is a very important factor in resolution, particularly where grainy photographic images are concerned. When testing lenses for air photography it is not desirable to use black and white objects, having a density difference of perhaps 2·0, because the total range of brightness of high-altitude views is only about 0·75 on the log scale. Measurements on actual details in air photographs have shown that a fairly representative figure for the test object contrast is a density difference of 0·2. Many details in air photographs will, of course, have higher or lower contrast than 0·2, but it is much closer to the probable mean contrast than 2·0. It must be said that in practice it rarely happens that the order of merit of lenses is inverted by changing from low to high contrast test objects, but the theoretical possibility exists, the practical possibility can be demonstrated, and as in many other branches of photographic science the safe course is to match the experimental conditions as closely as possible to practice.

It will be seen that photographic resolving power, determined with test objects of this kind, is an *ad hoc* measurement for a particular purpose and bears little relation to the resolving power of physical optics.

Definitions of Resolving Power.—For most photographic purposes resolving power is expressed in lines per millimetre, which is an expression of the quality of the definition at the image plane. The application of the tests in air photography, however, is generally to find out what sizes of detail will be visible from a given altitude. Let $1/r$ be the distance between line centres in the smallest Cobb object resolved, then the resolving power in the image is r lines per millimetre. Let the focal length of the lens be f mm., then the angle subtended at the lens by the resolved detail is $\theta = 1/rf$ Now the angle subtended by the object is the same as that subtended by the image, so that if the height is h and the size of detail just resolved on the ground is R, $\theta = 1/rf = 1/Rh$. The term " rf " is known as the angular resolving power and is measured, by definition, in reciprocal radians. Having measured the resolving power in lines per millimetre, we therefore multiply by the focal length and the product enables us to state the size of detail resolved on the ground from any height. Thus if the resolving power of a 20-in. lens is ten lines per millimetre, its angular resolution is $(20 \times 25 \times 10) = 5,000$, and from 20,000 ft. it resolves ground details 4 ft. apart.

The apparent sharpness of a picture depends on the resolving power in lines per millimetre, but not all pictures having the same lines per millimetre appear equally sharp. In general, grainy photographs look sharper than grainless images having exactly the same resolution. Although a certain level of sharpness is necessary for comfort in viewing air photographs, especially under magnification, it should never be forgotten that sharpness as such, without any specification of focal length, conveys no guarantee of good resolution of ground details. For example, a photograph taken from 20,000 ft. with a small camera fitted with a 2-in. lens will probably look much sharper than one taken at the same instant with an aircraft camera fitted with, say, a 36-in. lens, and will stand greater enlargement, yet it will have only about one-fifth of the resolution in terms of ground detail. In photographs taken on fast panchromatic film the image is satisfactorily sharp and will stand magnification to about four times if the resolving power for low contrast details is not less than ten lines per millimetre.

Measurement of Resolving Power.—For a complete resolution test of a lens, photographs must be taken at several different positions across the angular field and in several planes of focus. For short-focus lenses this can conveniently be done by setting up a row of test objects in a plane

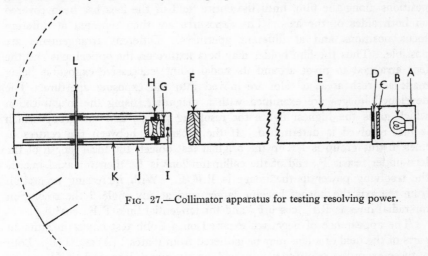

Fig. 27.—Collimator apparatus for testing resolving power.

opposite the lens and at such a distance (say more than ten times the focal length) that the latter behaves in the same way as when used at infinity. The focal length of aircraft camera lenses is generally so great that a set-up of this kind has to be out of doors, and even then the distances are often impracticably great. Moreover, the tests are then dependent on weather conditions, and are very difficult to repeat with precision. For these reasons a different approach is adopted.

Fig. 27 is a diagrammatic representation in plan of one form of apparatus used for the indoor testing of air camera lenses. A transparent test object D, uniformly illuminated from behind by the lamphouse A containing the lamp B and opal glass C, is fixed at one end of the collimator tube E at the focus of the collimator lens F. The light emerging from the collimator is parallel so that the test object is effectively at infinity. The diameter of the collimator lens must be sufficient for the front glass of all lenses tested to be completely filled with light. There are possible objections to the use of a collimator, as its faults might mask those of the lens being tested, but any such troubles are avoided by using a highly corrected telescope objective as the collimating lens and arranging that its focal length is considerably greater than that of the camera lenses. Air camera lenses up to about 50 in. focal length can safely be tested on a 100-in. collimator. The test lens G is mounted solidly in a flange H on a carriage J, which can pivot around a vertical axis through I so that the incident light strikes the lens at different angles and the image can be formed at different positions on the long strip of film held in the carrier L. The front glass of the lens is always positioned over I so that it does not move out of the beam of light from F as the carriage is rotated. The film holder L moves along rails for focusing. Various details such as the fine focusing adjustment and the arrangements for making the exposures are omitted for clarity. After visually focusing the lens a series of exposures are made at different angular settings by rotating J around I so that the test object is imaged at corresponding positions along the film, until the entire field of the lens has been covered on both sides of the axis. The exposures are then repeated at different focus positions and at different apertures. Different arrangements are possible. Thus the film holder may be a fixture on the optical axis and the lens arranged to pivot around its nodal point, successive exposures being made as fresh areas of film are moved into the exposing aperture. The developed images are examined with a magnifier, using the magnification which gives the highest figure for resolving power, and the group which is just resolved is determined. If the separation between the centres of lines in this group is $1/R$ in the original test object, the focal length of the lens under test is F_l, and of the collimator lens is F_c, then for axial images the resolving power in the image is $R.F_c/F_l$. With increasing separation from the axis the images become larger, and at any angle θ the resolution for radial lines is $R.F_c. \cos \theta/F_l$, and for tangential lines $R.F_c. \cos^2 \theta/F_l$.

The appearance of negatives exposed on a Cobb test object in different parts of the field of a lens may be gathered from Plates 1 (A) and 1 (B). Both of these examples relate to a 6-in. wide-angle survey lens, and the degree of enlargement was twenty times in each case. Super XX film was used, and in Example (A) it is obvious that the graininess of the emulsion plays a large part in determining the level of resolving power, though from separate measurements on the film with other lenses it is known that the defects of the lens are not without effect. In Example (B), however, although the graininess is still obvious, the optical quality of the image is evidently poor, and its imperfections are the main factor in fixing the resolution at a much lower level than in the first example. Example (A) was on the lens axis and Example (B) about half-way across the field in the zone of worst definition.

In the original work of Selwyn and Tearle the lenses were tested on three different panchromatic emulsions, viz., Super XX, Panatomic X, and Microfile. The first two of these were representative of types of emulsion which have actually been used for air photography; Panatomic X was about the slowest which could be used for that purpose; its speed was about one-third that of Super XX and its resolving power about 30 per cent. greater. Super XX was the fastest type normally used for daylight work. Microfile was of very much finer grain than the other two; its resolving power was about three times that of Super XX, but it had only about one-eightieth the speed. It was included because the difference in graininess and resolving power between Super XX and Panatomic X was so small that the influence of these characteristics on the combined lens-film resolution would not have been very clear. With Microfile in addition it was possible to see the influence of large changes in the emulsion factors which affect resolving power and to put in proper perspective any likely improvements in emulsion speed-graininess ratios. The development conditions were adjusted so that all three emulsions gave the same contrast, gamma being 1·6 approximately.

Cobb test objects were used throughout this work and the results were expressed in terms of " radial " and " tangential " resolving power. On the usual convention, which was adopted in this case, radial resolving power is measured on test objects orientated so that their length is radial to the optical axis, while tangential resolving power is measured on lines at right angles to this direction. Howlett (3) has pointed out that radial resolving power should strictly be measured on tangential lines and vice versa, and proposes to avoid the ambiguity by speaking of " resolving power on radial lines," where the usual phrase is " radial resolving power," and conversely. This suggestion has not yet been universally accepted, however, and throughout this book the convention first described will be used.

Results of Resolution Tests on Typical Lenses.—Selwyn and Tearle tested a range of aircraft camera lenses mostly designed before 1940, including focal lengths from 5 to 56 in. and maximum apertures from $f/2·5$ to $f/9·5$. Other workers in England, Canada, and the United States have since added very considerably to the total of resolution data, and all lenses of importance have been tested. It will be appreciated that the mass of experimental evidence, even from the original work, is too great to be treated in any but a summarised form, since every lens was tested at all apertures, several focus settings, at numerous points in the field, and on three different emulsions. Fortunately the results allow of a considerable degree of generalisation, and almost any of the lenses would serve as a reasonably representative sample of the whole series.

The simplest way of expressing the results of a resolution test is to plot resolving power against angular separation from the axis, giving so-called R/θ curves. It is desirable for the R values to be plotted on a logarithmic scale, as this helps to preserve a due sense of proportion when there are considerable variations in the level of resolving power. On the log scale equal fractional increments of resolution are shown as equal steps on the scale. This is correct since a change of, say, three lines per millimetre is much more important at a level of five lines per millimetre than at fifty lines per millimetre. In Fig. 28 a set of log R/θ curves are plotted for a standard type of 20-in. $f/6·3$ air camera lens on the three emulsions, Panatomic X, Super XX, and Microfile, at apertures of $f/6·3$, $f/11$, and $f/22$. Reading across horizontally the change of resolution with emulsions of decreasing graininess can be followed, while vertical reading shows the effects of change of lens aperture on any one emulsion. The full lines represent radial resolving power, and for this lens they always lie above the dotted lines which show the tangential resolving power.

It will first be noticed that nearly all the curves exhibit the same characteristic features. Resolution is highest on axis, falls off to a minimum, which always occurs at about ten degrees, then rises to a maximum at about seventeen degrees, and finally falls sharply to zero. The minimum is more pronounced for the tangential lines. This lens was designed to cover a

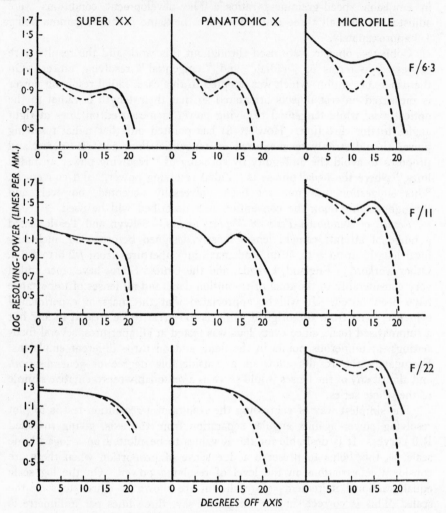

FIG. 28.—Resolving power of a 20-in. $f/6\cdot3$ air camera lens.

9 in. × 9 in. picture, which corresponds to a half-angle of approximately fifteen degrees, and it is apparent that over this angle there is a considerable variation in resolution. The variation is less on the coarse-grain than the fine-grain film and less at small apertures than at large apertures. The minimum, in fact, appears to be absent on the faster films at small apertures, but can still be seen in Microfile, whence its presence as a characteristic of the lens even at $f/22$ can be inferred. Reading across from the fastest

to the slowest emulsion it can be seen that while in general the change to finer grain raises the level of resolving power, the amount of the increase is not constant in different parts of the field. Where the lens is at its best on the coarsest grain film, the improvement produced by changing the film is greatest, but where the lens is at its worst little or no improvement results even on changing to Microfile. It is evident that the optical image, particularly at the larger apertures, is so bad in some parts of the field that nothing can be gained by a change of emulsion ; conversely, if the lens is improved by stopping down, the improvement is not fully realised in actual photography unless the finest grained film is used.

These curves show that the resolving power depends on the lens as well as the film, for the improvement on stopping down can only be associated with the lens. At the same time, the relationship between the two is by no means simple or obvious. The maximum possible resolving power of Super XX film, measured with a contact test object of contrast 0·2, is just over twenty lines per millimetre, a figure never reached with the lens, even on axis and at small apertures. At $f/6·3$ on axis the resolving power is only fourteen lines per millimetre, and the lens is well below its best performance, yet at the same aperture it reaches thirty-three lines per millimetre on Microfile. Evidently a lens may not be good enough to get the best out of a coarse-grained film and yet be capable of a considerably higher resolution on a film of much finer grain. On the other hand, with Panatomic X, a film of only slightly finer grain, the resolution is only very slightly increased. If the two films are compared at the apertures corresponding to their relative speeds, e.g., $f/6·3$ for Panatomic X and $f/11$ for Super XX, the average resolution is slightly higher for the faster film. This situation becomes even more complex if we extend the observations to visual resolving power where the film graininess is altogether eliminated. In Fig. 29 the axial resolving power for the same lens is plotted against aperture for the three emulsions and for visual observation of the aerial image. According to optical theory the resolution should decrease with increasing f/number in the manner shown by the upper curve, and in fact it does so fairly closely after passing through a maximum in the neighbourhood of $f/8$ to $f/11$. The photographic resolving power, however, moves in the opposite direction over most of the range, except that with Microfile a maximum is detectable at about $f/16$. It is reasonable to suppose that the coarser grained emulsions would also show more sharply declining resolution at some smaller apertures beyond $f/32$. The general picture is then of a shift of the aperture of maximum resolution to smaller apertures as we pass through the sequence : visual (high contrast), visual (low contrast), very fine-grain, fine-grain, and coarse-grain emulsions. At full aperture the lens is capable of visual resolving power many times greater than the maximum resolving power possible on Super XX, yet in conjunction with that film it never reaches that level of resolution. Visual and photographic resolution do not run parallel and are evidently governed by different laws. The hint of a connecting link possibly associated with the film graininess is provided by the shift in the aperture of maximum resolution already referred to.

All air camera lenses, whatever their focal length, aperture, or angle of view, give resolution curves similar in type to those of Figs. 28 and 29. Differences occur in the precise shape of the curves, the absolute values of resolving power, the deviation between radial and tangential lines, the positions of the maxima and minima, and the difference between visual and photographic resolution, but the typical features can be seen in every case. Theoretical explanations for these phenomena have been put forward and some will be discussed in a later section ; for the present the practical consequences will be considered.

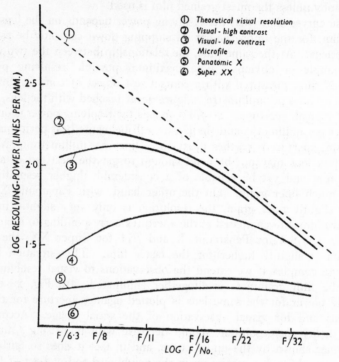

① Theoretical visual resolution
② Visual - high contrast
③ Visual - low contrast
④ Microfile
⑤ Panatomic X
⑥ Super XX

FIG. 29.—Axial resolving power of a 20-in. $f/6 \cdot 3$ air camera lens (No. 154107).

If the resolution tests are to be used for comparing different lenses on a quantitative basis it is first necessary to adopt some means of averaging the resolving power over the field. For this purpose the (Rθ) curves are not very suitable, because they take no account of the increase of area of the picture at increasing angles off axis. It is better to plot (R) against $\tan^2 \theta$ because the area included out to any angle θ is proportional to $\tan^2 \theta$. Beyond certain angles, however, the areas actually used begin to decrease again due to the square or rectangular form of the picture, and this should be allowed for. Fig. 30 shows a comparison between the same results plotted against θ and against $\tan^2 \theta$; the greater emphasis on the outer zones where resolution is low and the smaller importance assigned to good axial resolution should be noted. In test results issued by the National Research Council of Canada and the Royal Aircraft Establishment the resolution is plotted against the true area included out to each angular position, but Selwyn and Tearle adopted a form of averaging which was equivalent to a direct plot against $\tan^2 \theta$. Their averaged resolving powers are therefore strictly applicable to circular pictures only, but for the purpose of their investigation this did not matter.

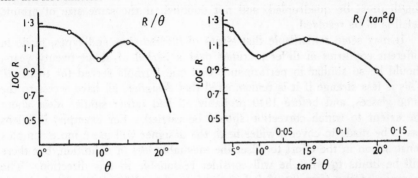

FIG. 30.—Comparison of R/θ and $R/\tan^2 \theta$ plotting of resolution figures.

Apart from matters of detailed construction the characteristics by which lenses are classified are the focal length, aperture, and angle of view. These factors have to be taken into account when comparing lenses of different types. Rather surprisingly, Selwyn and Tearle found that the average resolving power of all the lenses they tested could be expressed to a reasonable degree of approximation in terms of these factors only, and without reference to the make or construction. The average resolving power in lines per millimetre was given by

$$R = \sqrt{\frac{207}{FG} \left(\frac{f/\text{No.}}{\tan^2 \theta} \right)^{0\cdot3}}$$

where R is the average resolving power over the field ;

F is the focal length in inches ;

G is a factor describing the emulsion graininess as measured by the Romer-Selwyn method.

θ is the angle of view.

The average angular resolving power in reciprocal radians was given by

$$R = 25 \cdot 4 \sqrt{\frac{F \times 207}{G} \left(\frac{f/\text{No.}}{\tan^2 \theta} \right)^{0\cdot3}}$$

The chief significance of these formulæ was that they gave a certain degree of precision facts about photographic lenses which had previously been known in a rather vague and indefinite way. It was known that the image quality, which determines the resolving power at the image plane, was better in a general way for short-focus than for long-focus lenses. It was known that a wide angle of view could only be obtained by sacrificing definition and that definition improved on stopping down (though optical theory suggested that it should get worse). The formulæ linked these variables together and showed how the performance of a given lens could be predicted with fair accuracy from a knowledge only of its aperture, focal length, and angle of view. They also brought out some relationships of great importance in air photography. For example, if the operating height is doubled the formula for angular resolving power shows that the focal length must be quadrupled, and not doubled, if the same size of ground detail is to be resolved.

It may seem remarkable that lenses of diverse sizes and types, made in different countries at different times over a period of about twenty years, should be so similar in performance that one formula served for them all. This is less strange if it is remembered that designers all have access to the same glasses, and before 1940 probably all had rather similar ideas about the extent to which correction should be carried. For example, if a lens has to be made to cover a wider field, the designer will use a more complex construction in the effort to offset the inevitable loss of definition, but there will be limits to what he will consider reasonable in this direction. The presence of the term " $\tan^2 \theta$ " in the formula indicates that all designers have somewhat similar ideas about the compromise to be struck between a loss of definition which is tolerable and a practicable design effort and constructional complexity. The formulæ have therefore no absolute or permanent significance, and are liable to be rendered out of date by improvements in the standard to which lenses are designed. Something of the sort has, in fact, happened. A Wray 36-in. telephoto lens designed in 1944 gives a resolution figure some 35 per cent. better than indicated by the formula, while a 25-in. Ross Xpres, also designed in 1944, which should on the formula be 33 per cent. inferior to the old type of 36-in. telephoto, is actually about 15 per cent. better. In designing both of these lenses a deliberate effort was made to raise their resolving power above the highest level previously reached for their focal lengths. The success of the efforts shows the value of having precise figures for performance, as well as reflecting great credit on the designers concerned. Before the introduction of resolution tests there was no way of finding out whether improvements in lenses would lead to an improvement in the value of the photographs commensurate with the design work involved.

More recently (1949) the writer has seen photographs taken with a lens made by the Swiss survey firm of Henry Wild, and although no resolution tests were available the quality of the definition appeared to approach " perfection " all over the field.

Table 4 gives representative figures of average angular resolving power across the field for a number of lenses of different focal lengths and angles of view. It should be understood that these figures refer only to Cobb test objects of density difference 0·2 and Super XX type film developed to full speed and a gamma of about 1·6 in an active developer. Although the lenses are of widely different maximum apertures, the resolution data are all quoted for an aperture of $f/8$, which is an aperture used quite frequently in general daylight air photography. The data should be regarded as approximate, because individual lenses may vary slightly from these typical figures, and results obtained in different laboratories may differ by a small constant amount.

TABLE 4

Lens.	Normal Angle of View (across diagonal of picture).	Approximate Average Angular Resolution (Super XX).
3¼ in. f/5·5	94°	850
5 ,, f/4	70°	1,600
6 ,, f/5·5	94°	1,800
8 ,, f/2·9	41°	2,500
14 ,, f/5·6	24°	4,200
20 ,, f/6·3	35°	5,100
20 ,, f/6·3 *	35°	9,200
36 ,, f/6·3	20°	9,000
36 ,, f/6·3 *	20°	13,000

* New calculations.

THEORY OF PHOTOGRAPHIC RESOLVING POWER

Photographic resolution tests are very laborious to carry out, and it is natural to look for ways of predicting photographic performance from observations on the aerial image. It has already been pointed out that visual and photographic resolving power do not run parallel, and in the present state of knowledge it is not possible to relate one to the other in any precise way. Sufficient is known about the theory of the subject, however, to justify a cautious prophecy that it will eventually be possible to measure certain characteristics of the aerial image and put in factors for conversion to photographic resolution on chosen emulsions. A brief account will now be given of a current theory of photographic resolving power which will perhaps suggest the lines on which this may be done, and will also give a rational basis to the facts already described, which are quite inexplicable without some such addition to the older theory. In a book of this type it is only possible to give the outlines of the simple theory, and it should be appreciated that the subject is much more complex at almost every stage than might be supposed from this account. Those who wish to delve deeper should consult the original papers of Selwyn and others. (4) The subject is as yet in its infancy and much further development is to be expected.

Some Relevant Facts about Lenses.—The ability of a lens to resolve small detail must clearly be related to the size and nature of the image which it casts when focused on a distant light source of negligibly small size. It is shown in works on physical optics that the image of such a point source given by a " perfect " lens, *i.e.*, one free of all aberration, is a diffraction pattern of the general form shown in Fig. 31, A. The pattern consists of a central disc of light surrounded by alternate bright and dark rings. Over 80 per cent. of the total light goes into the central disc, 7 per cent. into the first bright ring, 3 per cent. into the second ring, and so on. In general the effective diameter of the diffraction pattern may be taken as the diameter of the central disc. The distribution of intensity across the pattern is also represented in Fig. 31, B. (The representation of the rings is negative for ease of reproduction.) Where two point sources lie very close together, they will not be clearly resolved by the lens until the centres of the diffraction patterns in the images are separated by a distance equal to the radius of the first ring. If this condition is fulfilled the bright centre of one disc falls in the dark ring of the other and there is a drop in intensity between the two peaks, which can therefore be perceived as separate. The principle is represented in Fig. 32 where the dotted line indicates the summed intensities. Strictly speaking, resolution could also occur at a somewhat smaller separation, but the coincidence of the centre and dark ring is a usually accepted condition. Distant points at much smaller angular separations than this will not be resolved; at any greater separation they will be clearly resolved.

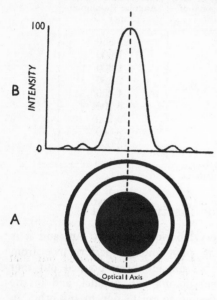

FIG. 31.—Diffraction pattern produced by perfect lens.

A, Appearance in focal plane, showing disc and first two rings.
B, Intensity distribution across pattern.

The distance between point sources which can be clearly resolved depends on the diameter of the diffraction pattern. This diameter is found to depend only on the wavelength of the light and aperture of the lens. For telescopes it is convenient to express the resolving power in terms of the angular separation between distant objects just resolved. Let this separation be θ, then it can be shown that

$$\theta = \frac{1 \cdot 2 \lambda}{D},$$

where λ is the wavelength of the light and D is the diameter of the objective lens. With photographic lenses it is generally useful to know the linear resolving power, i.e., the separation between points just resolved in the image plane. Let this separation be 1/R, then

$$1/R = 1 \cdot 22 \lambda f,$$

where f is the "f number" of the lens. Expressed in the usual form of "lines per millimetre," the resolving power is given by R. For green light of wavelength 5×10^{-4} mm., and $f/4$, the resolving power is about four hundred lines per millimetre.

So far we have only considered the case of aberration free lenses. Telescope and microscope lenses, which cover a very small field, can be made sub-stantially free of aberration, and for such lenses the theoretical resolving power is actually obtained. Photographic lenses have to cover much wider fields and the correction cannot be carried to such a high degree. In general, a considerable amount of residual aberration is present, such that at the full aperture of the lens the resolving power is determined by this rather than by the diffraction limit. The

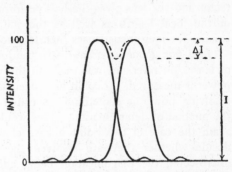

FIG. 32.—Resolution between two close images.

intensity distribution across the image cast by a photographic lens cannot be shown in any generalised form, because the aberrations vary so greatly in kind and degree, especially the off-axis types which give rise to unsymmetrical patterns. The simplest case is spherical aberration, which is symmetrical and can be represented by a pattern such as Fig. 33, A. The characteristic feature is a ring of light surrounding the central disc, of comparable

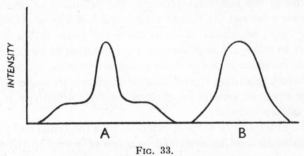

FIG. 33.

A, Large aperture with aberration.
B, Small aperture—no aberration.

intensity and much greater radius. In general, as the lens aperture is reduced the size of the patches of light due to aberration diminishes and at a certain aperture the lens may be regarded as " perfect," the image being determined solely by diffraction. Although the aberration fringes get smaller as the lens is stopped down, the diffraction discs get larger, so that the nature of the image changes in the manner suggested by Fig. 33, B. This is very important in the theory of photographic resolving power. The size of the aberration patches depends on the focal length of the lens, for a given state of correction, while the diffraction pattern depends only on the aperture. At long focal lengths the tendency is therefore for the definition to be limited by aberration, while at short focal lengths diffraction may be more important. As the lens is gradually stopped down from its full aperture the resolving power at first increases as the aberrant light is cut off, and then decreases again in accordance with the equation given. The aperture at which diffraction replaces aberration as the limiting factor and the lens gives the best performance of which it is capable depends on the focal length as well as the state of correction, and is in general smaller for long focus lenses than for those of short focus.

Lens-film Resolving Power.—In the foregoing summary of the properties of lenses no reference was made to the way in which their visual resolving power is measured. It could have been assumed from what was said that the resolving power is something associated with the lens and independent of the method of determination. This would not have been correct. Consider again the case of two point images close together (Fig. 32). In order to decide whether they are resolved the aerial image is examined with a microscope, the magnification being adjusted for the convenience of the observer and so chosen that whatever the level of resolving power the apparent size of the image is always about the same. The meaning of resolution is then that a variation in brightness can be seen across the patch of light which is the optical image of the two points. In Fig. 32 resolution is obtained so long as $\triangle I/I$ is greater than the contrast sensitivity of the eye, *i.e.*, so long as $\triangle I$ is greater than about 2 per cent. of I. ($\triangle I$ is the difference between the sum of the two intensities at the peaks and at the point where the curves cross.) It will be noticed that we have now introduced the properties of the image receptor into the definition of resolving power. If the receptor were not the human retina, and had a constant sensitivity of, say, 30 per cent., we should have to move the peaks of the curves much farther apart to make $\triangle I$ large enough for resolution to be perceived. The photographic emulsion is one of many possible receptors, it does not magnify the image before recording it, and its characteristics are quite different from those of the eye; in general its effective contrast sensitivity is lower than that of the human receptor.

It may be of interest to show in principle how the visual and photographic resolution anomalies can be explained in terms of energy distribution curves for the image of a point source. In Fig. 34 the pairs of curves refer to two hypothetical types of images; those on the left may be considered to represent a large-aperture lens giving an image with a strong central core surrounded by a fringe of aberrant light, while the others, which might correspond to the same lens well stopped down, are free of all aberration, but with a much broader peak. (The peaks have been made of the same height for convenience in comparison.) These two curves do not correspond to any real and measured images, but give a reasonable representation of what might occur with an actual lens. If the peaks of two such images are moved apart to various distances the fraction $\triangle I/I$ shown by the depressions in the dotted lines which are the summed intensities does not follow the same course in both cases. On the lower line I/R is five units; there is a small intensity drop between the peaks on the " large-aperture " pattern, but none on the other. On the upper line I/R is ten units; the drop is now greater with the " small-aperture " images. In Fig. 35 $\triangle I/I$ is plotted against I/R, the separation of the peaks, and since the curves cross over, the two types of image will lead to different resolutions on receptors of different contrast sensitivities. For a receptor such as the eye the " large-aperture " image

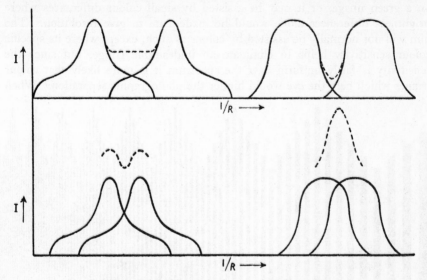

Fig. 34.—Pairs of images at large and small apertures.

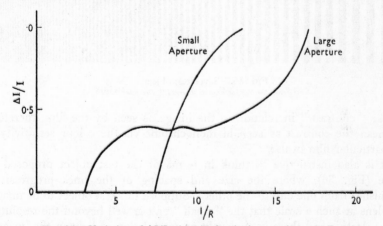

Fig. 35.—Variation of $\Delta I/I$ with $1/R$ for the images shown in Fig. 34.

gives higher resolving power, but at large values of $\triangle I/I$, as in photographic emulsions, the " small-aperture " type is superior. It will be clear that on lines such as these all the differences between visual and photographic resolving power could conceivably be given a complete quantitative explanation; the particular diagrams used here merely demonstrate the principles involved.

In this discussion no specific reference has been made to colour, but it will be appreciated that the presence of colour fringes in the image can exert a marked influence on the apparent resolution. Thus the eye may well overlook colour fringes in red and blue while tending to concentrate on a green image, or it may be assisted by small colour differences where brightness differences alone would be inadequate to give resolution. The film will not normally be assisted by colour as such, except where its specific colour sensitivity helps to eliminate an undesirable fringe, but since the sensitivity is fairly uniform over the spectrum it is more likely that colour fringes which help the eye would hinder the photographic separation. When

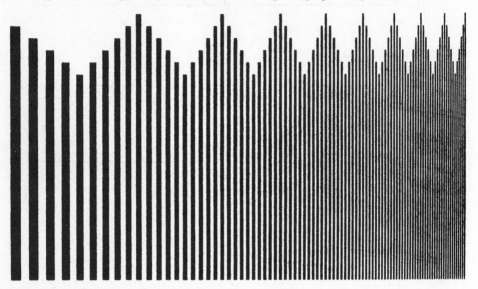

FIG. 36.—Sayce test object.
(*From the " Photographic Journal," December* 1940.)

we use " contrast " in relation to the image as seen by the film, therefore, we mean the contrast as seen in monochrome via the colour sensitivity of the particular film in use.

It is also instructive to think in terms of the test object proposed by Sayce (Fig. 36), where the size and spacing of the lines progressively diminishes from one end to the other. Suppose this test object to be imaged by a lens at such a scale that the " small " end is well beyond the resolution limit. At this end there is obviously no modulation of light in the image— the contrast of the object has fallen to zero. The very large lines suffer no loss of contrast, but as we move towards the small lines the image becomes progressively more blurred, light diffuses from the edges of the lines into the dark spaces and the contrast diminishes. At some point along the test object the contrast of the aerial image has fallen to a point where it equals the contrast sensitivity of the eye—this is the point of visual resolution. This conception of diminishing image contrast was introduced by Selwyn, and the curve relating contrast to image size is termed by him the " amplitude-reduction " curve for the lens. Its shape will naturally be determined by the characteristics of the image ; the curve in Fig. 37 is fairly representative, though it does not correspond to any actual lens. The ordinates in Fig. 37 give the fraction by which the test object contrast is multiplied in the image, or the contrast in the image of a test object of " unit " contrast, while the abcissæ give the resolving power (reciprocal of detail size). The short horizontal line cuts the curve at an ordinate corresponding to the contrast sensitivity of the eye ; the corresponding abcissa is the limit of visual resolution. Now when the image falls on the photographic emulsion it suffers a certain diffusion, which is relatively more serious the smaller the detail, and the result is a different amplitude-reduction curve displaced below that due to the lens alone. If we could view the image in the emulsion we should find the point of resolution moved to the left of that indicated in the figure. The image must be developed, however, and after development it has a grainy structure, which is equivalent to a random density fluctuation. The aerial image is a regular brightness variation, the photographic image may be regarded as the corresponding regular density variation mixed with a random variation due to the graininess. If we imagine moving down the test object with magnification increasing in inverse proportion to the size of the lines being viewed, then the random fluctuations will become progressively greater while the regular variation becomes less. At some point the regular variation becomes too small to be perceived above the graininess fluctuation—this is the point of resolution as determined by the graininess. In general the existence of the graininess means that resolution will require a higher image contrast, *i.e.*, the point of resolution must move to detail of larger size. A given graininess will, of course, act as a more serious limitation on resolution for a good lens than for a bad one, since in the latter case the image quality is poorer and the contrast may fall below the perceptible limit at a detail size where graininess is not noticeable.

It has been implicitly assumed so far that the photographic reproduction is at a gamma of unity, but if gamma can be increased to some higher figure, then the image contrast is effectively raised and the point of resolution will move towards smaller details. At lower gammas the converse is of course true.

It is not essential to think of the two emulsion factors separately in order to see the relation between lens and film in resolving power. The emulsion resolving power can be measured without using a lens at all, and its value can be determined for different test-object contrasts, giving a curve such as those shown in Fig. 37. Since the ordinates on the amplitude-reduction curve give the contrast in the aerial image at the detail sizes shown by the abcissa, the intersection of the two curves obviously determines the resolving power of the lens when used with the film in question. With any other film there will be a corresponding curve moved to right or left on the diagram, and the intersection will be at a different point. The two emulsion curves in Fig. 37 refer to Super XX and Microfile, and although the diagram is for illustrative purposes only, they cut the amplitude-reduction curve at the right order of resolving power for a good air camera lens.

To recapitulate, the essential factors in photographic resolving power, reduced to the simplest terms, are the contrast or amplitude-reducing property of the lens, the further reduction of contrast due to the diffusing properties of the emulsion, the raising or lowering of the contrast according to the gamma, and the obscuring effect of the graininess. In Selwyn's detailed investigations these factors were measured separately and when combined led to predicted values of resolving power fairly close to the figures obtained by direct means. It is beyond the scope of this book to discuss the mathematical treatment with which Selwyn develops the ideas here outlined in a simple way, but it should be mentioned that for convenience in the mathematics he introduces the conception of a " sine-wave "

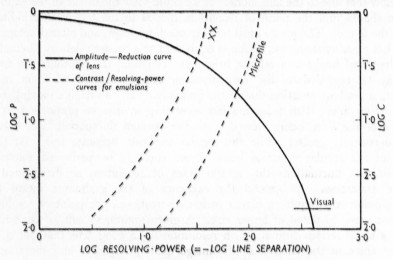

FIG. 37.—Amplitude-reduction curve for lens, showing visual and photographic resolution points.

test object. The ordinary type of test object may be regarded as a brightness modulation of square-wave form ; this has the disadvantage that the wave form becomes distorted as the resolution limit is approached and the contrast reduced, whereas the sine-wave type retains its essential shape unchanged. The contrast of the sine-wave test object is defined as the brightness modulation, i.e., as the ratio of the maximum difference of brightness from the mean to the mean brightness itself. This ratio is approximately equal to the density difference between the peaks and troughs of the waves for ratios up to 0·8. The sine-curve test object has been criticised on the ground that it is arbitrary or academic, but all kinds of test objects are arbitrary, and the sine-curve type seems to be, in this respect, no worse than any other.

The amplitude-reduction curve forms an illuminating way of looking at the problem of photographic resolving power, and expresses the essential characteristic of the lens in a way which is of direct interest to the user. On the other hand, it does not tell us why the lens behaves in this particular way, nor why one lens is better than another. All such differences, and the differences between visual and photographic resolving power, must ultimately be referred to the intensity-distribution curves for the images of point sources. Such curves must be determined with a receptor having the same colour sensitivity as the film. Little information has yet been published on this subject, but a start has been made.

It should be noted that the theoretical explanations which have just been described include as an essential assumption the existence, even on axis in lenses which are considered to be well corrected, of amounts of aberration which have a serious effect on the photographic resolution. These aberrations are known to be small relative to those present off-axis, and perhaps the most important result of modern work on photographic resolving power is the clear demonstration that even such small departures

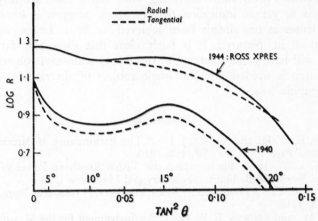

FIG. 38.—Improvement in 20-in. air camera lenses.

from perfect correction can influence the photographic performance of the lens. Without the information provided by the resolution tests and the theory which accounts for the results, designers would not have been justified in trying to improve the state of correction of lenses whose visual resolving power was far above that of the emulsion with which they were to be used. Once it had been shown that all improvements even up to "perfection" would lead to higher photographic resolving power, a more serious attack on the problem of reducing the residual aberrations was worth while. For small and moderate angles of view progress has already been made, as may be seen from a comparison of 20-in. $f/6\cdot3$ lenses covering the 9 in. × 9 in. field designed in 1940 and 1944. The average resolving powers, respectively 5,100 and 9,200, have already been quoted; they show an improvement of 80 per cent., which is a considerable achievement. The log $R/\tan^2\theta$ curves for these two lenses at full aperture on Super XX are given in Fig. 38. They show that the new lens has higher resolution than the old on axis and has a remarkably uniform performance over its entire field; indeed the superior average resolution is largely due to this fact. The lens is practically " perfect " over an appreciable part of its field and on axis shows no improvement on stopping down below $f/8$. It is considered unlikely that a better lens of this type could be made. What this difference of resolution in the field means in terms of actual air photography can be seen from the enlarged comparison photographs of Plate 2.

It should perhaps be mentioned at this point that various explanations based on the angle of incidence of the rays from the lens and the finite thickness of the emulsion layer have been advanced to account for the low resolving power of photographic lenses off-axis. The most direct answer to such theories is perhaps the improvements such as those shown in Fig. 38, which are entirely due to the reduction of the off-axis aberrations, but direct experimental tests have been made and show that the suggested effects are not operative, at least up to angles of 40 degrees. (5)

The problems involved in improving wider angle lenses are very difficult, and there is as yet no indication that so much progress is imminent for, say, 6-in. lenses as has already been achieved for 20-in. lenses covering the same 9 in. × 9 in. picture. It is fairly clear that something far short of perfection will have to be tolerated in these very wide-angle objectives, and much research is needed into the whole subject of aberrational tolerances for photographic lenses.

REFERENCES

1. SELWYN, E. W. H., and TEARLE, J. L. " The Performance of Aircraft Camera Lenses," *Proc. Phys. Soc.*, **58**, 493, 1946.
2. SELWYN, E. W. H. " Photographic and Visual Resolving Power of Lenses," *Photo. Journ.*, **88-B**, January-February and May-June 1948.
3. HOWLETT, L. E. " Photographic Resolving Power," *Canadian Journ. Res.*, **24**, 1 to 3, 1946.
4. ROMER, W., and SELWYN, E. W. H. " An Instrument for the Measurement of Graininess," *Photo. Journ.*, January 1943.
5. GREGORY, J. M. " The Effect of the Angle of Incidence of the Exposing Light on the Resolving Power of Photographic Materials," *Proc. Phys. Soc.*, **58**, 769, 1946.

Chapter Six

FURTHER NOTES ON PHOTOGRAPHIC RESOLVING POWER

As we have seen, photographic resolving power depends primarily on certain unchangeable characteristics of the lens and the emulsion, but it is also influenced by secondary factors which are liable to considerable variation. In Chapter Five these factors were assumed to be standardised, for without reducing the number of variables no just comparison could have been made between different lenses and emulsions. The resolving power obtained from a given lens and emulsion combination in actual air photography, however, will depend very largely on the secondary factors, some of which affect the nature of the optical image, while others are connected with exposure and processing. In this chapter some of these factors are considered in more detail and their relative importance is discussed. The image movements are also of the highest importance in air photography, but their influence on resolution is so profound that they are discussed in a separate chapter.

Contrast of the Subject.—Resolving power varies with the contrast of the test object in an approximately exponential way, and the desirability of testing lenses on objects of the same order of contrast as the subjects on which they will be used has already been mentioned. The precise importance of this will clearly depend on the shape of the amplitude-reduction curve for the lens and on the graininess and light-scattering properties of the emulsion, the arguments which apply being the same in principle as those used to account for the differences between visual and photographic resolving power. Romer (1) has shown that in an extreme case a change in the contrast of the test object can cause a great difference in the relative performance of different lenses. Two lenses, one having a very sharply shouldered amplitude-reduction curve and the other having a much more gradually sloping curve, were tested on Microfile film with a wide range of test-object contrasts. With black and white objects, the second lens gave two and a half times the resolution of the first, but at a contrast of 0·1 the resolutions were equal and at 0·01 the order was reversed. This was a rather exceptional and artificial case which does not come very near to practice, but it does demonstrate the importance of adhering to the right conditions in testing. In general the effect of decreasing contrast is to reduce the difference between different lenses. Fig. 39 shows the variation in resolving power with contrast on Super XX film for an 8-in. $f/4$ air camera lens and a 10·5 cm. $f/6$ lens designed to give theoretically perfect definition over a very small angular field. The convergence of the curves towards the lower contrasts is very marked, and at the very lowest contrast there is practically no difference between the two lenses, although the optical image given by one is " perfect " and that of the other is greatly softened by aberration. The general conclusion is that with gradually decreasing contrast the graininess of the film rather than the state of correction of the lens eventually becomes the limiting factor in photographic resolution, which can occasionally be observed in actual air photographs. It should also be noted, however, that it is only at the very lowest contrasts that the properties of the lens become relatively unimportant. In Fig. 39 the well-corrected lens gives higher resolution, even on the relatively grainy Super XX film, down to contrasts of the order of 0·01 density difference in the test object, and most of the important details in air photographs have contrasts of the order of 0·1 and greater.

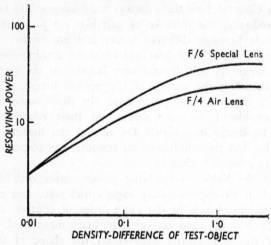

Fig. 39.—Dependence of resolution on contrast
(Super XX film).

The dependence of photographic resolving power on test-object contrast means that atmospheric haze, which lowers the contrast of a scene, must also reduce the effective resolving power ; this effect is discussed in Chapter Twelve.

Romer's experiments with test objects of different contrasts were accompanied by measurements of the resolving power of the eye on the same objects, and lead to some interesting deductions on the relative merits of the eye and the camera for recording distant details. In Fig. 40 angular resolving power is plotted against test-object contrast for the eye and for a number of lenses, the latter curves relating in each case to axial resolving power at $f/8$ on Super XX film. An important feature is the remarkably constant resolution of the eye over quite a wide range of contrast, whereas the photographic resolution falls away much more rapidly with decreasing contrast. This leads to the result that the 2-in. lens is almost equal to the eye on black and white objects, but is very much inferior at low contrasts. A 2-in. lens is commonly used in miniature cameras for ground photography, and it can be assumed that it would most frequently be used with a somewhat finer grained film such as Panatomic X. With this type of film the resolution would be about equal to that of the eye for detail of high and medium contrast, but would still be inferior for low contrasts. This explains why a 2-in. lens is about the shortest which can be used with any satisfaction on a miniature camera, except for very close subjects, and also explains the marked lack of detail in distant scenes taken with these cameras.

The 8-in. lens gives two and a half times the resolution of the eye at high contrast and is still considerably better than the eye at the typical

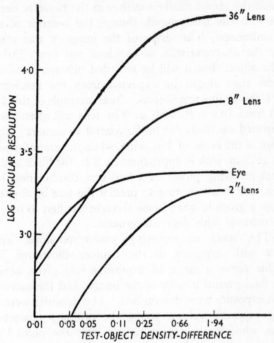

FIG. 40.—Effect of contrast on resolution—eye and different lenses.

contrast of 0·2, but at the very low contrasts the eye is superior. A curve has been added for the 36-in. lens on the assumption that the contrast relation is the same as for the 8-in. lens tested by Romer. Here the resolution is four times better than the eye at high contrast, but only twice as great at the lowest contrasts.

The importance of object contrast should be remembered when applying the results of resolution tests to actual air photography. If a lens is found to have an angular resolving power of, say, 1 : 2,000 for detail of contrast 0·2, it will resolve from 20,000 feet details 10 ft. apart on the ground if their contrast with their surroundings is 0·2, but much smaller objects will be seen in the negative if their contrast is high enough. White objects on a black background, for example, will be resolved if they are about 5 ft. apart. Conversely, objects of lower contrast than 0·2 will only be seen in the negative if they are larger and more widely separated than 10 ft. It should also be remembered that single objects will often be recorded at sizes smaller than the limit of resolution for two adjacent objects. As the camera gets farther away from an object, its image in the negative at first gets smaller in accordance with the laws of geometrical optics, but eventually a stage is reached at which the patch of light is the smallest that the lens will give. If the camera continues to recede the size of the image remains about the same, but its contrast with the background diminishes, since less flux enters the lens to be concentrated in the luminous patch. The distance at which the object finally vanishes in the negative depends mainly on its contrast with the background, though the contrast of the emulsion also has some influence. The shape of the image at this stage is mainly determined by the characteristics of the lens and bears little relation to the shape of the object, but it will be recorded in some fashion from much greater distances than might be expected from the resolving power as determined on Cobb or line test objects. As an example of this kind of effect, negatives taken from 10,000 ft. with an 8-in. lens will often show the white broken lines painted on roads for traffic control at corners ; the individual white patches are of the order of 3 in. wide, while the ground resolution from 10,000 ft. with an 8-in. lens is approximately 2 ft. for black and white lines.

The nominal resolving power of a lens-film combination has therefore to be used with care in attempting to predict the size of objects which can be recorded from a given height ; some thought has first to be given to their nature and the contrast with their background.

Exposure.—The level of resolving power obtained with a given emulsion varies with exposure in the manner illustrated by Fig. 17. In obtaining this curve a range of exposures was given behind the test object, and the background density of the images and the number of groups resolved at each exposure were determined. The densities were then plotted against the log exposure values, giving the ordinary characteristic curve of the emulsion, while the resolution figures were also plotted against their corresponding exposures, giving a curve of resolving power against log exposure. The resolving power curve passes through a maximum near the bottom of the straight part of the characteristic curve. This is in accordance with theoretical views on the nature of photographic resolving power. At very low values of exposure the resolution is limited mainly by lack of contrast, the slope at the toe portion of the characteristic curve being very small. With increasing exposure the contrast and resolving power increase together until maximum contrast is reached at the beginning of the straight line ; beyond that point no further increase of resolving power can take place. But the graininess increases all the time with density, and hence the resolving power must begin to fall off again soon after reaching its maximum. With very full exposures the shoulder of the characteristic curve would be reached, and with the decrease in contrast the fall-off in resolution would become more rapid. In the example shown in Fig. 17 the resolution has fallen to half value at a density of about 3·0. Correct negative exposure is therefore of great importance in obtaining the highest possible resolving power from any emulsions, and both under and over exposure must be avoided.

It was pointed out in Chapter Two that in any camera the illumination in the focal plane is a maximum on axis and decreases towards the edge of the field. This effect is not very serious with lenses of narrow angle, but is very marked with wide-angle survey lenses and is not without its effect on resolving power. It is in general more serious for large-aperture than for small-aperture lenses, because the more complex construction of the former makes the avoidance of vignetting more difficult. Lens manufacturers have been to great pains to avoid vignetting with their wide-angle lenses, and sometimes use extra large front and rear glasses to ensure that the full aperture of the stop is effective for all parts of the field. Some typical illumination curves are shown in Fig. 41, none of the lenses in question

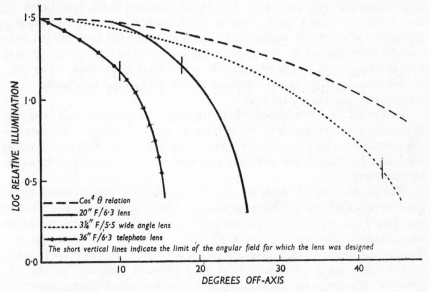

Fig. 41.—Relative illumination across field of air camera lenses.

being surface coated. The 20-in. lens, used on the 9 in. × 9 in. picture frame for which it was designed, gives about 80 per cent. of the axial illumination at the edges of the field, and about 40 per cent. in the corners. The fall-off in the corners is beginning to be serious, but the effect on resolution at the edges is negligible. The 36-in. lens, which being a telephoto type has rather a long barrel, shows a more serious falling-off, and it would be desirable to balance out the effect on resolution by having the optimum density about half-way across the field. The $3\frac{1}{4}$-in. wide-angle lens gives only one-tenth of its axial illumination in the margin of its field. If the exposure were such as to give maximum resolution on axis there would be a very serious reduction at the limit of the field due to the lower exposure level alone and assuming no aberrations. In fact, this lens, like all others of its type, has an inferior correction off-axis, and if the exposure is adjusted to give maximum resolution about half-way across the field the loss of resolution due to over-exposure on axis and under-exposure in the margins is not a very serious matter in comparison with the falling-off due to the aberrations. The uneven illumination is troublesome for a different reason, however. The log exposure variation across the field is multiplied by the negative gamma, which is usually about 1·5, and the resultant density variation is a great handicap to the printer. Devices such as a register glass or before-lens filter having a graduated neutral density are very useful in this connection ; they naturally reduce the axial illumination and hence require more camera exposure in proportion to the amount of compensation which they give, but this is unavoidable and the exposure is not longer than it would have to be even without the graded filter if the outer zones of the picture were to have adequate density. Although there is relatively little vignetting with the $3\frac{1}{4}$-in. lens its illumination curve falls below the $\cos^4 \theta$ curve. This is partly due to the increased importance of air-glass reflections at the wider angles, and coated lenses of the same design show a slight improvement in this respect, amounting to an increase of approximately 20 per cent. in the illumination at the limit of the field. The effect of distortion of the stop at extreme angles, mentioned in Chapter Two, may also be playing a part here.

It should be mentioned that attempts to produce full marginal illumination sometimes lead to inferior marginal resolution, because the stopping-down effect produced by vignetting has more effect in increasing resolution by cutting out aberrant rays than it has in reducing resolution by under-exposure.

The dependence of resolution on the illumination characteristics of the lens poses a problem for investigators in presenting their results. Selwyn and Tearle (*loc. cit.*) always gave such an exposure that maximum resolution was obtained whatever the angle off-axis. This has the advantage that the results express a single property of the lens-film combination. Howlett, on the other hand, prefers to work at a constant exposure, so that the densities vary across the field just as they would in actual photography with the lens, and the results can be interpreted at once in terms of practical use.

Howlett's procedure has the fault that the figures are of value only to the user, and then only for the case where he is working at the optimum exposure level. The lens designer cannot decide what success he has had in correcting the off-axis aberrations, because their effects are combined with, and possibly obscured by, the effects of a varying negative density. On the other hand, the constant-density procedure has the fault that users may interpret the results in an unduly optimistic way, crediting the lens with an off-axis performance which it may not attain in practice unless proper measures are taken to compensate for uneven illumination across the field. This is a case where standardisation is difficult, because the testing required for getting all the necessary information is very laborious. The preferred procedure is bound to be rather arbitrary and to be decided by personal opinion. The writer's opinion is that it is best to expose for a constant density, since the effect of density variation on the practical resolution can be reasonably predicted, whereas if the density is allowed to vary during testing one ends up with an ambiguous result. Whatever is done, however, it is essential that the exact procedure should be specified, *e.g.*, as to the use of constant density or constant exposure, use of any device such as anti-vignetting filters, etc.

One further point may be noted before leaving this subject. The exposure at any point in the focal plane is made up of the focused light which forms the image and the flare light which is more or less uniformly distributed. In general the flare light will not be so much weakened as the image-forming light at the edge of the field, and will therefore be relatively more important than on axis. At the edges of the field, however, the negative densities may fall in the under-exposure region of the characteristic curve, and the sum of the flare and focused lights may take the effective exposure to a point of greater slope than would be reached by the action of the focused light alone. This is no argument for leaving flare light in a camera, but it is of interest to note that over a limited range of exposure a certain amount of flare, or, for that matter, haze, can actually increase contrast in the negative.

Emulsion Graininess.—Slow emulsions in general have finer grain and better resolution than the faster types, but they are not necessarily the best for air photography on that account. The available light for exposure being fixed for any operating condition, a slower emulsion necessitates either a longer time of exposure or a larger lens aperture or some combination of the two. It is usually more convenient to keep the time of exposure constant at a figure determined by the image movements, and to vary the exposure by the lens aperture alone. Thus when a slow emulsion replaces a fast one the emulsion resolving power is raised, but the lens resolving power is effectively lowered, and the overall improvement may be small or negative, the exact results naturally depending on the particular lens and emulsions employed. The only slow type emulsions which are fast enough for air photography are the Panatomic X or Agfa " Aeropan " types, having about one-third or one-quarter the speed of Super XX and about 30 per cent. higher resolving power. In general there is a slight loss of overall resolution with these emulsions as compared with Super XX, because the deterioration of the optical image when the lens is opened up two stops more than counteracts the slight improvement in the emulsion graininess. A typical example is shown in Fig. 42, which gives the resolution on Super XX at $f/11$ and on Panatomic X at $f/6\cdot3$ for a 20-in. Ross survey lens manufactured in 1942 or thereabouts. The apertures of $f/6\cdot3$ and $f/11$ correspond to those required to produce the same density on the two emulsions when exposed for the same time under the same lighting conditions. The ordinates give lines per millimetre and the abcissæ values of $\tan^2 \theta$, so that the areas under the curves considered out to any angle give an indication of the mean resolving power over the film out to that angle. The 20-in. lens was computed for use with a 9 in. × 9 in. picture, the half-angle being about eighteen degrees, and it is clear that over this field the mean resolving power is much higher with the faster film. Only in a very narrow zone near the axis is the lens performance good enough to give higher resolution on the slower film.

This kind of result is fairly general for aircraft lenses made before about 1944. Plates 4 and 5 show results of a comparative air test made with two matched 20-in. lenses of somewhat better performance than the lens of Fig. 42. The films were a Super XX type and a film of one-quarter that speed, the lens apertures being set to $f/11$ and $f/5\cdot6$ respectively. It was known from previous tests that the shutter speed of $1/300$ sec. was adequate to stop all image movements. The examples were enlarged from portions of the negatives near the corner of the frame, and in the originals it can be seen that although the slow film gave a finer grained image it recorded less ground detail due to the greater influence of the lens aberrations at the larger aperture of $f/5\cdot6$.

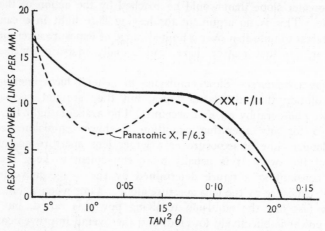

FIG. 42.—Resolving power of a 20-in. lens on Super XX and
Panatomic X films.

Some lenses produced for air photography since 1942, however, suffer much less than the older lenses from aberrations at full aperture and show little improvement on stopping-down, whence it follows that they might give better resolution with a finer grained film even when allowing for the slower speed of the latter. In any given circumstances much will depend on the image movements which are present. Well-designed anti-vibration mountings will generally allow an exposure time as long as $1/150$ sec. to be used with lens-film systems having a potential resolution of $1:10,000$, but most aircraft speeds are too high for anything longer than $1/300$ to be used except at very high altitudes. Given a sufficiently slow aircraft, however, there will be circumstances where a slow film can be used to advantage. After reading Chapter Eight it should be possible to make a sufficiently good assessment for any situation, but it should be said now that the possible improvement in terms of detail resolved on the ground must be relatively small even under the most favourable conditions, because the resolving power of Panatomic X and similar emulsions is only about 30 per cent. greater than that of the Super XX type. To obtain a really substantial improvement in ground resolution by way of a finer grained emulsion it would be necessary to accept a reduction of sensitivity to something of the order of one-tenth, which would require longer exposure times than are practicable at present.

Graininess as Affected by Processing, etc.—It is well known that the graininess of emulsions depends to a considerable extent on the composition of the developer and the way in which it is used. Lower graininess in general leads to higher resolving power, though when the solvent action of the common types of fine-grain developer is pushed too far there is a reduction of resolving power caused by a spreading of the image. Except under special conditions, however, fine-grain developers are excluded from use in air photography by the need for high contrast and full emulsion speed, as explained in Chapter Four. For similar reasons such methods as colour development are also ruled out. Within the range of practicable variation the effect of the composition of the developer on resolution is small in comparison with the effects due to the lens. All suitable developers such as pyro-metol or metol-hydroquinone, if applied in one or other of the standard formulæ for a time sufficient to give maximum emulsion speed, will give almost identical resolving powers. It will be appreciated that if the development is cut short in the attempt to reduce graininess the accompanying fall in contrast and speed may lead to lower and not higher resolving power, since high resolution in air photography does not depend solely on low negative graininess.

Judging from the more popular photographic literature and from general discussions with air photographers, there seems to be a good deal of misunderstanding about the influence of processing, exposure, etc., on graininess. The theory of graininess is highly complex and new knowledge is continually being added, but the influence of the important practical factors on graininess in the negative and print is easily understood, and a brief discussion will not be out of place. Reference may also be made to a good account by Schilling (2) which, however, deals mainly with conditions in amateur photography.

Graininess depends in the first place on the nature of the emulsion, and assuming correct exposure the choice of the emulsion does more than any other single factor to determine the graininess of the image. For any given emulsion, graininess as effective in the print increases progressively with density, and hence with time of development for a constant exposure. If, however, the exposure is varied so that a constant density is produced at all degrees of development, then the effect of development time is small, at least for degrees of development which are of practical importance in air photography. Fine-grain developers give a reduction of graininess at a sacrifice of speed. For the conditions of air photography the loss of speed for a given improvement in graininess is of the same order as the loss which would be suffered by using a slower film, but developing it fully in an active developer such as D19*b*. Inasmuch as the fine-grain developer will not always give adequate contrast even when development is prolonged to give maximum speed, the use of the slow film fully developed is a preferable way of obtaining the lower graininess.

Because of the increase of effective graininess with negative density, over-exposed negatives always give more grainy prints. Over-exposure is particularly undesirable in air photography, since with gammas of the order of 1·5, density builds up very rapidly. The apparent graininess in an air photograph depends very much on the atmospheric conditions at the time of exposure. In clear weather the contrast in the scene is relatively good and the negative can be printed on a fairly soft paper. In hazy weather the contrast in the scene is low and the mean density of the negative increases, unless the camera exposure is reduced. The negative, already more grainy by reason of its higher density, is printed on a more contrasty paper, which accentuates the density fluctuations of the graininess pattern just as much as the larger density variations which make up the picture. The eye, in striving to interpret the low-contrast detail of the hazy scene, is then very conscious of the increased graininess, although in the negative, on any area of uniform density, there will be no difference of graininess from that of a comparable area in the negative taken in clear weather. These effects often have more influence on the apparent graininess of an air photograph than anything to do with the processing conditions. The magnitude of such graininess differences is illustrated by the comparative air photographs of Plates 6 and 7. These are × 17 enlargements from two negatives exposed within half an hour, one over a large city and the other over a country area. The air over the city was very hazy, while that over the country town was clear. Both negatives were on the same roll of film, received the same camera exposure, and were developed together for the same time. The clear negative was enlarged on to normal bromide paper and the hazy one on to a contrasty grade. The difference in apparent graininess is due fundamentally to the difference in brightness range of the original scenes and the higher density of the hazy negative. This is a much greater difference than could have been produced by any practicable variation in the development conditions.

Special Techniques for increasing Resolution.—Special techniques for processing or after-treatment of the negative are periodically advocated in the belief that they will lead to increased resolution in air photographs. The after-treatment methods all seem to be based on the mistaken idea that if the graininess of a developed negative can be reduced its resolution will be increased. Stevens (3) has investigated a number of such methods of reducing the effective graininess of negatives, including both the chemical techniques such as bleaching and redeveloping in modified sulphide solutions, and the physical methods such as diffusing the image in projection printing. He worked with negatives on Super XX film developed in D19b, exposure being made to a Cobb test object with a 20-in. air camera lens. Some of the negatives were then printed in various ways, including the following :—

(*a*) Enlarging with the lens thrown out of focus to different degrees.

(*b*) Contact printing, by diffused light, parallel light at normal incidence, parallel light at oblique incidence, and all three conditions with the negative and printing material separated by 25 microns.

It was found that the apparent graininess of the negative could readily be reduced, but the maximum useful effect was a slight increase in

" smoothness " when the diffusion was too small to cause any appreciable loss of resolution. Amounts of diffusion sufficient to give a marked reduction in graininess caused serious lowering of the resolution.

In other negatives the graininess was reduced by bleaching in a ferricyanide-bromide solution and redeveloping in a 1 per cent. sodium sulphide bath containing different amounts of sodium thiosulphate. With appropriate concentrations of thiosulphate the silver halide image left after bleaching dissolves and diffuses a small distance before being precipitated as silver sulphide, thus causing a slight blurring of the graininess pattern. It was found that the diffusion of the graininess pattern was accompanied by a fall in resolution. Similar results would be obtained by other methods of chemically smoothing out the graininess.

In general, nothing can be done to a single image, once it is developed, which will increase the resolution. Printing on very contrasty papers, which might be thought useful, is of no avail, because the graininess pattern is accentuated at the same time as the regular density fluctuations of the image. This can readily be shown by making enlargements from a resolution test negative, using soft and contrasty bromide papers, and comparing the results. The contrast of the resolved groups is increased by the more contrasty paper, but the limit of resolution is unaffected.

Stevens showed, however, that the combination of several images, optically identical but taken on separate negatives, gave a marked increase of resolution as well as a reduction in graininess. Eight successive exposures were made on the test chart, and a print was built up by eight partial printings from these negatives, great care being taken to obtain exact registration of the images. The graininess of the composite print was much less than that of any single print fully exposed under any one of the negatives, and the resolving power was raised by about 60 per cent. The success of this method depends on the fact that any negative consists of a graininess pattern which is a random distribution of density, associated with the regular density distribution of the image. If the print is built up from partial printings of several negatives the image details will eventually reinforce each other and build up a full-strength image, but the random density differences of the graininess will tend to cancel each other out and given enough partial printings the graininess would eventually disappear altogether. The method obviously has no application to air photography, but is of considerable theoretical interest and throws light on the failure of other methods involving a lowering of the negative graininess.

REFERENCES

1. ROMER, W. " The Influence of the Contrast of the Test Object on the Resolving Power of the System Objective Sensitive Layer," *Sci. & Ind. Photo.*, **18**, 193, July 1947.
2. SCHILLING, A. " Feinkörnigkeit und Vergrössern." *Veröffentlichungen des Wissenschaftlichen Zentral-Laboratoriums der photographischen Abteilung Agfa*, **5**, 1937.
3. STEVENS, G. W. W. " The Effect of Diffusion on the Graininess and Resolution obtained from Processed Negatives," *Photo. Journ.*, **87-B**, May-June 1947.

Chapter Seven

PRINTING

PRINTING air negatives is a relatively straightforward process, free from the problems of personal taste and artistic convention which beset the pictorial photographer. A print which reproduces all the detail in the negative in a way which is clear to the interpreter is a satisfactory print, and no more can be asked of it. Prints are not always satisfactory on this criterion, however, their resolution falling below that of the negative at the ends of the tonal scale, though in the middle grey tones there is little if any loss of detail. Positive transparencies are better, and will record all the detail present in the negative, but paper prints are so much easier to handle that they are always used except for special purposes.

PRINTING MATERIALS

Air negatives are printed on the ordinary types of bromide or chloride papers which have to be developed after exposure. Bromide emulsions are sensitive mainly to blue, chloride mainly to violet. Since the aim is the reproduction of fine detail, and pictorial considerations are irrelevant, a white base, black image, and a glossy surface are the usual practice. The use of daylight printing papers would be quite impracticable in view of the very slow rate of output. Efforts are being made to improve the continuous tone printing processes based on the use of diazo compounds, which have the merit of requiring only " dry " development in ammonia gas. These papers have to be printed from an intermediate positive transparency, but this is no great disadvantage when numerous copies are required from each negative.

In Great Britain and many European countries bromide papers are used both for contact and projection printing, but in the American hemisphere most contact prints are made on chloride papers ; this corresponds to the respective national practices in general photography and is a matter of personal preference rather than technical advantages in favour of either type of emulsion. Bromide papers are faster and hence need less light in the printing box, are very tolerant to changes in developer composition and general mishandling in development, and are less liable to fading or staining when imperfectly fixed or washed. On the other hand, they have to be worked in a deeper orange safelight than the slower chloride papers, and judgment of print quality is correspondingly rather more difficult. Chloride papers are admittedly slow, but printing exposures are brief in the American printers using the violet argon discharge lamps, and the rate of printing is probably not less than with bromide papers. Chloride papers develop more rapidly than bromide, but are more liable to staining with over-development and general mishandling in the dark room. Chloride emulsions might be thought preferable for air photography because they can be made to give higher contrast than bromide, but the contrasty grades of the latter will give good prints from all but the flattest air negatives ; indeed, a negative which requires anything harder than the most contrasty bromide emulsion must be of very little value to the user. Thus no general recommendation can be made, and the choice between the two types of paper must always depend on individual preferences.

Since the contrast of printing papers cannot be varied very much in development, negatives of different density range are accordingly printed on papers of different contrast grades. In recent years manufacturers have produced " variable contrast " papers which combine in one emulsion coating the range of contrasts normally provided by five or more grades. In one example of this kind of paper there are two emulsions blended in the coating, one of which is a soft bromide type, and the other is a slow contrasty chloride, dye-sensitised to green. When exposed to half-watt light with suitable blue or yellow filters the emulsions can be used in any desired combination. Thus with a deep-yellow filter the bromide emulsion has no effective response, and the exposure is entirely on the contrasty chloride emulsion, while with a blue filter which passes no ultra-violet or far violet light full use is made of the greater speed of the bromide emulsion and the chloride does not respond, so that a very soft paper results. Once the complication of the filters has been accepted, these papers have very considerable advantages, because with only one type in stock the user can call upon the full range of contrasts he is likely to need, and can obtain intermediate contrast shadings not available in the grades of standard bromide papers. The storekeeping advantages are so great that it is rather surprising to see so little variable contrast paper in use.

Processing of Printing Papers

Chloride and bromide papers are usually developed in metol-hydroquinone, and suitable formulæ are given elsewhere in this book. Chloride papers should be developed in the Kodak formula D72 or in the formula recommended by the manufacturer, since they are rather liable to give stains if developed in unsuitable solutions. Bromide papers are much more tolerant and can be developed successfully in almost any standard metol-hydroquinone formula. D72 or ID20 are recommended, but it is quite possible to get good results with negative developers such as D19b and even D76. Nothing is gained by departing from the manufacturer's instructions, except under emergency conditions, when it may be useful to remember that D19b can be used.

During the progress of development the speed and contrast of printing papers increase in similar fashion to negative materials, but the time-scale is shorter, bromide paper being fully developed in about two minutes and chloride in one to one and a half minutes. Contrast approaches its maximum at an earlier stage than speed, so that within limits the density of a print can be varied with little effect on its contrast by varying the time of development. Very short development times are impracticable, however, because the density and contrast are changing rapidly in the early stages, say before one minute when developing bromide papers in their recommended formulæ. The practicable variation in the effective paper speed, sometimes called the " development amplitude," (1) is about 0·1 log exposure units either way. The contrast of bromide papers cannot be changed very much by any changes in the composition of the developer, but in an emergency, when the correct grade is not available, some amelioration of a difficult situation may be obtained by using an all-metol developer for softness or all-hydroquinone for greater vigour. Because of reciprocity failure it is also possible to modify the effective contrast of a paper by changing the intensity of the printing light; no precise guide can be given, because everything depends on the chracteristics of the emulsion in use, but it will be necessary to change the exposure time by a factor of the order of 100 to 1 to produce a noticeable change of contrast.

Papers are fixed in acid hypo, but hardening is not usually required. Formula IF4 is recommended for general use, while F1 may be tried in hot climates. An acid rinse (2 per cent. acetic acid) is advisable between development and fixation, especially with chloride papers. Fixation is best carried out by the two-bath method to ensure complete elimination of silver compounds which would cause staining of the highlights if left in the gelatine. After five minutes in the first bath the print is transferred to a second bath for a further five minutes. If operations start with two fresh baths and the prints always pass through the baths in the same sequence, the first one will remove most of the silver halide and the second will remain almost free of silver. When the first bath has been in use for some time it should be discarded and replaced by the second, which is then renewed. By following this method of fixing, the prints never enter the washing water direct from a fixing bath rich in dissolved silver complexes, which tend to become adsorbed to the emulsion and are not easily removed by washing.

Thorough washing of paper prints is much more difficult than washing plates or films, even with free exposure to running water. The bulk of the hypo quickly diffuses out of the gelatine film, but traces are held very firmly by the paper fibres, and complete removal by washing alone is almost impossible. The Agfa Company recommend that after a short wash the prints should be soaked for a few minutes in a weakly alkaline bath, *e.g.*, 1 per cent. sodium carbonate, then washed in the usual way for half an hour or more. (2) The alkaline bath is said to give complete hypo elimination by causing the adsorbed material to diffuse away in the final washing. Eastman Kodak have introduced a hydrogen peroxide hypo eliminator (formula HE1), which is applied for six minutes after half an hour's normal washing and converts remaining traces of hypo into harmless compounds. (3) A final wash of ten minutes is necessary.

Complete removal of hypo is naturally very desirable, especially if prints have to be kept for many years, but much more attention seems to have been paid to the subject in America than in Great Britain. Possibly this is associated with the greater use of chloride papers in America, since the finer grained image of chloride emulsions is more liable to hypo attack than the relatively coarse-grained bromide type. Like the author, many photographers will probably have in their possession bromide prints in perfect condition, made over twenty years ago and washed in rather crude conditions before their makers had realised that hypo cannot be completely eliminated by water alone. Slipshod work is certainly not to be encouraged, but sometimes it is more important to get prints out quickly than that they should keep in perfect condition for a very long time; when this is so, washing for a few minutes will probably be adequate and bromide prints at least will probably keep for a year or so. When very good keeping is essential, special precautions in fixation and washing are necessary, and the best source of information on this subject is the reference to Crabtree already given. (3) Reference 11 in Chapter Four may also be consulted. A summary is given here for convenience.

For complete removal of silver complexes, or for lowering their concentration in the print to a harmless level, the use of two fixing baths is almost essential unless one can accept a very high consumption of hypo, and three fixing baths are preferable. The preferred formula is F6. A single fixing bath must not be used for more than thirty 9×9 in. prints per gallon, and the first of two baths for not more than two hundred such prints per gallon, for good general purpose keeping (a few decades). For archival keeping, a single fixing bath should not be used for more than five prints of the size quoted, the first of two baths for more than seventy prints, and the first of three for more than one hundred. The sulphide test described in Chapter Four should not produce more than a faint cream tint when applied on the margin of a print that is to be stored for a long time. The depth of stain produced is a guide to the stain that might eventually develop when the print is stored not under ideal conditions.

As already mentioned, paper prints cannot be completely freed from hypo by water alone. If intended for good general purpose keeping they should be given an alkaline bath as described above, but for archival keeping the hydrogen peroxide eliminator should be used. The presence of hypo may be checked by placing a spot of acidified silver nitrate solution on the back of the print, when a brown stain of silver sulphide will develop.

SENSITOMETRY OF PRINTING PAPERS

The sensitometry of papers is more complex than that of negative emulsions, and there is less agreement about fundamentals; for example, there is as yet no agreed standard by which the contrast can be measured. Partly on this account less use is made of sensitometry at the printing stage than in making negatives. This is not so illogical as it might seem. The negative is essentially a straightforward transcription of the subject brightnesses into transmission densities, and this being a purely physical process can be controlled by the physical aid of sensitometry. With the making of the print, however, we have something which looks like the subject, and at once there enter those psychological factors of personal taste and preference and the psycho-physical factors involved in visual perception. This being so, it is not surprising that paper sensitometry has so far been the ally rather than the competitor of the judgment of skilled photographers, a research tool rather than a practical necessity. Fortunately, there is no reason to suppose that prints from air negatives would be any better if their densities were controlled by sensitometric methods rather than the experienced judgment of the printer.

The characteristic curves of printing papers are obtained by exposure to an intensity scale at an exposure time of the same order as the times used in actual printing, say a few seconds. After development and final drying the reflection density is measured at each step and plotted against the log exposure. Reflection density is defined by reference to the brightness of the paper base. If the brightness of the base is B, and the brightness of any exposed and developed area of the paper is B_1, the reflection density of that area is $D = \log B/B_1$. To avoid trouble from surface reflections it is usual for the paper to be illuminated at 45 degrees and viewed normally. In general photography the paper sometimes has a ribbed or " lustre " surface, with a different reflectance in different directions, and precautions have to be taken in the sensitometry to overcome this effect, but the papers used for air photography have a glossy surface and no difficulties of this kind are encountered.

Fig. 43 shows characteristic curves of a glossy bromide paper in " soft," " medium," and " contrasty " grades. They bear a general resemblance to negative curves, having a toe region of increasing gradient, merging into a straight-line portion which then gives way to a shoulder, with a definite maximum density. The toe is more pronounced in paper curves, however, and often extends over the greater part of the density range, while the shoulder is sharper, with a quicker transition to zero gradient than in curves of negative materials. The limited maximum density is, of course, a consequence of the positive reflectance of even the blackest surface. The maximum reflection density obtainable in bromide and chloride papers, assuming that an adequate coating weight of silver is used, depends on the surface finish. Glossy papers with suitable orientation of the illumination reflect the least light towards the eye and have the highest density, while matt surfaces are diffuse reflectors and send some light to the eye whatever the direction of illumination. In papers of the same make and contrast grade, matt surfaces may give maximum densities 0·3 lower than glossy. If the medium grade paper whose characteristic curve is shown in Fig. 43 had had a matt surface the curve would have begun to shoulder-off at a density of about 1·0, and the gradient would fall to zero at about 1·5. Other things being equal, matt papers cannot reproduce faithfully such a wide range of tones as glossy papers, and glossy surfaces, preferably glazed, are always used when it is necessary to show the utmost detail.

The sensitometry of negative emulsions and papers is approached from rather different viewpoints. In negative sensitometry the first aim is the definition and measurement of speed, for correct exposure being the foundation of success in photography and opportunities for correcting mistakes in the negative rare, the emulsion speed must be known before photography can start. Paper sensitometry takes relatively little account of speed, and no manufacturer publishes speed figures for his papers. At first sight this is remarkable, because the exposure latitude is far less in printing than in making negatives. It is just this need for precise exposure, however, which makes speed numbers of doubtful value, for without

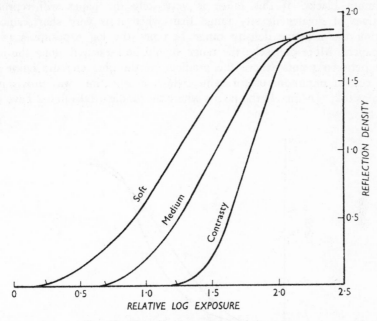

FIG. 43.—Bromide paper characteristic curves.

accurate measurement of the light reaching the paper through the negative they would not be particularly useful to the printer. Trial exposures must be made before each main printing job is started or when a new batch of paper is taken into use, and speed numbers could never be held from batch to batch with sufficient precision to obviate the need for this. In any case, the definition of speed for printing materials is even more difficult than it is for negative emulsions.

Broadly speaking, if the first task of negative sensitometry is the definition and measurement of speed, that of paper sensitometry is the specification of contrast. "Contrast," like its overworked companion "speed," is one of those words in the photographer's vocabulary which are the despair of the precise minded. Apart from any dictionary meanings, "contrast," according to its context, may mean the density range of a negative or print, the brightness range of a subject, or the property of a negative or positive material which determines the relationship between the brightness range of a scene and its reproduction. It is the last-named which is meant when we speak of the contrast of printing papers. Every photographer knows what is meant by the contrast of a paper, but its definition in precise terms is very difficult.

In discussing the contrast of papers reference may again be made to the characteristic curves of the three different contrast grades shown in Fig. 43; the positions of these curves on the log E axis are arbitrary and do not indicate their relative speeds. Contrast must obviously be related to the range of printing exposures which takes the paper from white to maximum black; if this range is very long the paper will reproduce negatives of greater density range than when it is very short, since in printing the negative density range becomes the log exposure scale for the paper. More precisely, the range should be measured along the log E scale between points where the gradient of the characteristic curve falls to a certain minimum useful value, which at one time was provisionally taken as 0·2. In Fig. 43 the points where the gradient falls to 0·2 have been

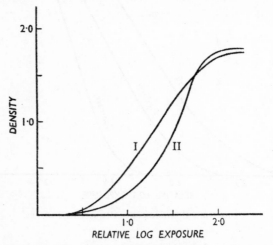

FIG. 44.—Curves of papers having the same scales but different slope characteristics.

marked on the curves, and the corresponding *total exposure scales* are: soft, 1·8; medium, 1·55; contrasty, 1·01. These figures indicate the maximum negative density ranges which the papers will accommodate without serious loss of detail in the extreme highlights and shadows, and to that extent are a measure of their contrasts. Later work has shown that the limiting gradient is not constant, but increases with the contrast of the paper, and is greater at the shoulder end of the curve than at the toe. Nevertheless, total exposure scale is of some value as giving a rough sorting of papers into their order of contrast.

The slope of the curve between the limiting points is clearly another factor of importance in determining contrast, but there is difficulty in deciding how it should be measured. Fig. 44 shows two characteristic curves which are hypothetical but sufficiently representative of actual papers; they have the same total scale, but the slopes vary between the limits in quite different ways, and they would evidently give quite different kinds of reproduction. Gamma is of no value as a measure of paper contrast, for in the curve marked I it would be fairly representative of the curve over most of its length, but in curve II it would be representative of only a small part at the shoulder end. Over a great part of its length curve II has a greater slope than curve I, and would be judged to have greater contrast, yet in the highlight region its slope is less. Evidently some means of averaging the gradients along the curve is required. The shape can be averaged with respect to exposure by dividing the total density scale between the limits by the total exposure scale, but this merely gives the slope of the straight line drawn between the limits. As can be seen from Fig. 44, this would be representative of the average slope of some types of curves, but not of others. Jones (4) considered that the slope should be averaged along the curve by equal density increments, but Renwick (5) preferred to take the average for equal steps measured along the length of the curve itself. Jones also points out that contrast in a print involves an *extent factor*, viz., the total *density scale*, in addition to the *rate factor*, which is the average gradient as defined by him, and gives a construction for obtaining the two via the curve which gives the differential of slope with respect to density. He concludes that the relative contrasts of different papers may be expressed by the product of the extent factor and the rate factor : $\Omega = (D_{max.} - D_{min.}).\overline{G}D.$ More recently Jones (1) has approached the subject along somewhat different lines by an examination of the sensitometric characteristics of large numbers of prints considered to be " good " by skilled photographic observers. It was found that the exposure scale of papers as determined by the limiting gradients of 0·2 was not in agreement with the scale actually used in the prints. In the best prints the minimum densities were often zero and the toe gradients much less than 0·2, while in the shadows the gradients were nearly always greater than 1·0. From the results of this work Jones concluded that the useful exposure scale, which is one method of expressing paper contrast, could be given sensitometric definition in a way which would correspond with the contrast as judged by a skilled printer. The method is illustrated in Fig. 45. Points *h* and *s* are found at the highlight and shadow ends respectively of the characteristic curve ; they are located by the relationship that the slope G of the straight line drawn from *h* tangential to the shoulder at *s* is ten times the gradient at the point *h*. The log exposure interval between the points *h* and *s* then gives the useful exposure scale.

Many other workers have studied this problem, but no agreement has yet been reached on the definition of contrast. We may note that any method arrived at by researches related to the general body of photographic experience may not be fully satisfactory for the purposes of air photography. In general photographic practice it is usual to make prints with a greater density range than in air photography, where the extreme toe and shoulder are avoided in order to keep the resolving power as high as possible throughout the tone scale. Jones's extent factor, for example, would give a high contrast rating to a paper with high maximum black, but in printing high-altitude air negatives density differences above about 1·4 are not in themselves of any interest ; all that matters is the gradient up to the highest density used, which is 1·3 to 1·4. Again, methods which average the gradient over the whole curve, including long toe portions with very low densities and gradients, are not realistic for air photography, for similar reasons.

The main interest of reaching an agreed solution of the contrast problem would lie in the possibility of grading papers in equal steps of contrast by sensitometric methods, which is not done by all manufacturers at present. This discussion may have served to show the air photographer that his papers can have characteristic curves of different shapes, and that his own opinion of the relative contrast of different grades may not always coincide with that of their maker. This is of little practical importance, provided that the fact is recognised and that the right type of paper can be found for the majority of negatives, which is certainly the case.

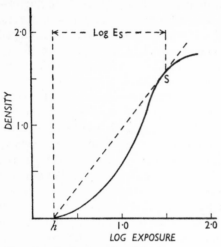

FIG. 45.—Derivation of useful exposure scale.

Contrast is one very important aspect in printing air negatives, but it should usually take second place to resolving power. Air photographers have found by experience that the best print for their purposes has no very low or very high densities. By making their prints in this way they avoid the very low gradients at the toe and shoulder of the characteristic curve, where the resolving power of the paper falls far below its maximum value. This also means that the useful exposure scale of any paper is less in air photography than it would be for ground photography, thus the paper whose characteristic curve is shown in Fig. 45 would be suitable for printing an air negative of density range 1·0, whereas its total exposure scale is about 1·5.

General Characteristics of Prints from Air Negatives

As we have already stated, experienced printers of air negatives do not use the full density range of the paper, and the ideal print is soft and " grey " in appearance with no areas of white or black. This is done from long experience of the kind of print preferred by interpreters, and although the tendency to softness has perhaps been overdone it is fundamentally sound. The most important reason for advocating soft prints has already been mentioned, viz., their superior resolving power in the highlights and shadows. There are some quite practical advantages, however, which may also be mentioned. Soft prints are usually on a soft paper, which means that unevennesses in print density are less liable to occur and mosaics are easier to make. Such unevennesses may be due to acceleration in focal-plane shutters, uneven illumination in the camera, or uneven lighting on the ground, and they are easier to shade out when soft prints are made. Another reason for preferring greyish prints may be that they give a closer representation of the appearance of an aerial view. Even if the printer has never seen the original subject, and is not interested in making his print look like it, he probably has sufficient general acquaintance with similar scenes to feel instinctively that black areas would be out of place in their representation. This is rather different from ground photography, where there is nearly always a subjective black somewhere in the scene, and on the usual convention black areas in the original are represented by black in the print. (6)   In this connection it may be pointed out that prints from low-altitude air negatives do not appear to be governed by the " no blacks " rule, which may be due to the existence of heavy shadows in such subjects.

RESOLVING POWER IN PAPER PRINTS

The resolving power in paper prints has not been investigated so thoroughly as resolving power at the negative stage. It would be expected that with the relatively low speed of bromide paper emulsions their resolving power would be much greater than that of fast panchromatic negative materials, and that all details in the negative could easily be reproduced in printing. In prints, however, as in negatives, the resolving power passes through a maximum, falling to zero at both ends of the characteristic curve. The negative resolving power can be retained only over a limited range, and there is always some loss in the highlights and shadows, while even at the maximum the print sometimes shows lower resolving power than the negative. Prints on diapositive materials reproduce the negative resolving power over a much wider range.

Overall Resolving Power Negative Print.—No information seems to have been published on the resolving power obtainable in bromide prints when printed from a test object of effectively unlimited resolution, but the resolving power in prints from negatives on fast panchromatic film has been investigated. J. B. Reid (7) determined the overall resolving power in prints on bromide paper and positive film from negatives made on Super XX air film developed in R.A.F. pyro-metol. A test object of density difference 0·2 was imaged on the film by a lens of extremely good correction and a range of exposures was made so that the negative resolving power could be determined over a wide range of densities from extreme under exposure to very full exposure. The resulting negatives were printed on different grades of bromide paper and on positive film, giving different printing exposures, taking special precautions to obtain perfect contact between negative and paper, and using parallel light ; the final resolving power in the prints could then be plotted against the exposures given to the negative emulsion. Some of Reid's results have been plotted to give the curves of Fig. 46. The abcissæ are the log exposures given to the negative material, and one of the curves shows the negative resolution at any exposure.

The other curves show in effect what happens when a negative containing this entire range of densities is printed on various positive materials, the printing exposure being adjusted so that in every case the peaks of the negative and positive resolving power curves are in approximate coincidence. It is necessary to keep clearly in mind precisely what is shown by these positive resolving power curves. They show what resolving power can be obtained in the final print if the negative is exposed on a range of test objects of different brightness but all of the same contrast (0·2 in this case). The

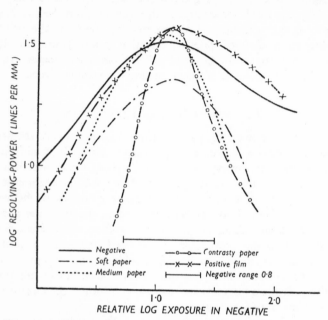

FIG. 46.—Resolution in negative and prints.

resolving power at the negative stage varies with the exposure in the usual way, rising at first with the gradient of the negative characteristic curve until the straight line is reached, then falling away with increasing density. (The characteristic curve has been omitted from Fig. 46 for clarity.) The curve of negative resolving power is then modified by the relation between density and resolving power for the particular positive material concerned, and the result appears as one of the positive resolution curves.

A study of the positive curves shows that the negative resolution can be reproduced satisfactorily on diapositives, but not on papers. A line of length 0·8 log exposure units, which is fairly representative of the brightness range in high-altitude views, has been drawn above the log E axis, disposed symmetrically about the peak of the negative resolving power curve. The resolution in the curve for positive film is close to that of the negative at all points, and it will be clear that by a slight adjustment to the printing exposure the negative resolution could be reproduced throughout the scale of 0·8. It is not possible, however, to reproduce the negative resolution over the whole of this range on any of the papers. The best average resolution is obtained on the medium grade, as may be seen by marking off a length of 0·8 exposure units and sliding it up the figure to meet the curves. It will be found that at the extreme ends of the range the resolving power drops to seventeen lines per millimetre for the soft grade, twenty-one lines per millimetre for the medium grade, and eleven lines per millimetre for the contrasty grade. For this particular subject range the best print is therefore made on medium paper. A subject of extremely short range, however, would give the best print on contrasty paper, as the resolving power of this grade is the highest over a very small range of exposures near the peak. It would also be possible to obtain high resolving power over any range of brightness by making several prints on contrasty paper at different exposures, so that small parts of the subject range in turn are brought to the peak of the paper resolution curve. The resolving power would then be higher than could be obtained by making one print on a soft paper, but would never be much higher at any point than the negative resolution. This is a very important conclusion and is a fundamental of photographic resolving power. Printing on contrasty papers makes it easier to see details of a flat negative larger than the limit of resolution, but will not reveal details appreciably smaller than that limit. It may be noted that the maximum resolution is about the same for the contrasty paper and for the positive film, although the gamma of the latter was much lower. The very narrow range of brightnesses over which high resolution can be obtained with the contrasty paper is, of course, due to the steep slope of its characteristic curve, which can only accommodate a limited range of negative densities before white paper is reached at one end of the scale and maximum density at the other.

The conditions of Reid's experiments were somewhat artificial, as he used a line test object and a lens of quite unusually high resolving power. It is not easy to devise a simple test which is exactly representative of practical conditions, and the subject has to be approached in different ways according to the particular point being investigated. Another informative experiment is illustrated by Fig. 47. Here the paper characteristic curve is plotted, together with a curve showing the resolving power at any value of reflection density. The negatives were again on Super XX film, their contrast was 0·1, and was made the same for all points on the exposure scale of the paper, whereas in Reid's experiments the test object contrast was modified by the varying slope of the negative characteristic curve. In other words, whereas Reid's curves showed the combined resolution of the negative and positive materials, Fig. 47 shows the resolution of the positive emulsion as restricted by a constant level of resolving power in the negative. This level was much lower than in Reid's experiments and has caused the flat-topped appearance of the curve. Fig. 47 shows that when the resolving power in the negative is of the order of sixteen lines per millimetre it can be satisfactorily reproduced on paper over a reflection-density range of about 0·1 to 1·2 or 1·3. For this particular paper the corresponding printing exposure range, which is equivalent to the negative density range, is about 0·75. Assuming a negative gamma of 1·4, the corresponding brightness range in the subject is about 0·5 log units. Even at the lower standard of resolution shown in Fig. 47 it is not therefore possible to reproduce a high-altitude negative on paper without some loss of detail in the light and dark tones (unless we accept the suggestion put forward in Chapter Twelve that it may be better to ignore the shadows altogether in high-altitude photography). The practical photographer's preference for soft prints from air negatives is thus well justified, because prints using the full density range of the paper would obviously suffer a very serious loss of fine detail at both ends of the scale.

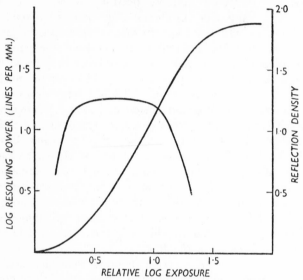

FIG. 47.—Characteristic and resolving power curves for
medium bromide paper.

At the toe end of the paper characteristic curve the falling-off in resolution must be mainly due to the lower gradient, which in Fig. 47 is less than unity for densities below 0·2. Approaching the shoulder end, however, the resolving power falls away before any great reduction in gradient can be seen, and the reason for this is not very clear. Possibly it may be due to diffusion of light at the interface between the emulsion and the baryta layer, which may also explain the fact that the maximum print resolution is often below the negative resolution, especially with the softer papers. The marked falling-off at somewhat higher densities is undoubtedly associated with lower gradient. Further investigations appear to be required on the whole subject of resolution in paper prints and its application to the printing of air negatives.

Practical Consequences.—Throughout this book stress is laid on the importance of obtaining the best possible resolving power in the air negative, and the reader may wonder if it is worth while in view of the limitations imposed by the printing paper. There are various ways of looking at this question. As a matter of general principle it would always appear to be worth while recording the utmost possible detail in the negative, even if some were lost in printing, because the air negative is a very valuable and almost irreplaceable record, but even on purely technical grounds the effort may be judged worth while.

We have to distinguish the two kinds of limitation on print resolution, one set by the limited *maximum* resolving power of the paper, and the other by the low gradients at the toe and shoulder of its characteristic curve, which cause the resolving power to fall towards zero at each end of the tone scale.

The first case is not of very great practical importance at present. Referring again to Fig. 46, it will be seen that only one paper, the soft grade, gave lower maximum resolution than the negative. This negative, however, had very high resolving power. The figures actually shown in Fig. 46 are probably artificially high, because Reid was working with a line test object, and it is known from much other work with Cobb test objects that the maximum resolving power obtainable on Super XX film at a contrast of 0·2 is twenty to twenty-two lines per millimetre. To bring Reid's data into conformity with the other figures in the book which relate to Cobb objects we therefore multiply them by two-thirds. Applying this to the curve for soft paper in Fig. 46, we conclude that it will give lower maximum resolving power than a negative having the best resolution that can be obtained on Super XX film. But few air negatives, in fact, have such a high standard of resolution as this, and ten lines per millimetre is probably a more representative average figure ; this is well below the fifteen lines which the soft paper will resolve at maximum, so that by making more than one print it is likely that all the detail in even the best air negatives could be reproduced on the worst paper of the three shown in Fig. 46.

Some loss of resolution at the ends of the tone scale cannot be avoided in one print from a high-resolution negative, unless its subject has a very short brightness range. If we again adopt the standard of ten lines per millimetre for the negative, however, we find that at least this level of resolution can be reached over a subject brightness scale of 1·0 for both soft and medium papers. With long-scale subjects, or negatives of higher resolution than ten lines per millimetre, it would be necessary to make more than one print, preferably not on soft paper, to avoid losses, but the majority of high-altitude negatives could be printed on to one piece of paper without seriously affecting their fine detail.

On the whole, then, the printing situation is fairly satisfactory in the present state of negative resolving power, but with any marked improvement in negative resolution this statement would need qualification.

DIAPOSITIVES AND DUPLICATE NEGATIVES

Diapositives are used instead of paper prints in various types of photo-grammetric plotting equipment. In general they are made on bromide or chloride emulsions of the kinds used for making lantern slides in general photography, and their use calls for no special comment. Being diapositive, their exposure is less critical than that of paper prints, at least from the point of view of retaining negative detail, and they will resolve all the detail found in the best negatives.

Duplicates of air negatives are sometimes required, and are usually made on a yellow-dyed cine positive type of emulsion. This has a lower inherent contrast than the same material undyed because the dye restricts the effective exposure to the upper part of the emulsion layer as well as performing the useful function of stopping any sideways diffusion of blue-violet light which might help to blur the image.

The general aim in duplication is to produce the most faithful copy possible of the original negative, but in air photography it is reasonable to improve on the original contrast if necessary. There are two stages in the duplication, a " master positive " being first made from the original negative and then printed to give a second transparency which is the duplicate negative. For faithful reproduction of the density ratios of the original both the master positive and the duplicate negative must be exposed so that their densities fall on the straight line part of the characteristic curve, and this line must be of unit slope. Alternatively, the products of the slopes in the positive and negative stages should be unity. The densities of the positive and negative need not lie entirely on the straight lines of the respective characteristic curves if these are, in effect, mirror images of each other, but this condition is difficult to fulfil with accuracy and straight line working is safer. With most materials a minimum density greater than 0·3 is necessary to fulfil this condition.

If sensitometric control methods are not available a rough check for unity gamma can be made by registering the master positive with the duplicate negative and examining the pair over a viewing light. With unit gamma straight-line reproduction the positive densities exactly cancel out the negative and the pair will appear to be a uniform density. If the positive has a greater gamma than unity the pair will appear to be a weak positive, and vice versa. The duplicate negative can be checked against the master positive in the same way.

It is usually rather difficult to keep the contrast low enough in duplication, because the tendency always seems to be for the master positive to have a gamma effectively greater than unity, due possibly to the slightly warm-toned image of the slow emulsion, which has a greater " printing density " than the visually measured density. A slight increase of contrast at the first stage is then multiplied up in the duplicate negative and the overall increase may be quite appreciable.

Complete development even of the special duplicating stocks will give a gamma considerably greater than unity, and a time of approximately five to eight minutes in a slow-acting developer such as D76 will be of the right order at 20° C. Trial and error will be necessary to find the exact times for local conditions.

Special Printing Materials

The base used for most photographic papers absorbs a great deal of water during processing, and the removal of this takes longer than the drying of the gelatine bearing the image. Prints can be dried more quickly by soaking in methylated spirit, and with expert handling the spirit can even be burnt off, but the need for this has been lessened by the introduction of the so-called " waterproof " papers. They are not perfectly waterproof, but the water absorption has been greatly reduced by a coating of a water-resisting lacquer, and in practice the drying time is very much shorter than with ordinary papers. It might be expected that waterproof papers would also lose hypo more rapidly in washing, but it would not be wise as yet to assume that washing could be as brief as with positive emulsions coated on glass or celluloid.

Waterproof papers in general seem to have lower resolving power than the ordinary types, though the difference is very variable. The author has seen many prints on waterproof paper in which the definition of good air negatives was seriously lowered, and others in which the results were almost as good as those obtained on normal papers. The trouble is possibly due to the thickness of the lacquer coating between the emulsion and the white base, and should not be difficult to overcome.

The requirements for minimum shrinkage in photogrammetric work have led to the production of special printing materials in which bromide emulsion is coated on to aluminium foil, or on to a special paper base having an interleaving of aluminium foil. These materials are processed normally and require no special mention here.

Special papers have been used for very rapid processing under military conditions, where it is not always possible to wait for the negatives to dry before printing. The surface of the emulsion is overcoated with a thin film of a synthetic resin soluble in alkalis but not soluble in water or acids. The paper may therefore be pressed into contact with the emulsion side of a negative wet with hypo solution and printed without any tendency to stick. On immersion in the alkaline developer the resin dissolves away and the development and fixation can proceed normally.

PRINTING EQUIPMENT

Negatives may be printed either by parallel light or by diffused light, the effect on contrast being small, though diffused light gives slightly greater contrast on account of the longer path for the light through the thickness of the image layer. If the negative image had no thickness and was in perfect contact with a paper emulsion also of negligible thickness, the same resolving power could be obtained with diffused light as with parallel light. If the negative has appreciable thickness, however, it is possible for lower resolution to be obtained with diffused light, since some rays then strike the image obliquely and may cause a slight enlargement of its effective boundaries (Fig. 48). The importance of this effect depends on the level of resolving power in the negative and the thickness of the emulsion layer. Up to at least twenty lines per millimetre in the negative fully diffused light introduces no loss of resolving power in the print. Parallel light printers have been made, using small distant point sources of light, but they are not strictly necessary and should be avoided unless there is some very good reason for their use, as, for example, bad contact in the printing head. The chief practical disadvantages of printing by parallel light are the difficulty of viewing the negative for shading or judging exposure, and the accentuation of scratches and other defects on the back of the film base. With diffused light the thickness of the base is normally sufficient for such defects to cast no shadow on the printing paper, but with parallel light they are illuminated from one direction only and are exactly stencilled.

Contact in Printing.—In diffused light printers perfect contact between negative and paper is essential. Some printers are badly at fault in this

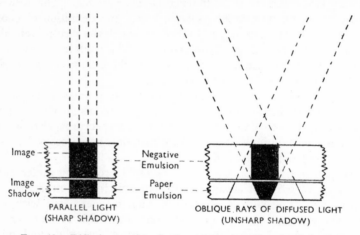

Image — Negative Emulsion

Image Shadow — Paper Emulsion

PARALLEL LIGHT (SHARP SHADOW)   OBLIQUE RAYS OF DIFFUSED LIGHT (UNSHARP SHADOW)

Fig. 48.—Diffusion at edge of a sharp image by diffused printing light.

respect and cause a serious lowering of the negative resolution in parts of the print. These areas of low resolution are popularly known as " soft spots," which is a graphic description of their very characteristic appearance.

Bad contact, as a characteristic of the printer itself, may be due to one or more of the following causes :—

(*a*) Pressure glass not flat.

(*b*) Pressure back not flat, not of uniform resilience, or its plane not parallel to plane of pressure glass.

(*c*) Insufficient pressure.

The glass in contact printers is usually $\frac{1}{4}$-in. plate, and the surface is good enough to meet all requirements for good contact. If the thickness is less than $\frac{1}{4}$ in., however, the glass may warp under pressure and give poor contact for a different reason.

The pressure back may be constructed in different ways according to the ideas of the manufacturer. The most successful type is probably the pneumatic bag with rubber walls thick enough to withstand a relatively high air pressure. The bag is convex to the paper, so that when it is clamped down the pressure is applied first in the centre of the negative and spreads outwards. It is essential for the bag to be strong enough ;

good results are obtained when the pressure applied to the negative is not less than 1 lb. per sq. in. The pneumatic pad has the advantage that the metal supporting plate need not be flat to a high accuracy.

Good contact can also be had with solid pressure pads made of rubber, felt, cork, or cork jointing material such as " Langite." It is essential, however, for the surface of such solid pads to be flat within 0·002 in. Moulded rubber of suitable resilience (Shore hardness 35 to 40) can be obtained within the necessary limits of flatness. If cork is used it is necessary to obtain the requisite flatness by grinding.

Wooden supporting plates for the pressure pad are useless as they warp in use, and light alloys must be aged before finishing. The printer must be made with sufficient accuracy to ensure that the planes of the pressure glass and pressure back are parallel, or one of the two should be flexibly mounted to allow them to come into parallelism.

It is sometimes supposed that bad contact is caused by air becoming trapped between the negative and papers as the pressure pad comes down. Some support is given to this view by the fact that both paper and negative are impervious to air and would tend to seal off any air trapped between them in small pockets ; such air could only leak away slowly through small gaps and would gradually work its way out to the edges. Moreover, it is well known that in some printers which give bad contact immediately after clamping down the pressure pad, perfect contact is obtained after a delay of a few seconds, suggesting that trapped air has leaked away and allowed the negative and paper to come into contact. It is equally easy to find arguments suggesting that the presence of trapped air need not be assumed. In any case the trapped air must be regarded as a secondary and not a primary cause of bad contact. Assuming perfectly flat pressure surfaces of uniform resiliency, air could not be trapped at all, since the surfaces could not come together until all air was excluded, but if the surfaces are not flat or have areas of different resiliency, then as they come together the air will naturally move to regions of lower pressure, i.e., where the contact is bad or the pad is weaker. It is extremely difficult to devise experimental tests which will settle the issue, but the question is one of academic interest only, because perfectly good contact can be obtained without any time delay if the surfaces are truly flat.

Even if the printer construction is above reproach, bad contact can be caused by the presence of foreign matter on or beneath the negative, or by small creases in the negative. The paper itself is not always perfectly flat ; apart from accidental kinks some sheets are marred by small ripples or irregularly shaped distortions which are associated with the drying of the paper after coating. These are normally " inspected out " by the manufacturer, but a few such faults sometimes slip through the most careful inspection. It is a wise precaution to examine the surface of each sheet under the dark room light before use ; these marks can nearly always be seen before the paper is wetted but not after processing. If it were not for the possibility of such flaws and such foreign matter as dust, hairs, flakes of gelatine, etc., a rigid pressure back could be used. A resilient back, however, provided that the pressure is sufficient, localises the area of bad contact when foreign matter is present, while a rigid back tends to distribute the bad contact over a large area. The pressure applied by most printers is surprisingly low, generally in the neighbourhood of $\frac{1}{2}$ lb. per sq. in. Vacuum pressure backs, as used in the process trade, apply pressure of the order of 9 lb. per sq. in., but they are too slow in operation for most air photographic work. A pressure of 1 lb. per sq. in. has been found to ensure good contact when printing air negatives, using pressure backs of solid rubber of the Shore hardness already specified, or the pneumatic type of back, or felt about $\frac{1}{8}$ in. thick.

The effect of bad contact on resolution naturally depends on the level of resolution in the negative, and the diffusion of the light. The following experimental data will illustrate the order of reduction obtained when the negative and paper are separated by definite distances. A negative bearing resolving power charts was printed with various thicknesses of cellophane between it and the paper, on a printer giving very good contact. The light source was a uniformly illuminated sheet of ground glass situated $3\frac{1}{2}$ in. below the negative. The following results were obtained :—

Resolution in negative . . .	21	lines per mm.
Direct contact print	19	„ „
Print with 0·0015 in. separation .	11	„ „
Print with 0·003 in. separation . .	$6\frac{1}{2}$	„ „
Print with 0·0045 in. separation .	$4\frac{1}{2}$	„ „

These figures illustrate the importance of accurate construction of the printer and the avoidance of dust on the negative when it is being printed. It may be wondered how it is that satisfactory prints are ever obtained from air negatives, in view of the very critical nature of the operation. Two comments may be made in this connection. Firstly, it is very common indeed to see " soft spots " in prints, even those made by reputable organisations. Secondly, these areas of bad contact form a relatively small part of the total print area, so that not many of the finer details are lost ; this is particularly true in the case of stereoscopic observation, where any point of the ground area depicted has two chances of being reproduced sharply.

Testing for Contact.—Bad contact in printers cannot easily be located by the use of resolution test negatives, because the whole area must be covered and inspection of very large numbers of resolution charts would be extremely tedious. There is, however, a simple and very sensitive test which only requires one print to be made from a test negative and shows clearly the position of all areas of bad contact, and the relative seriousness of the trouble at different parts. The test negative is a copy of a half-tone screen on film base of the same thickness as that of the negatives usually printed. Duplicating emulsion is suitable for making the copy, and the film base should be perfectly free from kinks or distortions of any kind. The screen should have a ruling of about a hundred lines to the inch. If a half-tone screen is not available, a sheet of wire gauze, about thirty-six wires to the inch, is a satisfactory substitute. The gauze sheet must be carefully selected to be free from creases and should be as flat as possible. The screen or gauze is held in contact with the copy film, preferably in a vacuum frame, and the exposure is made by parallel light. The copy should be examined under magnification to check that all the lines are perfectly sharp.

If the copy negative has been made from a rather coarse gauze, about thirty-six lines to the inch, the individual lines will be clearly visible in the contact prints, and the whole area of a good print should be covered with a sharp black-and-white pattern. With any lack of contact this contrasty pattern changes into a smooth grey tone, and the different appearance is very obvious on examination. In a copy made from a fine half-tone screen the lines are not visible to the naked eye if they are much closer together than one hundred to the inch, and the test works in a slightly different way. With good contact the print is covered by black-and-white areas as before, and over a wide range of printing exposures the black lines have the same density, viz., the maximum black of the paper, while the white spaces remain clear. The eye sees the print as a uniform grey tone if it cannot distinguish the lines, and the maximum density of this tone cannot exceed $0 \cdot 3$, because half the area is white. With bad contact light can spread outside the boundaries of the clear lines in the negative, so that areas which should be white in the print are more or less fogged, and the integrated density of the area can rise above $0 \cdot 3$. The areas of bad contact are therefore shown by areas of darker grey on a light grey background. This test gives no information on the absolute loss of resolution, but it is so sensitive that the user can feel confident that any printer which it shows to be satisfactory will lose none of the detail in the best air negatives at present produced.

REFERENCES

1. JONES, L. A., and NELSON, C. N. " Control of Photographic Printing by Measured Characteristics of the Negative," *Journ. Opt. Soc. Amer.*, **32,** 558 to 619, 1943.
2. WEYDE, E. " Über die Möglichkeiten, die Haltbarkeit photographischer Bilder zu verbessern." *Veröffentlichungen des Wissenschaftlichen Zentral-Laboratoriums der photographischen Abteilung Agfa*, **5,** 181, 1937 ; also *B. J. Photo.*, **82,** 376, 1935.
3. CRABTREE, J. I., EATON, G. T., and MUEHLER, L. E. " The Elimination of Hypo from Photographic Images," *Photo. Journ.*, p. 458, December 1940.
4. JONES, L. A. Papers in *Journ. Frank. Inst.*, summarised in Mees' " Theory of the Photographic Process," chap. 19.
5. RENWICK, F. F. *Photo. Journ.*, **27,** No. 1, 1937.
6. HOPKINSON, R. G. " A New Approach to the Problem of Tone Reproduction," *Photo. Journ.*, p. 542, September 1937.
7. REID, J. B. Unpublished Investigations for Ministry of Supply, London.

Chapter Eight

IMAGE MOVEMENTS

IMAGE movements are a characteristic feature of air photography and in general necessitate a shorter time of exposure than might be given from other considerations. For example, the requirement for high resolution indicates the need for a slow fine-grain emulsion, but the exposure would be so long even in the brightest light that the image movement would be excessive, and the ground resolution would probably be lower than with a faster emulsion and shorter time of exposure. So much is obvious from general principles; with the numerical data provided by resolution tests it is possible to study the subject in a more precise way.

Three classes of image movement can be recognised. The most obvious, if not always the most important, is the steady movement due to the forward velocity of the aircraft. Next are the vibratory movements of the airframe excited by out-of-balance forces in the engines or airscrews, or by aerodynamic forces; some of this vibration always reaches the camera, and in certain conditions it can be the most serious cause of image movement. The third and usually the least serious class is the slow-period movement of the aircraft as a whole about its mean orientation in flight. These movements of pitch, roll, and yaw are sometimes due to sudden impulses such as bumps, but even in still air they inevitably follow the movements of the control surfaces as the pilot makes the frequent corrections necessary to keep a constant mean height and course. The relative importance of the three classes of movement in reducing resolving power for ground detail depends on the speed and height of the aircraft, and whenever measures are taken to lessen the image movement this should be done in full knowledge of the situation.

TOLERABLE AMOUNT OF IMAGE MOVEMENT

The effect of image movement on resolution has always been somewhat obscure, and it usually comes as a surprise to find how much movement can be tolerated before its results appear as a blurring of the image. In the past it was usual to draw up tables of the longest exposure times permissible at various heights and aircraft speeds, the times being calculated in relation to an assumed " circle of confusion " of the lens. " Circle of confusion " is not a very useful term, however, and it is better to think in terms of the resolving power of the lens-film combination, the movement being related to the distance just resolved by the stationary camera. Resolving powers are now known for the lens-film combinations used in air photography, and the exposure times can be adjusted accordingly, more image movement being permissible when the resolution is low than when it is high. Often it is most convenient to think of the resolution in terms of feet on the ground, as this ties up with the aircraft movement in a very clear way.

Whatever the cause of image movement we always need to know its result in terms of the reduction of the resolving power of the stationary image. If the distance between points which can just be resolved in absence of movement is I/R and the distance moved by the image is d, we require to know the relation between I/R and d when the distance resolved in the moving image is just perceptibly greater than I/R. Assuming agreement on the meaning of " just perceptible," we can write

$$d = a.1/R.$$

A similar relation can be written for angular resolution.

There is no particular reason for supposing that a will actually be a constant factor for the diverse types of image encountered in air photography. The relation between movement and its effect on resolution will not necessarily be the same for the various types and contrasts of detail in air photographs, for films of different graininess and for optical images of different intensity distributions. Nevertheless, even an approximate estimate of the order of magnitude of the factor would be useful.

Selwyn (1) made a preliminary mathematical investigation of the problem and concluded that for sine-curve test objects the movement could probably be as much as one-half the distance just resolved in the stationary image before any serious loss of resolution would be apparent. At the time when this tentative estimate was first put forward it seemed rather surprising that so great an amount of movement could be tolerated, but later experimental work has shown that it is certainly of the right order.

J. M. Gregory (2) investigated the movement problem on a laboratory scale by photographing groups of Cobb test objects moving with a known velocity. The test objects were mounted on a pendulum swinging in a plane at right angles to the axis of an aircraft camera fitted with a 20-in. lens. The test objects were of high and low contrast and were orientated at different angles to the direction of motion. Exposures were made on Super XX film and the results plotted as resolving power against image movement for different lens apertures, orientations of the test objects, and positions in the field of view of the lens. Romer (3) made use of Gregory's experimental data, paying particular attention to the region where movement is small and just beginning to affect resolution. No simple expression of general application could be found for the distance resolved as a function of the movement, the relationship being different according to the contrast of the test object and its orientation and position in the field of view. Romer found, however, that in all cases the curve of resolution versus movement was convex to the movement axis in the region of small movement. A typical curve is shown in Fig. 49; the ordinates represent the relative angle resolved in the moving image divided by the relative angle resolved in the stationary image, while the abcissæ represent the angle moved divided by the angle resolved in the stationary image. The shape of the curve at its lower end has considerable practical significance, indicating that the movement can rise to an appreciable fraction of the resolving power limit before it seriously affects the latter. This is in agreement with practical experience, where it is common to find that movement is less serious than might be expected from the geometrical factors of scale, speed of aircraft, etc. Further up the curve the slope is constant and much greater than at the lower end ; while this indicates that the movement is then a more serious factor, it also shows that if movement is severe a relatively inaccurate attempt to compensate for it, as by moving the film, can produce a marked improvement in sharpness.

The form of the curve in its lowest portion means that the " least tolerable movement " cannot be very precisely determined. This does not matter very much, because in photographic practice shutter speeds are in any case varied by factors of two to one, and it would be unreasonable to work very close to the danger point. Romer assumed that movement at right angles to the bars of the test object, which has the most serious effect, would be the condition most relevant in actual air photography, and he made estimates of the factor a for this condition. He defined the " least tolerable " decline in resolution as an increase of I/R by 20 per cent., corresponding to a drop of 17 per cent. in resolving power. These assumptions seem reasonable enough, because a 10 per cent. change of resolving power is the smallest that is easily perceptible in laboratory resolution tests. Depending on the test object contrast and the position in the field, a was found to vary between 0·5 and 0·8. For low contrast detail the figure of 0·6 was finally adopted as the most representative. When the movement was such that $a=1·2$, the resolution was found to drop by 70 per cent., a serious reduction. For details inclined at all angles to the direction of movement the averaged drop in resolution was found to be 12 per cent. for $a=0·6$ and 45 per cent. for $a=1·2$.

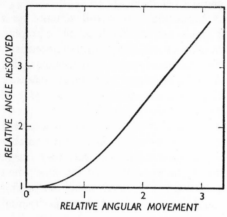

FIG. 49.—Effect of movement on resolution.

Experimental air photographs have been taken in which known and controlled amounts of image movement were introduced, and study of the detail in such photographs supports the conclusion that the tolerable image movement can equal but not exceed 0·6 of the resolution in the stationary image.

Plates 8 and 9 show comparative enlargements from air negatives taken to verify these relationships. The photographs were taken under strictly comparative conditions, and the only difference between the members of a pair is the amount of image movement which was allowed. One camera had a moving-film mechanism and was controlled so that the image movement due to the forward movement of the aircraft was nil, within the accuracy possible with the equipment used. In the other camera the film was stationary during exposure, and by flying at different heights and speeds the image movement was varied as desired. The image movement was calculated from the ground speed of the aircraft, the scale, and the nominal shutter time of 1/400 sec. These shutters were of focal plane type, about 60 per cent. efficient, and the use of the nominal time is somewhat arbitrary ; however, the accuracy of the experiment would hardly justify any closer estimate of the real time of effective exposure. The time of 1/400 sec. was short enough for all other image movements to be negligible, and the lenses were known to give identical resolving power. The enlargements clearly show that when movement is 0·6 times the distance resolved in the stationary image its effects can scarcely be perceived, while at 1·2 times the effect on resolution is serious.

Although this experimental demonstration refers only to image movements due to the forward velocity of the aircraft, it seems reasonable to adopt the factor of 0·6 for general use in all problems of image movement, however the movement is produced. The lens and film conditions in which it was derived might be approximately described as the optical image free from very serious asymmetrical aberration, resolution limited to some extent by the film, and detail of low contrast. So long as the conditions do not depart very obviously from these the factor of 0·6 will probably apply, but any marked asymmetry of the optical image or any marked change of graininess might well require a different factor.

Magnitude of Image Movements

In air photography we are interested in the angular resolving power or the ground resolution rather than the linear resolving power in the image plane, because the object of taking the photographs is to record ground details of the smallest possible size. For this reason it is generally more useful and less confusing to think of image movements as angular movement or movement of the ground.

Forward Movement of the Aircraft.—At any height h the angular velocity ω of the ground, due to the steady forward velocity of the aircraft, is given by

$$\omega = v/h.$$

If the time of exposure is t, the angular movement θ is given by

$$\theta = \omega t = vt/h.$$

Strictly speaking, θ is not known precisely unless the shutter is 100 per cent. efficient, but the error introduced with shutters of the usual 60 to 80 per cent. efficiency is not important. The velocity v is, of course, the true ground speed of the aircraft, and the air speed must be corrected for wind. Thus the angular movement varies inversely as the height, while the apparent ground movement is, of course, independent of the height.

Vibration.—The aircraft camera is a heavy piece of equipment, but is not massive enough to be unaffected by the vibrations transmitted from the supporting parts of the airframe. These vibrations are very complex and vary from one aircraft to another. For the present purpose we are only concerned with the vibration which actually filters to the camera through the absorbing medium of the mounting. The details of anti-vibration mounting design for air cameras have not been worked out in a completely satisfactory manner, but good designs reduce the amplitude of the applied vibrations to a point where they are not very serious. The performance of mountings is best expressed as the average angular velocity of the mounted camera. (Strictly speaking, as the root mean square velocity, which gives a better index of performance.) With simply constructed mountings employing sponge rubber as the medium giving elasticity and damping, a common construction, the average R.M.S. velocity of the camera is in round figures 0·01 radian per sec. This figure is an average of figures obtained in single and twin engine military aircraft built before 1944, all of which gave results of the same order. There is some evidence that better results might be obtained in certain types of civil aircraft, and in the future jet aircraft seem likely to be very much better. It is not likely that any of the aircraft which might be used for air photography would have substantially worse vibration than the examples to which the figure of 0·01 rad.-sec. refers, and it is about as representative as any such figure can ever hope to be.

The angular velocity of the camera due to vibration is substantially independent of the height of the aircraft so long as it is operating normally within its designed height range. The effect of rotational vibrations of the camera on ground resolution increases in direct proportion to the height.

Aircraft Unsteadiness.—It is obvious that considerable angular velocities must be developed when the aircraft goes into a steep turn or dive, but as seen from the ground its motion in straight and level flight appears to be very steady and uniform. Closer examination shows, however, that the motion is never quite along a straight line. In bumpy air there will naturally be continual violent movements, but even at high altitudes and in calm weather the aircraft is continuously making small deviations from the mean line of flight. Continual slight changes of the control surfaces are necessary to maintain a constant average course, and with each change an angular velocity of pitch, roll, or yaw may be developed. The magnitude of these irregular movements depends not only on the air conditions but also on the characteristics of the aeroplane and the skill of the pilot. A skilful pilot, flying with the aim of reducing such angular velocities to a minimum rather than keeping the best mean course, can help by making all corrections slowly and smoothly, even at the cost of slight wandering from the desired heading. Automatic pilots are generally better from the present point of view than the best human pilots, possibly because they anticipate the need for corrections somewhat sooner and hence reduce their magnitude. Many years ago, with the slow aircraft then in use, it was possible to make flat turns on rudder only, and it is probable that the average angular velocities in such aircraft were less than in modern types where correction of heading introduces a slight roll.

Photographic flights are carried out whenever possible in steady weather away from bumpy air. The angular velocities encountered under these conditions are therefore much more important for photographic purposes than those met in bumpy weather. Romer has measured the angular velocities of pitch and roll in various aircraft, using the well-known method of flying over a light when using an open-shutter camera at night. Other investigators have made similar measurements. Romer found in Wellington and Mosquito aircraft, flown manually in good weather, at heights of the order of 10,000 ft., that the highest figure for the mean angular velocity measured over runs of 10 to 20 seconds' duration was 0·017 rad.-sec., while the lowest was 0·0014 rad.-sec. From a number of such measurements he derived an average R.M.S. figure of 0·009 rad.-sec. for good manual piloting. During individual runs the maximum figure was 0·03 rad.-sec. With very careful manual piloting the averaged figure over the run could be as low as 0·005 rad.-sec. With the automatic pilot the R.M.S. velocity for several runs was 0·00028 rad.-sec.

Romer concludes that the R.M.S. figure of 0·009 rad.-sec. best represents the likely average angular velocity with good normal piloting. This means that the angular velocities due to vibration and to the aircraft unsteadiness are of very similar order, when the aircraft is manually piloted. With the automatic pilot in use the vibration is much more serious than the pitch and roll movements. Needless to say, these figures are indicative only of the order of magnitude of the movements to be expected, and must be subject to considerable variation according to the kinds of aircraft and automatic pilot used.

As with vibration, the effect of the aircraft unsteadiness on ground resolution must increase directly with the height.

Relative Importance of the different Types of Image Movement.—The three types of image movement acquire different relative importance under different conditions of flying and photography, and it is always desirable to have some knowledge of the apparent ground movement in relation to the maximum ground resolution possible with the lens-film combination in use. Exact comparisons are not possible, because the movements are never known with precision, but it is at least feasible to see how things stand to a first approximation. For such comparisons it is often convenient to consider the two irregular movements together as one, because both increase in importance directly with the height, whereas the effect of the steady forward movement on ground resolution is constant and independent of the height. Moreover, under many conditions the two irregular movements are of the same order of magnitude. According to Romer's work, the figure of 0·0134 rad.-sec. is representative of the combined movements due to vibration and the unsteadiness of the aircraft, when using a sponge-rubber type of anti-vibration mounting and assuming average manual piloting. These are probably the most representative of the varied conditions of vibration and flying encountered in air photography.

The relative importance of the irregular movements and the steady forward movement will naturally depend on the height and speed of the aircraft, and one way of illustrating this is shown in Fig. 50. The ordinates in Fig. 50 give the maximum ground resolution obtainable in absence of movement, from the altitudes shown on the abcissa scale, with the lenses whose focal lengths are indicated against each of the dotted diagonal lines. These resolution figures are for Super XX film, a test-object contrast of 0·2, and are averages across the 9 in. × 9 in. field at $f/8$. The ordinate scale also shows apparent ground movement, and the horizontal line is drawn at the value of ground movement corresponding to 1/200 sec. exposure time at a forward velocity of 240 m.p.h. Other lines could be drawn to correspond with other conditions of movement, e.g., for 120 m.p.h. at the same shutter

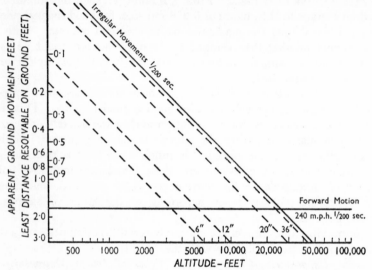

FIG. 50.—Interrelation of image movements and ground resolution.

speed the line should be moved up to an ordinate value half that shown in the figure. The diagonal line marked " irregular movements " gives the apparent ground movement in 1/200 sec. due to vibration and the aircraft unsteadiness, based on the representative figure of 0·0134 rad.-sec. ; to find the apparent ground movement from any altitude follow vertically upwards from the appropriate abcissa point and take the ordinate value at the intersection with the " irregular movements " line. For other shutter speeds than 1/200 sec., parallel diagonal lines can be drawn, displaced up or down as required.

Suppose we are using a 6-in. wide-angle lens ; the angular resolution is very low, and we can come down to just over 3000 ft. before the ground resolution equals the ground movement as shown by the horizontal line. To comply with the condition that the movement shall not exceed 0·6 of the resolution in absence of movement, we move down the 6-in. lens line until the ground resolution is 1/0·6 times the ground movement; this is found to be at approximately 5000 ft. In this case the irregular movements are insignificant, being less than one-quarter of the steady forward movement in terms of the effect on ground resolution. Much longer times of exposure than 1/200 sec. are, in fact, permissible with this lens, on account of its low resolution, and even at 1/50 sec. the irregular movements are not serious. At heights of 15,000 ft. and upwards, which are commonly used in topographic surveys, the 6-in. lens could safely be used at 1/75 sec., assuming a mounting of good anti-vibration characteristics as implied in the irregular movements figure of 0·0134 rad.-sec. However, not all mountings used for survey cameras are as good as this, and it would be well to allow a certain factor of safety by regarding 1/100 sec. as the longest safe exposure time.

As a very different case we may consider the use of a 36-in. telephoto lens of the best modern type. With this lens the smallest distance resolvable on the ground is practically the same as the apparent ground movement due to the irregular movements; if the full resolution is to be obtained a shutter speed of about 1/320 sec. must be used for this reason alone, however great the altitude. The apparent ground movement due to forward velocity introduces an unacceptable amount of image movement at all altitudes below 40,000 ft., assuming 1/200 sec. as shown in the figure, and at the more likely altitude of 30,000 ft., 1/300 sec. should be regarded as the longest safe time.

At very low altitudes, such as 500 ft., the forward movement of the aircraft outweighs all other causes of low resolution, even with the 6-in. wide-angle lens, and some form of movement compensation becomes essential for vertical photography, since there is rarely enough light to allow the use of the shutter speeds of the order of 1/1000 sec., which the diagram shows to be necessary at 240 m.p.h. The irregular movements are so small relative to the forward movement and the possible ground resolution with a 6-in. lens, which is the sort of focal length most likely to be used at 500 ft., that anti-vibration mountings could probably be dispensed with, even with movement compensation and a shutter time of 1/200 sec.; they would certainly be unnecessary at a shutter time of 1/1000 sec. without movement compensation.

These examples have shown the importance of studying the image movements in relation to the ground resolution that is required and that is possible with the lens-film combination in use. Short-focus wide-angle cameras in general cannot give high resolution, and image movement is a much less serious problem than with long-focus high-resolution equipment, the use of which is only justified if care is taken to see that all image movements are kept down to the necessary low level. There is little point in using a high-resolution camera and spoiling its performance by inefficient mounting or by using too slow a shutter speed; it would be better to use a camera of wider angle and cover more ground at each exposure.

The data used for Fig. 50 are about as typical of conditions in air photography as any one set of data could be, but they should be regarded primarily as a demonstration of general principles which each photographer must apply according to the details of his own problems.

REFERENCES

1. SELWYN, E. W. H. Unpublished work for Ministry of Supply, London.
2. GREGORY, J. M. Unpublished work for Ministry of Supply, London.
3. ROMER, W. Unpublished work for Ministry of Supply, London.

Chapter Nine

REDUCTION OF IMAGE MOVEMENTS

In Chapter Eight we have considered the magnitude and relative importance of the image movements which are present in the aircraft camera under average conditions of use, these being the vibratory movements which get through the mounting, the steady movement due to the forward speed of the aircraft, and the pitching and rolling motion of the aircraft as a whole. Some attention will now be given to the means which have been adopted for keeping camera vibration down to the lowest possible level and compensating for the forward movement when this becomes excessive.

The three kinds of image movement have different relative importance at different heights and aircraft speeds, and it is not surprising that in the development of air photography, with continual changes of height and speed, the technique for dealing with them has also been modified from time to time. In balloons, no doubt, the only problem was unsteadiness of the platform, but this branch of air photography is not well documented. The early photographers in mechanically propelled aircraft seem to have been troubled mainly by vibration, if we may judge from records of the First World War. This was eventually overcome by the development of adequate anti-vibration mountings, which reduced the angular velocities of the cameras to a point where they were not very important in relation to the level of resolution obtainable at that time. From then until the beginning of the Second World War vibration as a limiting factor seems to have very largely disappeared, perhaps because of the shifting of emphasis to shorter focal lengths for survey photography. The lessons which could have been learned from a proper study of the successful anti-vibration mountings seem to have been rather overlooked, however, judging from admittedly limited information. Between the two wars commercially available mountings seem to have been very stiff, practically equivalent to rigid mounting of the camera to the airframe, or if reasonably soft the damping was not adequate. In terms of absolute performance such mountings were inefficient, but in practice they often allowed the full resolution of the cameras to be obtained, and thus were quite satisfactory to the user. Their successful use was no doubt due in part to the fact that the speed of aircraft was going up and faster shutter speeds were required to cope with the increased forward movement. Fortunately the sensitivity of panchromatic emulsions was also increased, and the need for reduced exposure time could be met. Vibration does not seem to have become any worse; it may even have become less due to better engines and airframes. When operating heights increased, focal length and angular resolution had to go up at the same time, and the need for better mountings became acute. The problem was solved by the same methods which had been used before, and vibration again receded as a limiting factor. Aircraft speeds were still going up, but no further increase in emulsion sensitivity took place, and still shorter times of exposure could not be used. Attention was then directed to means for compensating for the forward velocity, mainly for low-altitude work at first, but with the realisation that it would sooner or later be necessary even at higher altitudes. At present there are few occasions when vibration need be a problem, but forward movement is often a very serious drag on resolution, notably in large-scale town surveys, because of the high speeds of modern aircraft. Possibly the helicopter will solve this problem in the course of time and thus save the surveyor the headaches involved in the use of movement compensation devices.

Compensation for Forward Movement

The effect of forward movement on ground resolution is theoretically independent of the height or scale, but in practice large scales and low altitudes are used for the purpose of recording the smaller ground details, and the movement is in effect much more serious than at higher altitudes. The most obvious way of combating the movement is to reduce the time of exposure, but little can be done in this direction, at least for vertical photography. If the normal time of exposure at high altitudes is, say, 1/300 sec., and this is just sufficient to stop the movement, then at ten times the scale 1/3000 sec. would be required to give the full advantage of working at the lower altitude. Even if it were mechanically possible to give such extremely short exposures they would be ruled out by the limited sensitivity of the film. The brightness of shadows is much less at low altitudes than at high, and correspondingly more exposure is required. There is not enough lens aperture in reserve to cope with the need for much shorter times of exposure while still producing a well-exposed negative, even when allowance is made for the fact that the yellow filter can be dispensed with because of the lesser importance of haze, and the obvious course is to introduce some compensation for the steady forward movement.

At low altitudes the improvement to be expected from movement compensation is very marked. Referring to Fig. 50 in Chapter Eight, we see that at 500 ft., 240 m.p.h., and 1/200 sec. exposure time the limit set to ground resolution by the forward movement is 20 in., by the irregular movements less than 1 in., and by the lens-film resolution 3 in., assuming the use of a 6-in. lens. Therefore we stand to improve the ground resolution some six times if the effect of the forward movement can be eliminated, the effect of the irregular movements being altogether negligible. We could, in fact, afford to *increase* the time of exposure, which would be useful in view of the dark shadows just mentioned, but this should not be pushed too far, because there will always be errors in the accuracy of compensation, while the irregular movements may be more serious at low altitudes than is shown by the figure, and the shorter the exposure time the greater the residual movement that can be tolerated. Low altitude vertical photography is the field where the most outstanding advantages can be claimed for movement compensation, but in high-altitude verticals also it is bound to have applications as the speed of aircraft continues to increase.

Methods of Compensation.—Several methods have been suggested for movement compensation in vertical photography. They may be divided into two classes :—

(*a*) Methods which move the film in the focal plane with the same velocity as the image, or give the image, by optical means, a velocity equal and opposite to that imparted by the aircraft movement.

(*b*) Tilting of the camera axis during exposure so that it continues to point at the same point on the ground in spite of the forward displacement of the aircraft.

Methods of the first class include moving film magazines and "slit" cameras, cameras with rotating prisms before the lens, cameras which move the lens parallel to the focal plane, and cameras with a rotating glass plate between the lens and the film.

The moving-film principle is the simplest of all methods, and has the advantage that the compensation is the same at all parts of the field, while no synchronisation with the moment of shutter release is required as with moving lens and rocking camera methods. It has probably been used more than any other technique.

Tilting the camera has had a certain vogue, but it is not always convenient to arrange mechanism for swinging a large and heavy camera, and the compensation is not uniform all over the field. However, the errors only become appreciable for angles of view greater than 35 degrees. For example, with an 8-in. lens used on a 5×5 in. field the error at the edge of the field is 10 per cent., while if a $3\frac{1}{4}$-in. lens is used on the same camera the error is 50 per cent. With the rotating plate method the error at the edge of the field would be 15 per cent. for the 8-in. lens. These errors could be reduced in practice, however, by dividing them between the middle and edges of the field, thus leaving a smaller error which would not often be serious. Nevertheless, the moving-film method is generally so much simpler to apply that it has been almost universally used.

Slit Cameras.—Slit cameras are suitable only for low altitudes, below 1000 ft. The film is wound continuously past a slit positioned in the focal plane at right angles to the direction of film travel and the line of flight. The speed of the film is, of course, made equal to the speed of the image. There is no shutter in the conventional sense, the time of exposure being determined by the width of the slit and the speed with which the film is wound past it. The width of the slit is adjustable to allow for correct setting of the exposure time at different heights and speeds. It will be clear that for a constant time of exposure the width of the slit will be proportional to the scale of the photograph and directly proportional to the velocity of the aircraft over the ground. The entire length of the film is exposed in a continuous strip without frame divisions, hence the alternative name "strip camera." This means that in the simple form it is not possible to take overlapping pictures for stereo relief. A stereo form is made, however, in which the two lenses are used to give two strip photographs side by side on the same film. The axes of the lenses are parallel, but are slightly displaced relative to each other along the line of the film travel, and at right angles to the slit; thus one records a given point on the ground a fraction of a second before the other and hence a parallax difference is obtained. A separation of 3 to 5 degrees gives ample relief. The stereo cover is, of course, obtained at the cost of a smaller scale or less ground covered by each strip.

The slit camera has been widely used for work at very low altitudes, where it has outstanding advantages over any other type, arising from the very rapid rate of film movement. This may be seen from an example :—

Let aircraft velocity $V = 300$ m.p.h. $= 440$ ft. per sec.
  focal length $f = 5$ in.
  height $h = 200$ ft. $= 2400$ in.

Then the film speed $v = \dfrac{Vf}{h} = 11$ in. per sec.

Suppose that under these conditions a conventional type of camera is to be used, giving pictures with the usual overlap of 60 per cent. between successive frames. If the picture width is 9 in., the image of a point on the ground will take 9/11 sec. to travel from one side of the frame to the other, but for stereo cover the same point must appear in two pictures taken at an interval 0·6 of this, i.e., 0·5 sec. approximately. Therefore the film would have to move alternately at 11 in. per sec. and at some greater speed fast enough to ensure that the necessary windover took place. The whole cycle of exposing, winding on film, and resetting the shutter would have to be done in less than half a second. This can be done if the camera is designed for the job, but it is very much simpler to wind the film continuously without using a shutter at all.

Although the slit camera is so well adapted for work at very low altitudes and high speeds, it has disadvantages which make it unsuitable for heights much greater than 500 ft. The longest time of exposure which can be given while still obtaining pictures free from blurring due to vibration, inaccurate compensation, etc., is about 1/100 sec. To get this time at the smaller scales, the slit has to be very narrow. If the time is t and the slit width S, then $S = Vft/h$. For the case already quoted, $S = 0·11$ in. If the height is increased to 800 ft. the slit must be reduced to 0·027 in. With widths of this order two troubles which are present but not serious at the larger scale become much more obvious. The first trouble is a periodic density variation or ripple along the length of the strip, the transverse bands of different density corresponding to slight variations in the speed of travel of the film, which cannot easily be avoided in a system using gears. A more serious fault, however, is a distortion of the image, due to the fact that successive points on the ground are recorded behind the slit at intervals of time which are quite large compared with those in, say, a focal-plane shutter camera. In the latter, points at opposite edges of a 9-in. frame are exposed within about 1/20 sec., but points 9 in. apart along the strip will be exposed at an interval of over three seconds in the case of photography at 800 ft. quoted above. This would not matter if there were no vibration and the aircraft held a perfectly steady course, but these suppositions are not true in practice, and the image suffers considerable distortion due to the oscillations of the camera axis about its mean position. This distortion is visible even in low-altitude photographs, but is not then serious enough to interfere with the recognition of objects. The amount of the distortion, being due to an angular movement of the camera, increases directly with the height, and at 1,000 ft. and above is sufficiently serious to make small objects quite unrecognisable.

In recent years the distortions have been reduced by use of gyroscopically stabilised mirror systems in front of the lens, but the complication would hardly be justified in conditions where the conventional type of camera is satisfactory.

Moving-film Cameras with Shutter.—Up to date most of the moving-film cameras other than strip cameras have been made by modifying the magazine parts of existing equipment. This was the natural line of development; the means already existed for winding the film over rapidly after exposure, and additional mechanism could be added to give the slower continuous motion needed for compensation. This also fitted in well with the normal practice of using different lens cones with the same camera body and magazine. There are obvious advantages, however, in designing a moving-film magazine and camera as one unit, *e.g.*, it will be possible to incorporate the time-interval control as part of the moving-film mechanism, obtaining correct compensation together with correct time interval for 60 per cent. overlaps.

In most designs the compensating movement is obtained by applying the separate drive through some kind of overrunning clutch, though this is not the only way of moving the film.

The film has normally been held flat during the exposure by whatever means the designer had previously employed to get flatness with a stationary film, thus American models use vacuum, while British rely on a glass pressure plate backed up by a metal pressure pad, the film being pulled through the narrow slot between them. The success of the latter scheme depends on two facts, the remarkable uniformity in the thickness of film base and the relatively great depth of focus of aircraft camera lenses. The film base used in air photography is of nominal thickness 0·0055 in., and different specimens rarely vary from the normal by more than a few ten-thousandths. Thus with a clearance of 0·007 in. between the register glass and pressure pad the film will always move easily, especially if the pad is relieved over part of its area. The resolving power of most aircraft camera lenses averaged over the picture area is scarcely affected by moving the film a distance of plus or minus 0·002 in. from the position of best focus. This is true even for the shorter focus lenses, because these are generally of wide angle and hence of low resolving power. Thus a $3\frac{1}{4}$-in. wide-angle lens can be moved in and out from the best focus position over a range of 0·012 in. without seriously affecting its average resolution. Moreover, at low altitudes, where short-focus lenses are most likely to be used with moving-film magazines, the ground resolution is in general limited by movement rather than by the lens-film resolution.

Accuracy of Compensation required.—The accuracy required in movement compensation depends very much on the kind of photography being undertaken. At very low altitudes and high aircraft speeds the potential gain in ground resolution from even partial compensation is very substantial. A 6-in. lens at 500 ft. offers a possible ground resolution of 3 in., which is of the order of ten times better than a 36-in. lens will give from 30,000 ft., and the low-altitude photograph is relatively much better than the figures suggest, because of improved rendering of shadows and other dark tones in absence of haze. Even a two to one error in compensation would still leave a great margin of improvement over the high-altitude photograph, assuming the same time of exposure in each case. Under different circumstances we might require to use a slow, fine-grained emulsion for good resolution at a higher altitude, with a relatively long time of exposure. Here the margin of error for compensation speed is much less, and if the residual image movement is too great the expected improvement in resolution will not be obtained.

The accuracy required in compensation can be calculated for any chosen case. The residual movement which can be tolerated will depend primarily on the time of exposure and the resolving power of the lens-film system, but the relative magnitude of the irregular movements may also have to be taken into account. If they are negligible the requirement is that the angular velocity must be reduced to a point where the angular movement during the exposure is not greater than 0·6 times the angular distance just resolved in the stationary image. If they are not negligible, then the steady movement should be reduced to the point where it makes no noticeable difference when both movements are added together as root mean squares ; nothing is gained by further reduction.

Let λ be the angle resolved without movement.

E be the percentage error allowed in compensation.

v/h be the angular velocity due to the forward motion of the aircraft.

t be the time of exposure.

θ_e be the residual uniform angular velocity due to the error in compensation.

θ_i be the irregular angular velocity.

The allowable error in compensation may be expressed as a fraction or percentage of the uncompensated velocity. Thus the percentage error is given by

$$E = \frac{100\theta_e h}{v}.$$

If the irregular movements are negligible, then compensation is just accurate enough when

$$t\theta_e = 0\cdot 6\lambda,$$

and in this condition we then have

$$E = \frac{100h0\cdot 6\lambda}{vt}.$$

When the irregular movements are not negligible they will be the factor controlling resolution if the compensation for the uniform movement is perfectly accurate. If the compensation is not perfect the residual uniform movement will add on to the irregular movement which is already reducing the resolution possible with the stationary camera. The further reduction due to the added uniform movement will depend on the ratio of the irregular movement to the static resolution, so that a given fractional increase in the sum of the movements will not always produce the same reduction in the final resolving power. No simple expression is therefore possible for the maximum tolerable addition of uniform movement, and to avoid undue complication it seems reasonable to adopt an arbitrary convention. Romer considered that the R.M.S. velocity resulting from the addition of the two movements should not exceed by more than 20 per cent. the velocity of the irregular component. In this condition we have

$$\sqrt{\theta_e{}^2 + \theta_i{}^2} = 1\cdot 2\theta_i,$$

whence

$$\theta_e = 0\cdot 66\theta_i,$$

so that

$$E = 100\frac{h}{v}.0\cdot 66\theta_i.$$

The additional reduction in resolution due to this error will be from 5 to 15 per cent., depending on the amount of irregular movement present.

We may now calculate the permissible compensation error for some specific cases.

We will first take the case of photography from 600 ft. at 240 m.p.h., with a 6-in. lens of angular resolution 1 : 1800 and an exposure time of 1/100 sec. At this altitude the irregular movements are negligible and we have

$$E = \frac{100.600.0\cdot 6.100}{1800.342} = 5\cdot 6 \text{ per cent.}$$

It may be repeated that the tolerable error is inversely proportional to the time of exposure, so that at 1/400 sec. the error could be 22 per cent., without detracting at all from the lens performance. In practice much larger errors than this would be tolerated because the low altitude picture is so much better than the high altitude that the full quality of the former is not always necessary.

The scale in the first example was 1 : 1200. The same scale could be obtained with a 36-in. lens from 3600 ft., and to a first approximation the ground resolution would be the same, because the angular resolutions are approximately in the ratio of the focal lengths. The irregular movements are not now negligible, as they have been in effect multiplied by six due to the increased height. We therefore have, assuming the same aircraft speed and the representative figure of 0·0134 rad.-sec. for the irregular movements,

$$E = \frac{100.3600.0 \cdot 66.0 \cdot 0134}{342} = 9 \text{ per cent.}$$

In this case the time of exposure does not enter into the formula, since the loss of resolution due to inaccurate compensation depends only on the ratio between the uniform and irregular movements. Needless to say, the resolution would be increased by reducing the exposure time, since both movements would be cut down in the same ratio, but the permissible error in compensation would remain the same.

The accuracy needed for any other case can be derived on similar lines. In general it can be seen from the formulæ that if the irregular movements are negligible, as at very low altitudes with short focus lenses, then the error in compensation is inversely proportional to the time of exposure and directly proportional to the distance resolved on the ground in absence of movement ; when the irregular movements are not negligible, the tolerable error is directly proportional to the height and the magnitude of the irregular movements and inversely proportional to the aircraft speed.

Determination of Compensation Speed.—The fundamental difficulty in using methods of movement compensation is the determination of true ground speed during the period of exposure.

Ground speed can be measured directly by a sighting method if an observer is available to work the instrument. In principle all that is necessary is a telescope for observing the ground, with a moving graticule in the eyepiece. The speed of the graticule is varied until no relative movement is discernible between it and the image of the ground ; it could be arranged that the speed control knob also regulated the film movement so that the operation would be semi-automatic. The method is probably capable of an accuracy of at least 1 per cent. if properly developed, though no equipment designed specifically for the purpose seems to have appeared as yet. Tachometric sights have, of course, been produced for use in determining time interval with survey cameras, and further development along these lines is indicated. This method is not suitable for use at very low altitudes, because changing ground height often changes the required compensation speed within a few seconds, and these rapid alterations could not be followed with a visual sight.

The ground speed can be calculated by the methods used in air navigation, *i.e.*, measurement of air speed and wind vector. If the latter is based on the meteorological estimate for the locality errors of 25 m.p.h. may well occur, and the accuracy of compensation will not be very good. On the other hand, the wind can now be found with some precision by the use of the Air Position Indicator, and if this instrument is available the true ground speed can probably be found to within 3 per cent., which is good enough for most purposes in movement compensation.

The altitude must also be known, and at high or moderate altitudes the accuracy of high precision barometric instruments is generally good enough. At low altitudes, however, the barometric altimeter is of little use, particularly with varying ground contours, and the radio altimeter seems to offer more hope. Radar methods may also be developed which will give direct reading of ground speed.

An automatic method for controlling the compensation speed at low altitudes has been developed by the American firm of Chicago Aerial Surveys, who specialise in strip cameras. The method involves the use of a photocell and amplifier. An image of the moving ground is cast on a grid of transparent and opaque lines located in front of the cell, producing an alternating current whose frequency is proportional to the speed of movement and the number of lines in the grid. The amplified cell output controls the compensation speed automatically via servo gear.

This device covers a film speed range of 1 to 40. It is only intended for use at low altitudes at present, the highest altitude catered for being 1000 ft. at 220 m.p.h., and the accuracy claimed is plus or minus 10 per cent.

ANTI-VIBRATION MOUNTINGS

Mountings for aircraft cameras have to perform several functions. In the first place they have to support the camera firmly in the chosen position in the aircraft and to withstand quite considerable forces. Cameras may weigh up to some hundreds of pounds, and the effective weight may be much greater during turns or due to landing shocks. Although photographic aircraft do not normally indulge in aerobatics, it is customary for the mountings to be stressed to withstand accelerations of 6 G. The basic mounting design should be adaptable for holding the camera in any required position without sacrifice of the anti-vibration qualities. Rotation about the vertical axis for setting drift and about the fore and aft and transverse axes for levelling are usually called for. Whatever means is adopted for absorbing vibration must require the minimum of servicing or adjustment. Only the anti-vibration properties of mountings are considered in this chapter.

It will be clear that transverse movements of the camera along any of the three axes will have no effect on definition, but a relatively small rotational movement during exposure corresponds to a relatively great movement on the ground. The purpose of the anti-vibration mounting is therefore to absorb any rotational vibrations which might be transmitted from the airframe and to ensure that transverse vibrations of the support are not transformed into rotational movements of the camera.

Methods of testing Mountings.—The efficiency of anti-vibration mountings can be tested in the laboratory up to a certain point, but the conditions of vibration in aircraft are so complex that they cannot easily be reproduced, and final testing must always be done in the air.

The general principle of laboratory testing is to apply forcing vibrations to the mounting with camera installed and to study the response of the camera over a range of frequencies. A simple but sensitive method was used by J. B. Reid (1), and his apparatus is shown diagrammatically in Fig. 51.

A rigid framework of some 8 ft. long is arranged to pivot around a horizontal axis at B, which is fixed to the stout girders of a steel-framed building. At the other end the framework is suspended from the ceiling girders by rubber cords C, which retain it horizontal when loaded with the camera but allow complete freedom for vertical oscillations. A variable speed motor M with out-of-balance weight on the shaft allows any desired frequency of vibration to be applied. The frame can only move up and down, and since it is long relative to the amplitude of movement induced by the eccentric weight the vibrations it executes are substantially vertical. The amplitude of these vibrations is measured by observing through a microscope the length of the apparent line of light produced by the movements of a very small steel ball imaging a small lamp. Amplitudes up to 0·01 in. can be measured to an accuracy of 0·0001 in. The camera K on its mounting is fixed to

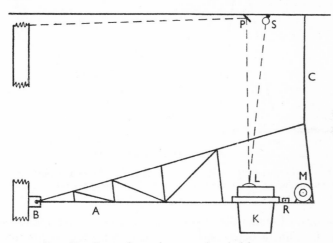

FIG. 51.—Set-up for testing mountings in laboratory.

the frame near the motor. An optical system incorporating a mirror on the camera throws a spot of light on a distant wall and is equivalent to a lever 65 ft. long. When a forcing vibration of constant frequency is applied to the framework by running the motor at a constant speed the spot of light describes a path of shape and size depending on the characteristics of the vibration induced in the camera. The track of the spot is most easily recorded by tracing along it with a pencil. The amplitude of rotational vibration of the camera is then found from the appropriate constants of the system. In testing a mounting it is fixed to the framework, and the camera, with any accessories such as leads or drive cables, is fastened in place. The motor is then run over the required range of speeds and at each frequency the amplitudes of the applied and induced vibrations are recorded. The results are expressed as the ratio of the amplitude of the forcing vibrations applied to the frame to the amplitude of the vibrations induced in the camera. The units employed by Reid were radians-inch, *i.e.*, radians of rotational vibration of the camera per inch of forcing vibration of the frame or milliradians per thousandth of an inch. The response ratios are then plotted against frequency, a typical curve being shown in Fig. 52. By altering the arrangement of the frame it is possible to apply the forcing vibrations in a horizontal direction.

While mountings can be roughly sorted out and their characteristics analysed by a vibrating frame such as this, it cannot replace flight testing, and indeed is often used rather as a means of finding out why some mountings are better than others on flight test. The particular form of frame described here can only be used to determine the efficiency with which a mounting absorbs vertical or horizontal vibrations which are harmless in themselves, and to demonstrate whether they are transformed into rotational vibrations

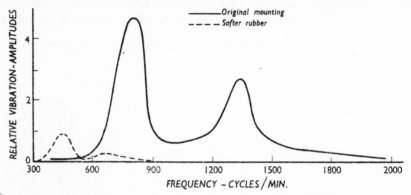

FIG. 52.—Response curves of two mountings. (" Vibration amplitudes " are rotational vibration of camera for vertical vibration applied to mounting.)

of the camera. Rotational vibrations as such cannot be applied and their effect on the camera determined. The chief justification for this kind of vibrating table is that airframe vibrations always have vertical and horizontal components which cannot be allowed to reach the camera, where they would inevitably be transformed into rotations except in those cases where the camera is mounted exactly at its centre of gravity.

The most satisfactory practical test for a mounting is that developed during the First World War, which involves flying over a light at night-time with an open shutter. The light is interrupted at a known frequency, which enables the track to be analysed by obvious means. During the Second World War some vibration tracks were obtained in daylight by flying over a large convex mirror, which gave an image of the sun in a restricted angle of view. A mirror of 36 in. diameter and 100 in. focal length enabled tracks to be obtained up to 5000 ft. The camera shutter was opened just before entering the field of the mirror, and steps were taken to reduce the exposure by using small stops and neutral filters in the lens. The method is troublesome, as the mirror requires attention to keep the cone of light vertical and tracks cannot be obtained from high altitudes. At night the shutter is left permanently open and a 100-watt lamp enables tracks to be obtained up to at least 10,000 ft.

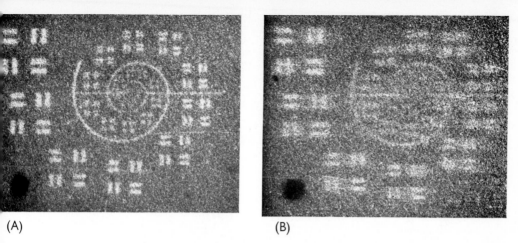

(A)   (B)

Enlargement from typical lens-test negatives, showing Cobb test-objects
Both taken on fast panchromatic film
(A) on axis (B) in zone of poor definition

(C)

Infra-red photograph of typical haze layer with well-marked " top ". The lower stratum evidently contains large particles which scatter all wavelengths almost equally, while the smaller particles of the relatively clean atmosphere above scatter very little light of the wavelengths used to take the photograph (circa 0·70 to 0·85 micron)

Plate I

Comparative photographs, taken simultaneously from 20,000 feet; ×5 enlargements from the corners of the 9 × 9 field

(B) Ross Xpres 20″ f/6·3 lens (1944 construction)

(A) Old type 20″ f/6·3. lens (1940 construction)

Plate 3

(A)

An extreme example
of directional scatter
from haze

(B)

Low altitude photograph. Example of photograph taken with moving-film camera (F52, 20″ lens). Altitude 1500 feet. 1/150 sec, f/8. Speed 150 m.p.h. In spite of the low altitude and large scale movement is not apparent

Comparative photographs taken from 20,000 feet on fast and slow panchromatic films, using matched 20″ Aviar lenses.   Enlargement × 17

Plate 4   Super XX type, 1/ 300 sec., f/11. Plate 5   Panatomic X-type. 1/300 sec. f/5·6

Plate 4

Plate 5

Difference in effective graininess due primarily to differences of subject contrast. The negatives were exposed from 18,000 feet, all photographic conditions being identical except that Plate 6 was enlarged on normal paper and Plate 7 on contrasty. Enlargement × 17

Plate 6 Clear country air Plate 7 Heavy city haze

Plate 6

Plate 7

(8A)   No movement

(8B)   No movement

Plates 8 and 9. Effect of image movement on resolution. All taken with
20″ lens, fast panchromatic film, ×5 enlargement.

Plate 8

(9A)   Movement—1·2 × resolving power

(9B)   Movement—0·6 × resolving power

Plate 9

(A)

(B)

Comparative photographs taken over (A) city and (B) country areas under constant conditions of exposure, development etc. Note the contraction of the brightness scale mainly from the lower end in the hazy scene

Plate 10

(A)

(B)

Effect of aircraft altitude on brightness-characteristics of a scene

(A) was taken from 1,000 feet, (B) from 12,000 feet, all photographic conditions being identical

Plate 11

(A)

(B)

Plate 12

Haze penetration by different wavelengths of visible light—moderate haze

Plates 12 and 13. Haze penetration by different wavelengths of visible light—moderate haze. Focal lengths, 8″; height, 10,000 feet. All enlargements × 4.

Plate 12A: Minus Blue filter—soft paper.
Plate 12B: Tricolour Blue filter—contrasty paper.
Plate 13: Tricolour Blue filter—soft paper.

Plate 13

(A)

(B)

Plate 14

Haze penetration by different wavelengths of visible light—
heavy industrial haze

Plates 14 and 15. Haze penetration by different wavelengths of visible
light—heavy industrial haze. Focal lengths, 8″; height, 10,000 feet. All
enlargements × 4 on contrasty paper.

Plate 14A: Tricolour Red filter.
Plate 14B: Minus Blue filter.
Plate 15: Tricolour Blue filter.

Plate 15

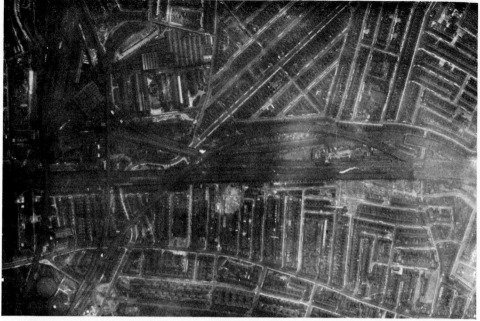

(A)

(B)

Comparison of panchromatic and infra-red emulsions
Examples taken from 18,000 feet—20″ focal length. Contact Prints

(A) Panchromatic emulsion—Minus Blue filter
(B) Infra-red emulsion—Tricolour Red filter

Plate 16

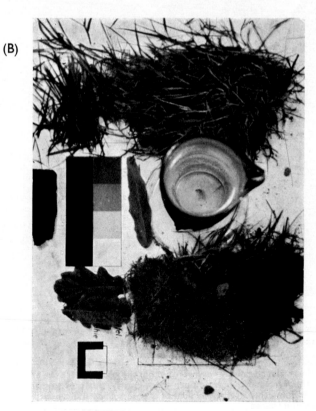

(A) Infra-red   (B) Panchromatic

Plate 17

(A)

(B)

(C)

Laboratory simulation of effects of haze and graininess
(A) The original scene—no haze
(B) Average haze—contrast restored to equal (A) but
    shadow detail lost
(C) Heavy haze—contrast could not be restored

Plate 30

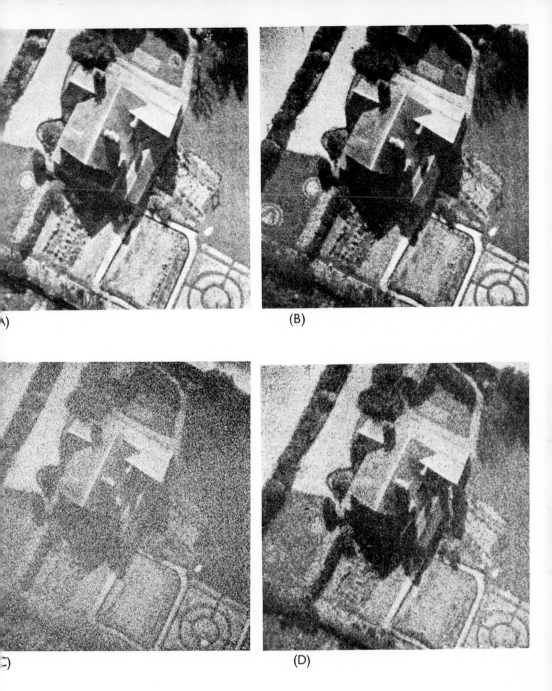

(A)

(B)

(C)

(D)

Laboratory simulation of effects of haze and graininess
(A) High altitude photograph of original scene—no haze
(B) as (A) but with average haze
(C) as (A) but heavy haze
(D) as (B) over-exposed

Plate 31

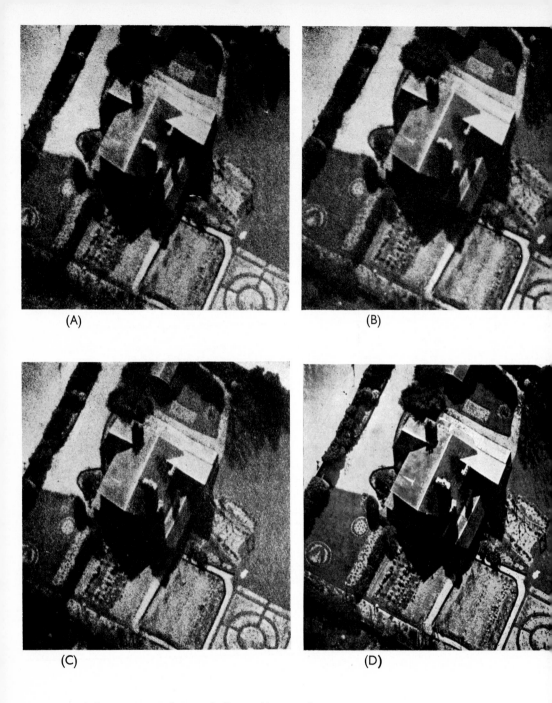

Laboratory simulation of effects of haze and graininess
(A) High altitude photograph of original scene-average haze-fast emulsion D. 19b
(B) as (A) D. K. 20—fast Emulsion
(C) as (A) Panatomic X—D 19b
(D) as (A) Microfile-dilute metol developer

Plate 32

Design of Air Camera Mountings

General Considerations.—There are some problems of vibration insulation which allow a very satisfactory solution to be obtained by relatively simple means. Such problems are exemplified by machinery whose vibration causes objectionable disturbances in a building, or delicate apparatus which will not function properly on a vibrating floor. In such cases there is often a predominant frequency of vibration; for example, that due to imperfect balancing of an electric generator running at a constant speed. There are well-known methods for dealing with such problems.

It is shown in simple vibration theory that the response of an elastically mounted mass to forcing vibrations depends on the ratio of the frequency of the forcing vibration to the natural vibration frequency of the system. In Fig. 53 a mass M is mounted on resilient supports and has a certain freedom in the vertical direction. The stiffness of the suspension is expressed as C dynes per centimetre, where unit stiffness is the force required to cause a displacement of 1 cm. The body on its mounting then has a natural frequency n for vertical vibrations given by

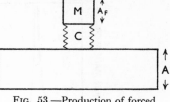

Fig. 53.—Production of forced vibrations.

$$n = \left(\frac{1}{2\pi} \sqrt{\frac{C}{M}} \right).$$

It can be shown that under the above conditions, if the support is given a vibration of frequency f and amplitude A, then the mass M will take up a forced vibration of the same frequency and amplitude A_f, where

$$A_f = A \Big/ \left(1 - \frac{f^2}{n^2} \right).$$

The ratio of the amplitudes of the support and the vibration induced in the mounted body is evidently a measure of the value of the mounting arrangement. The ratio of A_f to A is given by

$$1 \Big/ \left(1 - \frac{f^2}{n^2} \right),$$

and Fig. 54 is a plot of A_f/A against f/n. Starting from the left-hand side of the figure and referring to the full line, a zero ratio of forcing frequency to natural frequency means that the mounting is infinitely stiff, *i.e.*, the mounted body is rigidly fixed to its support and will describe the same vibrations. Passing from this hypothetical case, bodies mounted with considerable stiffness (high natural frequency) follow the vibrations of their support with an amplitude which rapidly increases to a very high value when the natural and forcing frequencies are the same. This is the condition of resonance, when the vibration is worse than a rigid attachment to the support. When the forcing frequency becomes slightly greater than the natural frequency the induced vibration begins to decrease and at a ratio of 1·4 the body again follows the vibrations of the support with the same amplitude. As the forcing frequency gets greater and greater than the natural frequency of the mounted body, so the amplitude of the induced vibration diminishes, and when the ratio is of the order of three or four very little vibration gets through. The full line in the figure illustrates the theoretical response for an elastic system without damping, but is a fair approximation to the behaviour of lightly· damped systems for absorbing vibration, such as suspension on springs or "Lord" and similar rubber

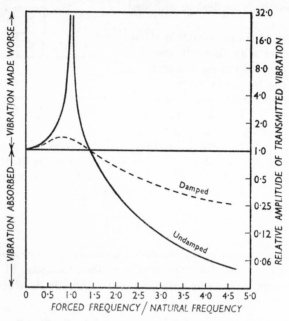

FIG. 54.—Response curve of a simple vibrating system.

suspensions. The introduction of damping to cause a more rapid decay of induced vibration is illustrated by the dotted curve. It will be observed that the resonant effect is greatly reduced, but the efficiency of absorption for frequencies well away from the resonant point is also much lower than in the undamped mounting.

In applying these results to the insulation of, say, instrument panels it is only necessary to mount elastically on springs or rubber in such a way that the natural frequency of the suspension is several times lower than that of the forcing vibration. There are limits beyond which this cannot be pushed in any particular case, because the lower the natural frequency of an elastically mounted body the "softer" is the suspension and the more easily it is displaced by random disturbing forces. Moreover, the deflection of the mounting under its load may be inconveniently great. These considerations may not always be of any great consequence. For example, a heavy generator can have a low natural frequency when mounted without any great inconvenience, because its inertia is great enough to withstand most shocks. Light equipment is more difficult, but as a rule a considerable amount of freedom can be allowed. Aircraft cameras, however, cannot be allowed much freedom, and the absorption of low-frequency vibration is consequently difficult.

Mounting equipment in aircraft is particularly difficult because of the wide range of frequencies encountered. The most serious vibrations are usually at engine frequency, or some multiple of it, of the order of 2000 cycles per min., but the range extends at least from 500 to 10,000 cycles per min., so that the mounting has to have a very low natural frequency if it is to insulate well for all possible vibrations. A suspension with a natural frequency of 500 cycles per min. affords about 60 per cent. insulation for a 1000-cycle forcing vibration, and deflects about 0·15 in. under load, which gives some idea of its stiffness. This would not be unreasonable for an instrument panel or similar installation. Attempts to apply such principles directly to the mounting of air cameras have not been successful. The reasons for this can be appreciated by following investigations made by Reid. (1)

Development of Sponge-rubber Mountings.—The investigation started by analysing the performance of a standard type of camera mounting in which the weight of the camera was taken through a metal frame on four buffers made from a moulded type of sponge rubber. The mounting was rather stiff, and gave a vibrating frame test indicating strong resonance with vertical frequencies of 800 and 1300 cycles per min. (see Fig. 52). These frequencies are present in most aircraft, the higher being close to a common engine frequency. Vibration tracks showed that strong resonance occurred in the aircraft also and caused rotational vibration of the camera. (It did not affect the definition in the photographs very much in exposures of the order of 1/400 sec. because of the limited angular resolution of the lens normally used.) The mounting was then modified in two ways. In the first modification the rather hard rubber buffers were replaced by a pile of rings cut from " Medium " Sorbo sponge rubber. This changed the natural frequencies to 500 and 830 cycles per min., as shown by the response curve in Fig. 52, and the amplitude of the transmitted vibrations was much less at resonance. Vibration tracks showed that whereas the mean angular velocity of the camera in the standard mounting was 0·03 rad.-sec., it was only 0·01 rad.-sec. in the modified version. The improvement was clearly due to the lowering of the natural frequencies well below the strongest frequencies in the aircraft. In attempting to effect a further improvement the natural frequencies were made lower still, but this time the Sorbo rubber was replaced by " Isoflex " units. The Isoflex unit is representative of a class of vibration absorbing devices available commercially. Their advantage over ungraded sponge rubber is that their mechanical properties are listed with some precision, and it is possible to design a mounting to any desired specification of natural frequency from this data. The Isoflex unit in this case consisted of a small wheel with rubber spokes bonded to a metal rim and hub. The load is taken vertically on the hub, while the rim is fixed to the support in a horizontal plane, thus the camera floats suppoited through the spokes. The natural frequencies of this mounting were 380 and 550 cycles per min., so that even better performance might have been expected than with the experimental Sorbo mounting. In fact, very poor results were obtained, the average angular velocity in the aiicraft being almost as great as with the standard mounting, although the vibration tracks agreed with the vibration frame tests in showing that the higher frequencies were being filtered out in a very efficient way. The angular movement was being caused by low-frequency vibrations close to the natural frequency of the mounting, one of the tracks showing a frequency of 500 cycles, which was found to be a characteristic of the aircraft used in the tests. Another Isoflex mounting having a natural frequency of 350 cycles about all axes gave even worse results.

The obvious difference between the Isoflex and Sorbo mountings was one of damping, and further work, confirmed by theoretical and practical investigations of other workers, showed that a high degree of damping is an essential feature of mountings for aircraft cameras. Referring again to the curve for a damped suspension in Fig. 54, this shows that when the ratio of forcing to natural frequency is less than about 1·5 the damping reduces the vibration of the suspended body, and is especially valuable in reducing the amplitude at the resonant point. Thus if it is not practicable to give the mounting a sufficiently low natural frequency to avoid resonance or near resonance with the lowest aircraft frequencies, damping will help by keeping down the amplitude of the resultant vibrations. This will be achieved at the cost of less perfect insulation for the higher frequencies, but the well-damped mounting may be a better practical compromise. The quality of the results actually obtained must depend on achieving the right balance of damping and natural frequency for the conditions of use, and it was clear that the Sorbo mounting had led to a better balance than the undamped Isoflex mountings.

The aircraft vibrations are not all transmitted through the mounting, but some disturbances are liable to enter along the electrical leads or any drive cables, etc. Here again damping will help by stopping the build-up of strong resonances.

Any shock applied to a mounted mass will tend to set it oscillating at the natural frequency of the system, but if damping is present the vibrations will soon die out. Now the aircraft camera is not completely isolated from its surroundings, but is liable to receive shocks from stray draughts, bumps, sudden slight changes of aircraft altitude, etc., all of which will tend to set it vibrating at its natural frequency. With high damping the energy of such disturbances is quickly dissipated and the vibration does not assume serious proportions. It has been shown theoretically that accelerations of the order of 0·01 G, acting during periods of the order of two seconds, can produce in undamped low-frequency mountings angular velocities of the same order as those excited by imperfectly absorbed engine vibrations, and this is a further argument for having damping.

When the need for damping had been demonstrated, mountings incorporating sponge rubber were designed for different types of camera.

The virtue of sponge rubber for this purpose is that it provides a very convenient means of obtaining a low natural frequency with a certain degree of damping, and the damping requires none of the adjustment or maintenance that would be necessary with such devices as dashpots or friction pads. The damping action is probably due to the viscous friction of the air inhaled and exhaled through the numerous pores of the material or compressed and expanded through holes in the interior of the mass, and to friction of the outer surfaces of the rubber against the sides of the containing box. The damping is not under control, however, and practically all that can be done is to select the grade of rubber by trial and error, with some experimenting on the loads applied and the added mechanical friction. Good results have been obtained with " Dense " and " Medium " Sorbo and " Medium " Dunlopillo. A typical mounting for a camera weighing 80 lb. employed a total area of 84 sq. in. of " Medium " Sorbo rubber sheet, 1 in. thick, arranged around the camera in four strips, each consisting of two thicknesses of the material, 12 in. long and $1\frac{3}{4}$ in. wide. The natural frequency for vertical vibrations was 580 cycles, and the rotational frequencies were somewhat lower. Due to the large area of sponge rubber employed the damping was good. The performance of this mounting was excellent, the average angular velocity found from vibration tracks being 0·005 rad.-sec. when tested in a twin-engined military aircraft. This performance was unusually good, and was probably associated with a high degree of friction. Sponge-rubber mountings in general give figures of 0·007 to 0·009 rad.-sec. ; 1/200 rad.-sec. means that in an exposure time of one-hundredth of a second the apparent ground movement from 20,000 ft. would be 1 ft., about half the distance resolved by the longest focal length lenses commonly used at that altitude. Thus by using an exposure time of 1/200 or 1/400 sec., which is generally required to arrest the forward movement, the vibration becomes a negligible factor in definition.

Although it is fairly obvious, the point is perhaps worth stressing that the reduction of troublesome vibrations becomes easier as the weight of the camera increases, because the greater mass suffers less displacement from the action of a given disturbing force. Experience shows that it is indeed more difficult to get satisfactory mountings for a small camera than for a large one. The performance figures quoted in this chapter refer to cameras weighing between 20 and 80 lb. ; better results are likely to be obtained with heavier equipment, and the results with lighter cameras may be worse. Where an installation of several cameras is involved there is much to be said in favour of coupling them rigidly together, thus increasing the effective mass available to oppose disturbances.

In view of their excellent performance and the ease with which they are constructed it is not surprising that sponge-rubber mountings have been widely used. The design is not highly critical, if only because the subject is not well enough understood for it to be made so. In general the natural frequency should be low, less than 700 cycles for vertical and horizontal freedom, though the rotational frequencies should be above 300 cycles to give reasonable stability. An indication of natural frequency is given by the depression of the rubber under the weight of the camera. If the deflection is D and the natural frequency is N cycles per min., the approximate relation is

$$N = 188\sqrt{1/D}.$$

Thus if the deflection under load is 0·11 in., the natural frequency is 564 cycles per min.

The vertical and horizontal frequencies should be approximately the same. Assuming the use of " Medium " Sorbo sheet of 1 in. thickness used in a double layer, the natural frequencies will be of the right order and damping will be adequate if the area of rubber supporting the camera is 1 sq. in. per lb. weight supported.

Centre of Gravity Support.—From a restricted theoretical viewpoint, the ideal anti-vibration mounting would be had by supporting the camera on frictionless bearings at its centre of gravity with complete rotational freedom. Granted truly friction-free bearings no rotational disturbance could possibly reach the camera through them, and translational disturbances could not be transformed into rotations by coupling, given sufficiently accurate location of the point of suspension in the centre of gravity. In practice, however, a simple mounting of this type, *e.g.*, a gimbal suspension with ball-bearings, is almost useless. With good ball-races and accurate location of the centre of gravity the high-frequency vibrations can be filtered out very effectively, but there is always enough friction in the bearings for a certain amount of low-frequency vibration to get through and set the camera oscillating. Moreover, there is nothing to restrain the action of forces operating directly on the camera, *e.g.*, draughts or vibrations transmitted along electric leads, etc., against which the mounting provides no protection, while the changing weight distribution as the film is wound through the magazine disturbs the accuracy of location of the centre of gravity at the suspension point. No doubt because of these practical difficulties encountered in the most direct application of the centre of gravity principle, some designers maintain that it has no value in air photography, or even that it is basically incorrect. With a full understanding of the case, however, there is no difficulty in seeing that the principle is quite valid ; the difficulties lie in applying it in isolation from disturbing factors. Experimental mountings have been constructed in which the theoretical conditions were very closely approached, and when all necessary precautions were taken they were found to have a very fine performance.

The centre of gravity principle naturally applies to the sponge-rubber type of mounting, but very exact location of the centre of gravity in the plane of support is not essential at the level of performance normally obtainable, and the shifting film weight normally causes little trouble. Nevertheless, there is no need to invite coupling by mounting at points far removed from the centre of gravity of the camera.

As already stated, mounting at the centre of gravity is sometimes criticised on the ground that if it is accompanied by low natural frequency about rotational axes the camera is easily set swinging by random forces such as draughts or rolling of the aircraft. Such oscillations, as we have seen, can be largely overcome in a practical mount by good damping. It is further suggested, however, that a better mounting system would have considerable stiffness about rotational axes with much greater freedom for translational movement. The argument is that if the camera is free to move vertically or horizontally it will move in these directions only, and mountings have been designed using bell-crank systems for vertical freedom, or rubber in shear for horizontal freedom. These arguments are not correct, because giving the mounting translational freedom cannot transform rotational vibrations of the support into translational movements of the camera, while if the centre of gravity is not correctly placed the translational vibrations will still be liable to give coupling.

Translational freedom mountings are often used and give acceptable results, but this merely shows that the vibrations they pass are not serious in relation to the limited angular resolution of the cameras used in them. Naturally there is no reason why they should not be used so long as the pictures are satisfactory, but they are unsatisfactory with high-resolution cameras. The results obtained will vary according to the characteristics of the particular specimen, but one test may be quoted in which a vertical freedom type gave an average angular velocity of 0·025 rad.-sec., while a sponge-rubber type gave 0·007 rad.-sec. in the same aircraft on the same flight. All camera mounting systems so far developed are compromises, and cannot be otherwise because of the wide band of vibration frequencies in aircraft and the presence of stray disturbances, but comparative tests show that the sponge-rubber or other damped suspension fulfilling the centre of gravity condition is the most efficient yet available.

Further Mounting Development.—Simple sponge-rubber mountings will reduce the angular velocity of the camera due to aircraft vibrations to 0·01 rad.-sec. or less, and with exposure times of the order of 1/300 sec. it is then less important than other movements. Interest in further mounting developments is therefore dependent on the improvement of resolution by other means, or the use of movement compensation to allow of slow exposures with a fine-grain film. For example, it would probably be feasible to use a film of about 20 Weston at an exposure time of the order of a fiftieth of a second, thus achieving a marked reduction in graininess, given accurate movement compensation. Depending on the focal length of the lens, the angular resolution might then be high enough for the mounting to be a limiting factor. It seems unlikely that simple sponge-rubber mountings can be made much better than they are at present, but Romer (2) has improved their performance at the cost of increased complication, by introducing a gimbal system between the rubber and the camera. Gimbal mounting has the advantage that the axes can be made to intersect in the centre of gravity of the camera, and provided that the centre of gravity does not shift, one of the fundamental requirements for good mounting has been met. We have then only to insulate against rotational vibrations of the support, which is easily done by giving the system a low natural frequency around the gimbal axes. While damping of the rotational vibrations is then required, this can be achieved, experimentally at least, by friction devices, one element serving for each gimbal axis. In Romer's design the gimbal suspension was provided by Silentbloc bushes instead of ball-races and was built up on the base board of a standard type of sponge-rubber mounting; this ensured that translational vibrations were greatly reduced before reaching the gimbals, so that the effect of any displacement of the centre of gravity was lessened. The translational frequencies were about 600 cycles and the rotational about 100. Dry friction dampers, consisting of steel blades rubbing between Paxolin pads, were used for the gimbal axes. The mounting gave a mean angular velocity on vibration track test of 0·0025 rad.-sec. with very little film in the magazine and accurate positioning of the centre of gravity. With a full 500 exposure spool at one side of the film magazine, the centre of gravity being then shifted 2·8 cm. upwards and 1·5 cm. sideways from the intersection of the gimbal axes, the figure was 0·0042 rad.-sec. This performance represents a considerable advance on that of the best sponge-rubber mountings, but the setting of the friction dampers is troublesome, and it is doubtful if the mounting in its original form would be suitable for general use. Nevertheless, its performance is of considerable theoretical interest and confirms the general theoretical arguments on mounting design which have been put forward in this chapter. Other workers have obtained very satisfactory performances with damped springs of various kinds.

Aircraft Unsteadiness

The image movements due to pitching and rolling of the aircraft about its mean course do not seriously affect resolution even with manual piloting, so long as the exposure time is less than about 1/200 sec. and the angular resolving power is less than 1 : 10,000. With increased exposure times, which might be used with a slower film in the quest for higher resolution, the aircraft unsteadiness would become a limiting factor, and steps would have to be taken to reduce the angular velocities. A first step would be the use of the automatic pilot, but this has limitations, and for exposure times very much longer than those at present used some form of camera stabilisation, perhaps by gyroscopic means, would be necessary.

References

1. REID, J. B. Unpublished researches for Ministry of Supply, London (1942-45).
2. ROMER, W. Unpublished researches for Ministry of Supply, London (1942-45).
3. NAGEL, M. " Kompensation der Bildpunktverwanderung durch mechanisches Nachführen der Aufnahmekammer während der Belichtung," *Jahrbuch der deutschen Luftfahrtforschung*, **5,** 1939.
4. BAUER, W. " Kompensation der regelmässigen Bildwanderung bei Luftbildaufnahmen durch dreikeile," *Jahrbuch der deutschen Luftfahrtforschung*, **5,** 1939.

Chapter Ten

ESTIMATION OF NEGATIVE EXPOSURE

THE estimation of exposure for most of the air negatives made at the present time is probably done with the aid of tables or calculators, supplemented by the experience of the photographer, and exposure meters are relatively little used. Most skilled photographers have their own systems, or combinations of system and " instinct." The object of this chapter is to give a fairly detailed analysis of the factors affecting exposure in air photography, in the hope of clarifying ideas on the subject. Certain principles are put forward on which, it is felt, any logical system should be based, but the author does not feel convinced that any system can be fully satisfactory which does not involve photometric measurements of the brightness of the subject.

The accurate exposure required in air photography is often obtained without difficulty, but this is partly accounted for by the constancy of daylight illumination in the clear weather conditions suitable for work of a high standard. In air survey, for example, photography will often continue for many successive days over one tract of country, early and late hours will be avoided because of long shadows, and the sky will of necessity be almost free from cloud. After one or two tests the photographer can estimate his exposure with sufficient accuracy, and on moving to new territory, or resuming after an interval of time, a further test will enable him to continue with confidence. If the ground can be observed while photography is in progress, the exposure can be varied to suit the changing brightness of different types of country, *e.g.*, dark forests or snow-clad hills, and the density of the negatives will remain fairly constant. The position is less satisfactory when camera-men of skill and experience are not available, when there can be no camera-man, and the exposure has to be set many hours ahead of the operation, or when photography must be undertaken in dull weather or at early and late hours in rapidly changing light. If a meter is not used under these difficult conditions the exposure is liable to be in error, but the better the photographer understands his subject the less serious these errors are likely to be. Accurate exposure is desirable under all circumstances, but above all in small-scale and high-altitude work, for the amount of detail recorded depends very closely on having the optimum negative density. Bearing in mind that lens resolution improves with reduction of aperture, and that emulsion resolution falls off with both over and under exposure, the photographer must decide on the shutter time which will arrest image movement and then select the smallest lens aperture which will give the requisite density. He must avoid under-exposure at all costs, but by over-exposing he throws away resolution with both hands.

At this stage it is desirable to define the meaning of " exposure." " Exposure," in the true sense, is the product of illumination and time, but in the photographic world, by a typical ambiguity, its common meaning is the combination of lens aperture and shutter time by which the true exposure is regulated. Jones and Condit (1) suggest the term "camera exposure" to indicate particular settings of aperture and shutter speed, and for the sake of uniformity their proposal will be adopted.

Several factors have evidently to be considered in estimating camera exposure. In the first place the brightness of the subject will vary with the intensity of the daylight which falls on it, and ordinary experience shows that this intensity varies irregularly under different weather conditions and in a regular way according to the time of day and year. Different subjects vary in their reflectance, *e.g.*, dark woods reflect less light than snowfields, and so on. Moreover, the darkness and importance of shadows depend on the altitude from which they are seen. When all factors external to the camera have been considered, allowance has then to be made for "camera constants," such as emulsion speed, shutter time and efficiency, lens aperture, and so on. The camera constants, however, are quite straightforward in their nature, being under the user's control, and the purpose of this chapter is to discuss the external factors which affect the brightness characteristics of the subject. These may be listed as :—

(*a*) Regular variations in the quality and intensity of daylight.
(*b*) Irregular variations in effective subject brightness due to changing atmospheric conditions.
(*c*) Reflectance characteristics of the subject.
(*d*) Aircraft altitude.

DAYLIGHT VARIATIONS

Even to casual observation it is very clear that there are two kinds of variation in the intensity of daylight, a regular annual and diurnal variation connected with the solar altitude, and irregular variations due to changes in the weather and state of the sky. In compiling exposure tables and calculators some relationship is first assumed between the solar altitude, which can be calculated in advance for any time and place, and the illumination effective for photography in perfectly clear weather. The basic exposure at any solar altitude is then multiplied by factors to allow for the effects of different weather conditions and different types of subject. Ordinary experience also shows that the colour of daylight varies during the course of the day.

Hurter and Driffield were probably the first to make systematic measurements of the variations in daylight illumination. (2) They measured the intensity of "diffuse daylight" continuously during the year 1885-86 and concluded that the illumination under constant weather conditions was proportional to the sine of the solar altitude. The "diffuse daylight" was apparently the illumination from the north sky, but their curves do not show a very good agreement with the sine curve, and their conclusion was an undue simplification of the facts. Nevertheless, their work marked a step forward, and they used their data to construct exposure tables and calculators. On the variation of the diffuse illumination with changes in the weather they say : " We thus found that the diffuse light at any given hour of any given day is seldom less than 25 per cent. of the maximum light possible at that hour, except when it is foggy or raining, but in those circumstances no one thinks of taking photographs outside." In broad principle these remarks have not been challenged by any later work, and they are not irrelevant to the estimation of exposure for air photographs, which also are seldom taken " when it is foggy or raining." Numerous other exposure tables have appeared since those days, but until comparatively recent times they appear to have been based on Hurter and Driffield's data or to have been thinly disguised copies of each other, (3) and no attention was paid to the wealth of information about daylight illumination collected by physicists and illuminating engineers over the intervening years. In 1941 the author and J. B. Reid prepared exposure tables for air photography, using the illumination data published by Elvegard and Sjostedt, (4) and in preparing the American Standard Exposure Tables first issued in 1942, but probably drawn up some time before that date, Jones and Condit (*loc. cit.*) have examined all the relevant information available. Their paper forms a very comprehensive and detailed account of the subject, and although written from the standpoint of ground photography it will well repay close study.

REGULAR VARIATIONS IN THE QUALITY AND INTENSITY OF DAYLIGHT

The quality and intensity of the daylight falling on the earth's surface in perfectly clear weather are affected by three principal factors, viz. :—

(*a*) Distance of the earth from the sun.

(*b*) Solar altitude, *i.e.*, the angular distance of the sun above the horizon, which determines the angle at which the sunlight strikes the earth, and also determines

(*c*) The thickness of atmosphere traversed by the sunlight.

The sun's distance from the earth varies appreciably during the year, and winter sunlight is stronger than summer, other things being equal. However, the difference is only 7 per cent., which is negligible for photographic purposes, though easily measured photometrically. The solar distance has no effect on the quality of the sunlight, and need not be considered any further.

The solar altitude, and hence the effective thickness of the atmosphere, affect both the quality and intensity of the sunlight.

Solar Altitude and Air Mass.—The solar altitude can be calculated for any time of the day and year by a formula which is well known to astronomers and sailors, viz. :—

$$\sin h = \sin \phi \sin \delta + \cos \phi \cos \delta \cos 15t,$$

where h = solar altitude in degrees,

ϕ = geographical latitude of the place,

δ = declination, *i.e.*, the sun's angular distance above the celestial equator,

t = time in hours before or after true noon.

The time should strictly be corrected from clock time to solar time by the so-called " equation of time," but this can be neglected for most photographic applications. The necessary corrections and figures for declination at different times are given in astronomical and navigational tables.

A simple form of calculator was devised in 1941 by J. B. Reid for determining the solar altitude at any time and place with sufficient accuracy for photographic work. The setting of two transparent scales was made in a few seconds and the result could be read off directly as a camera exposure.

The effective thickness of the atmosphere, known to astronomers as the " air mass," can be calculated accurately by a formula due to Bemporad ; it varies approximately as the secant of the sun's zenith angle (zenith angle $= 90° -$ solar altitude), but the accurate formula takes account of atmospheric refraction. The air mass for a zenith angle of zero is taken as unity, and masses for a few solar altitudes are given in Table 5 for illustration ; it will be seen that for high suns there is little change of air mass with altitude, but as the sun declines the air mass rapidly increases.

TABLE 5

Air Mass at various Solar Altitudes

Solar altitude (degrees) .	5	10	20	40	60	90
Air mass . . .	10·40	5·60	2·90	1·55	1·15	1·00

Sunlight and Skylight.—The illumination at any point on the earth's surface is made up of two components, direct light which has come in straight lines from the sun, and diffused light from the sky. In addition there is often secondary illumination by reflection of the primary sources from terrestrial objects, but we are not at present concerned with this.

The sunlight casts fairly sharp shadows, because the rays are almost parallel, the sun's disc subtending only half a degree at the earth's surface. The skylight is, of course, sunlight which has been deflected from its original path and arrives after many scatterings or reflections by atmospheric particles ; it reaches an unobstructed point on the surface of the earth from the whole hemisphere of sky and casts no shadows. Skylight, indeed, is the main source of illumination for shadows, which are very dark when the air is clear and there are no nearby objects to reflect light into them. On clear days the sunlight illumination is usually much stronger than that due to the sky, though the relative intensities depend on the height of the sun above the horizon as well as on the state of the atmosphere. While the unobscured sun is enormously brighter than the sky, the angular subtense of the latter is so much greater that its contribution to the total illumination is not negligible. On a clear day, at a solar altitude of 40 degrees, the illumination from the sky is of the order of one-quarter of that from the sun ; towards dawn and sunset the sunlight decreases more rapidly than the skylight, and when the sun is less than about five degrees above the horizon the skylight is the stronger.

Atmospheric Absorption and Scattering.—Atmospheric absorption and scattering change the energy distribution of the sunlight over the whole range of its radiation spectrum. Our chief concern is with the visible spectrum, but it is of interest to note that ozone in the upper air absorbs ultra-violet light in the region of 0·3 to 0·4 micron, while water vapour absorbs infra-red in the photographic region 0·7 to 1·0 micron. The most important changes in the visible region, however, are due to scattering. Even in perfectly clear air free of water vapour the sunlight is affected by scattering at the gas molecules, the amount of energy lost from the direct beams in this way being inversely proportional to the fourth power of the wavelength, so that the transmitted light is weaker and the scattered light richer in shorter wavelengths. The scattered light is not all lost, a fraction eventually reaches the earth after repeated scattering and is the source of the brightness and colour of the blue sky. Additional scattering, inversely proportional to the second power of the wavelength, takes place at the minute water drops and dust particles which are always present to some extent even in the cleanest natural atmospheres. All of these effects increase in proportion to the thickness of air traversed by the sunlight.

The intensity and spectral energy distribution of the solar radiation after traversing different air masses has been studied in great detail over many years by workers in different parts of the world. The measurements fall into two classes ; in one the illumination is measured by visual photometry or with photo cells corrected to have the same spectral sensitivity as the eye, and in the other the sunlight is dispersed into a spectrum and the heat energy at each wavelength is recorded. The first type of record only provides information on the total radiation in the visible range as integrated by the eye, with no reference to the energy distribution. The second type of record usually extends well beyond the visible range and shows how the energy distribution changes according to the thickness of atmosphere traversed by the sunlight ; it conveys no direct information about illumination as such, but the illumination can be derived if the energy at each wavelength is multiplied by the appropriate relative luminosity figures and by the maximum luminous efficiency of radiant energy, which is 650 lumens per watt at 0·55 micron. The energy records are thus the more fundamental and more generally useful in physical problems, while the direct illumination measurements are of value to illuminating engineers.

Variations in the Spectral Quality of Daylight.—The spectral sensitivity of photographic emulsions is not in general the same as that of the eye, and visual illumination measurements on light of changing colour are not strictly applicable to photography. On the other hand, there is no standard emulsion sensitivity which would be truly representative of " photographic sensitivity." While the nominal aim of general photography is to work at the same spectral sensitivity as the eye, widely different combinations of emulsions and filters are in use, and the corresponding sensitivities are sometimes greater than the eye at the red end of the spectrum and sometimes at the blue end. The eye curve is probably not far from the average of the commoner photographic sensitivity curves, and is about as representative as any photographic curve could be, and the usual practice of assuming that visual illumination measurements apply directly to photography is reasonably well justified. It would hardly be justifiable to correct for the spectral sensitivity of the emulsions used in air photography unless some allowance was also made for the colours of different objects, which would be a very serious complication and one hardly worth considering, because the colours of outdoor objects *on the average* do not depart appreciably from neutral. (5) In view of other errors of a much more serious nature

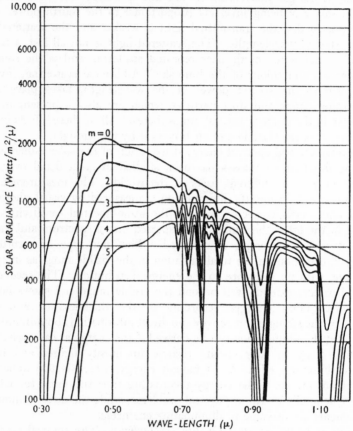

FIG. 55.—Spectral energy distribution of sunlight at various solar altitudes.
(Redrawn from Moon, "Journ. Franklin Institute," Vol. CCXXX.)

which enter into the calculation of photographic exposure, it is not considered to be unreasonable to assume that the variations in the colour of daylight cause little difference between its visual and photographic intensity.

After a careful study and weighting of all available data, Moon (6) published average curves showing the energy in absolute units in sunlight at wavelengths between 0·3 and 1·2 microns, for different air masses in clear weather, *i.e.*, with no clouds or haze but with the traces of dust and water which are never absent from the clearest atmospheres. Some of these curves are reproduced in Fig. 55 ; the ordinates are " watts per square meter per micron." In studying these curves it should be remembered that the most generally representative emulsion sensitivity for air photography is probably an almost uniform response between 0·5 and 0·65 micron, while infra-red emulsions usually have maximum sensitivity at 0·8 micron or thereabouts.

It will be apparent from Fig. 55 that the sunlight loses a great deal of energy in passing through the air, the progressive weakening of the ultra-violet, violet, and blue with increasing air mass being especially marked. This has less effect on the eye or on panchromatic emulsions than on the old " ordinary " (blue-sensitive) emulsions, which became relatively less sensitive at low solar altitudes when exposed on sunlit scenes. In the middle of the panchromatic range of sensitivity an air mass of 5 (solar altitude 11 degrees) reduces the radiation to less than half its intensity at unit air mass. The absorption bands in the near infra-red region suggest that the exposure in infra-red photography might have to be increased rather rapidly as the sun declines in the sky. Over the photographic region used in panchromatic air photography the balance of energy does not change very seriously between unit air mass and air mass 3, which is just below 20 degrees solar altitude. Since most air photographs are taken for preference at higher solar altitudes than this to avoid long shadows, there will be few occasions when the changing colour of sunlight is likely to lead to errors in exposure. It should also be remembered that as the air mass increases the skylight becomes relatively stronger and the total radiation on any object exposed to both sunlight and skylight does not change very much in spectral composition. Selwyn and Pitt have shown (5) that the average or "integrated" colour of outdoor scenes does not change much in the course of a day, but gets slightly *bluer* towards sunrise and sunset; thus, while there will always be some objects which are illuminated predominantly by sunlight, which gets redder with increasing air mass, this need not be regarded as any more serious than the normal variations of colour within a scene at any time.

Regular Variations in Daylight Illumination.—Having discussed the changes in the quality of daylight with varying solar altitude, we may now pass on to consider the corresponding variations in illumination. As already indicated, it will be assumed that camera exposure should vary in inverse proportion to illumination as evaluated by the eye or equivalent receiver.

In attempts to reveal the underlying order in the variations of daylight illumination it is necessary in the first place to use only those observations made in clear weather, since haze and clouds introduce irregular disturbances. The exact meaning of " clear " is naturally rather hard to define, and some minor discrepancies between results obtained in different parts of the world are no doubt due to different interpretations of the word. Kunerth and Miller (7), working at Ames, Iowa, U.S.A., took readings only on " perfectly clear days," while Elvegard and Sjostedt (*loc. cit.*) say that their results, based on the observations of Auren in Sweden and Lunelund in Finland, refer to " relatively clear and translucent air . . . neither extremely clear, as often in mountainous regions, nor markedly filled with vapours, as in industrial districts." Nevertheless, it is a fair assumption that all the results which have been published were obtained in air containing so little suspended dust and water that variations in the amount were unimportant, because figures obtained by several different observing stations in America agree fairly well with each other and with the Scandinavian figures. An atmosphere of this order of clarity is rare in England, and would probably be classed as " exceptionally clear."

Illumination measurements must be referred to some standard reference plane, and in considering daylight illumination there are three possibilities, viz., the horizontal plane, the vertical plane, and the " normal plane," *i.e.*, the plane which is always at right angles to the direction of the sun. Solar energy curves, such as those of Fig. 55, are usually given for the normal plane, but the horizontal plane is apparently the best suited for the illumination

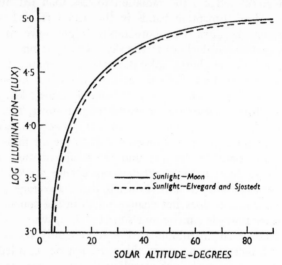

FIG. 56.—Variation of the illumination on a horizontal plane : sunlight only.

measurements to be used in air photography. It is most convenient to express the illumination as a function of solar altitude.

Jones and Condit (*loc. cit.*) made a very thorough comparison of the data on sunlight published by Elvegard and Sjostedt and by various American workers. Some of the American figures were direct illumination measurements, others were derived from solar radiation curves. After taking all the evidence into account Jones and Condit concluded that the illumination curve derived from Moon's standard solar radiant energy curves was " the most probable representation, for all parts of the world, of the illuminance on the horizontal plane due to direct sunlight for the atmospheric condition characterised by the visual judgment as clear " ; this curve is shown in Fig. 56. It is of interest to compare this standard curve with the curve based on the Scandinavian data. The latter include no figures for solar altitudes above 50 degrees, because of the high latitude of Sweden and Finland, but Elvegard and Sjostedt deduced an expression for the illumination as a function of the solar altitude, and in Fig. 56 the curve of their equation is plotted up to 90 degrees. The expression is

$$S = 123{,}000 \sin h . 10^{-0.1M}$$

where   S = illumination in lux on the horizontal plane,
   h = solar altitude,
   M = air mass for h.

The differences between Elvegard and Sjostedt's curve and the proposed standard curve are negligible for photographic purposes.

Published measurements for the illumination due to the clear blue sky do not agree so well as the sunlight data, which is not altogether surprising in view of the sensitivity of the sky brightness to small changes in the scattering properties of the atmosphere.   Jones and Condit again considered

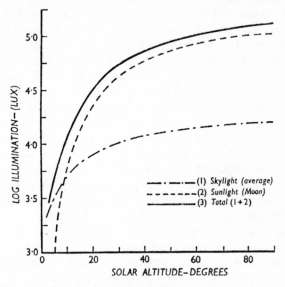

FIG. 57.—Variation of the illumination on a horizontal plane : sunlight and skylight.

all the available data and finally averaged the American and Scandinavian figures to produce the curve shown at 1 in Fig. 57.   Curve 5 in Fig. 58 is the plot of Elvegard and Sjostedt's expression for the skylight,

$$H = 16,300\sqrt{\sin h},$$

where H = illumination on the horizontal plane,
   h = solar altitude.

Curves 2 and 3 in Fig. 57 respectively show the sunlight illumination and the total illumination on a horizontal plane in the clear condition.

ATMOSPHERIC CONDITIONS

The " clear " atmospheric condition, *i.e.*, cloudless blue sky with little or no visible haze, is not very common, and high-altitude air photographs often have to be taken with more or less haze or cloud present.   Photography is not possible, however, with continuous sheets of cloud beneath the aircraft, and in air survey it is usual to consider 2/10 cloud the maximum tolerable.

It is not always feasible to work to this standard, but nevertheless it is true that high-altitude photography is only possible under a limited range of conditions ; clouds may be present, but they must be sufficiently broken and detached to allow a reasonable amount of ground to be seen and illuminated by direct sunshine. High-altitude photographs can certainly be taken underneath the continuous sheets of cloud which sometimes form up to about 15,000 ft. in England and probably higher in hot countries, but the absence of direct sunlight on the ground gives pictures of very low contrast and the results are of small value. At lower altitudes and larger scales quite satisfactory photographs can be taken when the whole sky is covered with clouds and there are no shadows. Nevertheless, the majority of air photographs are taken without much cloud from fairly high altitudes.

Haze.—At ground level haze lowers the apparent brightness of a scene by intercepting part of the direct sunlight, but the scattered light illuminates the shadows, raising their brightness and shortening the brightness scale. Very heavy haze, dense enough to obscure the sun's disc and eliminate shadows, reduces the general illumination and may justify an increase of camera exposure.

In air photography the illumination at ground level is not the sole consideration, for the haze scatters light upwards as well as downwards and modifies the apparent brightness characteristics of the scene. The effects of this upwards scattered light are very complicated, depending on the solar altitude, the polar scatter characteristics of the haze, the height of the aircraft, and the height distribution and density of the haze. Over cities, or where a temperature inversion holds the haze particles below a definite level in the air, the conditions approximate to a simple case in which the haze all lies over the ground in a relatively shallow stratum well below the aircraft, which is in the clear upper air. Such a haze layer scatters light upwards more or less uniformly and may be regarded as having a uniform brightness which is added to the various brightnesses independently of the height of photography. The added brightness raises the lower subject brightnesses relatively more than the higher, and the brightness scale therefore contracts from the lower end. Some contraction may also take place from the upper end, especially in smoky areas where the haze particles absorb as well as scatter light, but in clear atmospheres the maximum brightness does not change very much.

Haze does not always lie near the ground in relatively shallow layers, but may extend up to altitudes of 30,000 ft. or more, yet it is true in a general way that the concentration decreases with height, so that the tendency is always for the air to be clearer above the aircraft than below it. With increasing altitude the camera looks through an increasing column of haze, and the minimum scene brightness rises accordingly. Increasing altitude therefore produces a similar effect to increased concentration of haze. The rise of minimum scene brightness under hazy conditions is easily shown by comparative photographs, but it is not always obvious to the eye, which presumably estimates the brightness of a scene by the brightest parts rather than the darkest. Certainly hazy areas often *look* very dark from above, but the author has yet to see proof of any case where the haze did not raise the minimum brightness. This applies even to the dense smoke haze over the English Black Country, which looks very dark indeed from above but scatters enough light upwards to call for less camera exposure than clear areas under the same illumination. It is, of course, conceivable that in tropical countries the dust haze, which sometimes rises to a great height, may be dense enough above the aircraft to cut off a great deal of light and lower the minimum scene brightness, but from general experience it is clear that under such conditions high-altitude photographs would be of very little value on account of the lack of shadow on the ground. It will be assumed throughout this book that haze which is thin enough to allow good air photographs to be taken always raises the minimum scene brightness, thus causing a contraction of the brightness scale from the lower end as compared with the same scene under clear conditions.

Clouds.—High-altitude photographs are generally taken under clear skies or with a proportion of cloud small enough to allow a reasonably unobstructed view of the ground. Within this limit general experience indicates that the effective illumination of shadowed areas is increased by the presence of the clouds, and this is understandable in view of the common use of yellow filters which weaken the light from the blue sky. Opinions seem to differ, however, about the illumination in shadows as measured visually at ground level. Thus Jones and Condit maintain that on the average cloudy skies are no brighter than blue skies, since the additional light contributed by the parts of the clouds in full sunshine is offset by the lower brightness of the parts in shadow. Elvegard and Sjostedt, on the other hand, indicate without reserve that the blue sky is markedly less bright than a sky filled with white clouds. Some of the older exposure tables indicated less exposure for a blue sky with white clouds than for a cloudless blue sky, but the recent British and American Standard Exposure Tables do not indicate any difference between the two conditions. This is rather difficult to understand, because it is quite usual to find higher illumination in the shade with white clouds, and the author at least has never yet found a case where the converse was true, though he has often measured decidedly higher shadow brightnesses in the same scene under *grey* clouds than under a clear blue sky, at the same solar altitude.

Cloud conditions are extremely difficult to describe with precision and brevity, and they vary so much that it would hardly be possible to predict the illumination with any accuracy once the clear sky condition has been left. Elvegard and Sjostedt have made the attempt, however, and give formulæ for a few stated conditions. They conclude that the illumination can be expressed as the sum of a fraction of the sunlight plus another fraction of the skylight, according to the cloud conditions. In general the formulæ are written as

$$W = xS + yH,$$

where W = illumination on a horizontal plane from the clouded sky,
    S = sunlight,
    H = skylight.

Their three equations are :—

　(a) " Illumination in the shade from a sky with light white clouds and a bare sun."

$$W = 0 \cdot 08S + 1 \cdot 02H.$$

・(b) " Total illumination when the sun is screened by a thin film of cloud."

$$W = 0 \cdot 35S + 0 \cdot 89H.$$

　(c) " Total illumination from a clouded sky."

$$W = 0 \cdot 26S + 0 \cdot 54H.$$

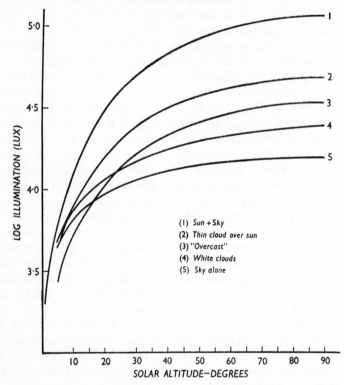

(1) Sun + Sky
(2) Thin cloud over sun
(3) "Overcast"
(4) White clouds
(5) Sky alone

FIG. 58.—Illumination in typical sky conditions (Elvegard and Sjostedt).

Unfortunately, attempts to give a verbal description of cloud conditions are so ambiguous that the precise meaning of Elvegard and Sjostedt's conditions are not clear. It seems fairly certain, however, that Case (a) refers to a condition where high-altitude air photography would be possible, i.e., detached clouds in a clear blue sky with the fraction of cloud somewhere between 1/10 and 9/10. Case (b) probably covers the case where a thin film of cloud has built up to the point where shadows have just vanished, but it is not a very definite condition. Case (c) from another of these authors' publications (8) seems to refer to the condition where grey clouds have increased to the point where no blue sky is visible, since they describe it as " completely overcast."

These equations have been used to plot the curves shown in Fig. 58. The difficulty of specifying cloud conditions suggests that the curves should be interpreted with caution, but it is interesting to note that over a large part of the useful range of solar altitudes they indicate that the illumination in shadows increases with increasing cloud, at least as far as the " overcast " condition, and air photography has little concern with heavier cloud conditions than that.

Use of Illumination Data in Estimating Camera Exposure

We will now consider how the available information on daylight illumination might be used to estimate the camera exposure required on any occasion. The general idea is clear enough ; there is less light when the sun is low than when it is high, and more when the sun is unobscured than when the sky is heavily overcast, we therefore set our camera exposure according to the time of day and year and our estimate of the weather conditions. Ultimately this means that we are making an estimate of the brightness of the scene. In general photography the nominal aim is to vary the camera exposure in inverse proportion to the *minimum* scene brightness so that the minimum negative density is fairly constant for all scenes, that at least is to be deduced from most photographic literature on the subject of exposure. There would be some theoretical justification for such a procedure, but in general it appears to be a conventional fiction rather than a method which is actually applied in practice. Nevertheless, it will serve to illustrate the difficulties of setting camera exposure accurately under changing sky conditions.

Any scene may be regarded as a series of surfaces of different reflectance, the brightness of each being determined by its reflectance and the illumination which falls on it. To simplify matters at this stage reflectance will be ignored and the problem considered in terms of illumination only. Surfaces in sunlight are exposed to the total illumination from sun and sky, those in shadow will in general be illuminated by skylight only. In some cases, *e.g.*, in closely built-up town areas, some of the shadow illumination may be due to reflection of sunlight from adjacent buildings, but the shadow areas where this reflected light is important are necessarily small, and most of the larger shadowed areas are open to a considerable expanse of sky. Basing the camera exposure on the minimum scene brightness therefore means that it must be varied according to the illumination received from the sky by the darkest shadow area. If all shadows were exposed to the whole, or the same fraction of the whole hemisphere of sky, it might be reasonable to vary the camera exposure at different solar altitudes according to the curves for sky illumination. Real shadows, however, are exposed to widely differing fractions of the whole sky hemisphere, and indeed the illumination varies quite considerably within individual shadowed areas. Moreover, the sky is not of uniform brightness, even when perfectly free of clouds, and the distribution of brightness varies with solar altitude. The minimum scene brightness cannot therefore be predicted with any accuracy even in the clear weather condition for which the illumination from the whole sky is fairly precisely known.

The clear condition is rare, however, and the illumination from the sky is liable to be modified by clouds or haze in an unpredictable fashion. It is perhaps possible to predict the order of illumination which may be expected under certain specified sky conditions, but these at best are merely steps on a long scale and cannot possibly be representative of all the conditions that may be encountered. The precision of estimating the minimum scene illumination therefore becomes even lower when we depart from the clear sky condition. Moreover, in air photography the problem is further complicated by the light scattered upwards from the atmospheric haze, which modifies the scene brightnesses, sometimes quite profoundly. When this is added to the variations due to different amounts of cloud in the sky it can be seen that the task of predicting the minimum scene brightness with any precision is quite hopeless.

It was pointed out in Chapter Three that there is little or no latitude in high-altitude air photography if the best resolution is required, how then can the camera exposure be set with the necessary accuracy, assuming that means for the measurement of the minimum scene brightness are not available ? Strictly speaking, the camera exposure cannot be set to give a *constant minimum negative density*, but this does not mean that it cannot be set to give *good negatives*. To explain this statement it will be necessary to consider the precise meaning of " correct exposure " in air photography, when we shall see that the *exposure*, as distinct from the *camera exposure*, can be allowed to vary according to the nature of the subject. Once we recognise that the densities of correctly exposed negatives can be different for different subject conditions the exposure problem can be simplified, because we can abandon all pretence of estimating the changes of minimum scene brightness under different atmospheric conditions and can allow the minimum negative densities to vary within relatively wide limits.

Estimation of Camera Exposure for High-altitude Photography.—It is now suggested that for any given solar altitude the camera exposure should be left constant irrespective of the amount of cloud or haze. With correct choice of the level of *camera exposure* the *exposure* will automatically adjust itself so that the densities keep reasonably close to the optimum values under all conditions in which high-altitude photography is possible, viz., haze from " perfectly clear " to complete extinction of the ground view, and cloud up to about 7/10. The variation of camera exposure for different solar altitudes will be considered at a later stage.

Haze.—It has already been pointed out that haze in general contracts the brightness scale and raises the lowest scene brightnesses, and the effect in terms of photographic exposure can best be visualised by a particular experiment, which nevertheless illustrates a quite general principle. In the course of this experiment several vertical photographs were taken within a few minutes over a large industrial city and over a country town from the same altitude of 18,000 ft. All the photographs were on the same roll of film exposed in the same camera, and all conditions such as lens aperture,

filter, processing, etc., were exactly the same, so that differences between
the negatives must have been due to the brightness characteristics of the
scenes and to nothing else.   The city atmosphere was extremely hazy and
the haze *looked* very dark, being much contaminated with industrial smoke ;
the air over the country town was unusually clear for England.   Two
negatives were selected from the roll, one showing the clear area and the
other the hazy area ; their maximum and minimum densities are marked
on the characteristic curve of the emulsion, which is shown in Fig. 59 ;
$D^H_{max.}$ and $D^H_{min.}$ refer to the maximum and minimum densities in the
hazy negative, and $D^c_{max.}$ and $D^c_{min.}$ to those in the clear negative.
Perpendiculars dropped from these densities to the log E scale determine
the log brightness scales, BS^H and BS^C, in the two scenes as imaged in the

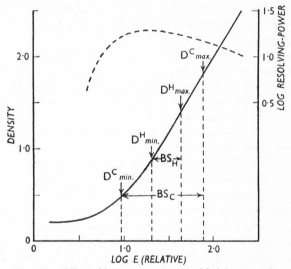

FIG. 59.—Effect of haze on exposure and brightness scale.

camera.   Above the characteristic curve the curve for resolving power on
low-contrast detail is drawn.

The brightness scale in the hazy scene has contracted from both ends,
the marked reduction in maximum brightness being presumably associated
with the smoky nature of the haze.   The camera exposure is seen to have
been such that the densities in the " clear " negative are disposed about
the maximum of the resolving power curve in a fairly satisfactory way.
The same camera exposure given over the hazy area has yielded a negative
whose densities are still about the most satisfactory for the circumstances,
because the contraction of the brightness scale has moved them all nearer
to the peak of the resolving power curve.   If the haze had been " clean "
and the maximum brightness had not fallen, the density range would still
have been fairly satisfactory, though a small reduction of camera exposure
could have been tolerated.   It should be especially noted that *increasing*
the camera exposure over dark haze, which is sometimes advocated, would
be entirely wrong, for the negative densities would increase, graininess would

become worse with no benefit of greater slope in the characteristic curve, and the resolving power would fall away. Plate 10 shows prints made from negatives adjacent in the roll to those from which the density measurements of Fig. 59 were taken. The printing exposure was exactly the same for both negatives, which were on sheets of paper from the same box and were developed together for the same time ; the tonal difference between the two prints may therefore be taken as a pictorial illustration of the negative density characteristics and hence of the brightness characteristics of the subjects. It will be seen that the heavy city haze, which looked so dark to the eye, has markedly raised the general shadow brightness, and in the originals it is possible to see that the highest brightnesses are somewhat lower than in the clear area. A similar result was obtained with reversal " Kodacolor " film exposed under the same conditions. For a constant *camera exposure* the transparencies of the hazy area had a lower mean and maximum density than those of the clear area.

Fig. 59 refers only to one particular set of clear and hazy conditions, but they were chosen because between them are included practically all the conditions in which high-altitude photographs are normally taken ; few days occur, at least in England, on which the air is clearer than in the clear example, while photographs taken in much hazier conditions are of little use. All other haze conditions will fit between by adjustment to the lengths of the brightness-scale lines in Fig. 59.

The basic camera exposure has to be chosen with care so that the best balance is preserved between clear and hazy conditions. In the clearest conditions the exposure in the camera has to be sufficient to ensure adequate contrast in the rendering of what little shadow detail is present, yet it must not be too great or the sunlit parts of the scene, where the most important details are usually found, will be recorded at unnecessarily high densities and resolution will be lost. If the camera exposure is set at the optimum for the haziest condition it is liable to be on the under side for the clear condition, and some compromise is required. It seems best to arrange matters so that the brightness scale of the average high-altitude view is recorded symmetrically about the peak of the emulsion resolving power curve ; on clearer than average days the shadows will then be recorded at somewhat less than optimum contrast, but this can probably be tolerated just because it *is* clear, while in hazy weather the densities will not be excessive. For European conditions the brightness scale of the average high-altitude view as imaged in the camera is approximately 5·5 to 1·0 or 0·75 on the log scale, while longer scales than that shown for the clear condition in Fig. 59 must be rare. If the minimum negative density in average clear conditions normally runs at about 0·3 to 0·5 above fog the basic exposure level is reasonably correct and no change need be made for any variation in the haziness of the atmosphere.

It could equally well be argued that since there is always enough haze in high-altitude scenes to wipe out practically all shadow detail (see Chapter Twelve), the latter need not be considered when estimating exposure. In that case the minimum negative density could well be lower than 0·3 above fog, thus bringing the middle of the subject brightness range nearer to the peak of the resolving power curve, at a density of about 0·9. However, it is never possible to determine the negative densities with such precision as this, and in view of the very rapid decline of contrast and resolving power on the toe of the characteristic curve it is probably better to work a little higher up, as originally suggested, in the interests of safety. The loss of resolving power in the middle tones of the subject will be quite negligible, and much less than would be suffered as a result of accidental under-exposure.

Clouds.—From what has already been said it should be clear that clouds need not be considered in setting the camera exposure for high-altitude air photography. More or less cloud means more or less shadow illumination, leading to variations in the brightness scale, but all of these are included in the statement that the average brightness scale is 0·75 and the practical maximum 0·9. If the basic camera exposure is correct it will accommodate all these variations without serious loss of quality.

Air photographs are often taken when an appreciable fraction of the ground is in cloud shadow, and there is a rather common belief that the camera exposure should be increased in such cases. There might be some justification for this belief if the basic camera exposure for clear weather were not sufficient to bring the shadows on to the correct part of the characteristic curve ; a moderate degree of under-exposure might escape notice on small shadowed areas, but is less likely to be tolerated in the much larger area of a cloud shadow. If the exposure is adequate in clear weather, however, it need not be increased when cloud shadows are about.

The illumination in a cloud shadow cannot be less than in the shadow of a terrestrial object, though it may well be greater, because the cloud-shadowed area is exposed to the whole hemisphere of sky ; this may seem to be very obvious, and is only mentioned because in the author's experience many air photographers strongly hold to the opposite belief. Even if the cloud cover increases until most of the ground is in shadow, the illumination does not in general fall below that of shadows under a clear blue sky, as can be seen from Elvegard and Sjostedt's curves in Fig. 58, and can be confirmed by photometric measurements or by taking photographs at ground level (see Appendix). Much of the confusion about exposure for cloud shadows arises from the lack of detail, which is their most obvious characteristic in air negatives. Photographers are accustomed to associate under-exposure with lack of shadow detail, and when confronted with a negative having featureless areas of cloud shadow they instinctively diagnose a need for more camera exposure. Some negatives shown to the author as examples of " under-exposure " in cloud shadows have had minimum densities greater than 1·0, and would have benefited by a reduction rather than an increase in exposure. The lack of detail in properly exposed cloud-shadowed areas is primarily due to the absence of any directed light within the areas, so that objects cast no shadows and can only be distinguished by their different reflectances ; a further reduction of contrast is caused by the haze light, which has a greater flattening effect at the low-brightness end of the tone scale, the contrast is then so low that only the larger objects are above the resolution limit (see Chapter Twelve).

Clouds do, of course, cast their shadows on the haze as well as on the ground, so that a part of the haze column is not fully illuminated, and the fraction not in sunlight increases with increasing solar altitude, but this effect is not of very great significance. The most convincing argument for ignoring cloud shadows in setting camera exposure comes from a study of the densities of actual high-altitude negatives with cloud-shadowed areas. All shadows in such negatives are found to have much the same density, and the cloud shadows are neither much denser nor much less dense than the average.

Camera Exposure as a Function of Solar Altitude.—We have seen that the camera exposure for high-altitude air photography can be left constant under different atmospheric conditions at any solar altitude. How should the basic setting vary at different solar altitudes ? We have already decided that it cannot logically be related to the illumination of the shadowed areas, and the only other obvious possibility is that it should vary inversely as the illumination on sunlit areas. It should be realised that this is not an attempt to forecast the brightness of any part of the scene with precision ; no more is involved than the recognition that the high-altitude view in general has a restricted brightness scale whose absolute brightnesses must vary according to the solar altitude. The length of the brightness scale itself will also vary with the solar altitude, as may be seen from the curves in Fig. 58, but given a suitable basic exposure level a camera exposure which follows the illumination on the sunlit areas can hold the negative densities within a reasonable range, the same arguments applying here as in the case of varying amounts of haze.

Until comparatively recently exposure tables for general photography had been based on the assumption that the camera exposure should be inversely proportional to the illumination on a horizontal surface, and the same assumption has been made up to this point in this chapter. Jones and Condit, however (*loc. cit.*), show that the assumption has no logical justification in ground photography, since the subjects commonly photographed contain surfaces inclined at all angles, the horizontal being without special significance. They point out that so long as light is evaluated as *illumination* some definite receiving plane must be invoked, but since no plane whatever can be claimed to be representative of the variety of planes encountered in photography, the only logical course is to abandon the conception of illumination altogether, and evaluate the light in some other way. This way they find in the concept of " luminous density," by which the luminous energy traversing the object space is estimated in complete independence of the direction from which it arrives. The original paper should be consulted for a fuller account of luminous density and the units in which it is measured ; for the present purpose it may be regarded simply as a measure of the total *luminous energy* which enters the object space independently of any *illumination* to which it may give rise. Illumination, by definition, implies that the luminous energy strikes some surface ; without material objects no amount of luminous energy can produce any illumination, but luminous density is still a valid conception in a perfectly empty space, which under the right conditions could have a high luminous density while appearing quite dark. Luminous density may in fact be regarded as *potential illumination*.

The variation of luminous density with solar altitude is shown for the clear atmospheric condition in Fig. 60, a curve for the illumination from sun plus sky on a horizontal surface being shown for comparison. It will be seen that the luminous density curve rises more rapidly from the lowest values and flattens out earlier; this is because the energy in the sunlight entering the hemisphere of sky is limited only by the air mass, whereas the *illumination* on the horizontal plane is further reduced by the cosine factor of the angle at which the rays strike. If luminous density provides the correct guide to camera exposure the same setting could be held down

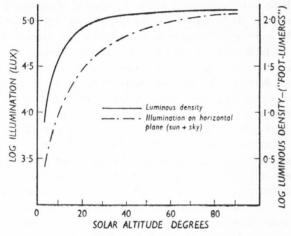

Fig. 60.—Variation of luminous density and illumination with
solar altitude.

to much lower solar altitudes than is suggested by the illumination curve. In practice this means that there would be less difference between summer and winter and between high and low altitudes than is shown by the older exposure tables. Jones and Condit contend that these older tables are incorrect and that the luminous density curve is in close accord with the camera exposures given by skilled and experienced photographers.

At the time of writing only the first part of the Jones-Condit paper has appeared, and a proper appreciation of their views has not been possible, but there is certainly a great deal to be said for the luminous density theory in ground photography. The author has found that the camera exposure required for ground photographs and low to medium altitude air obliques on reversal colour film, which is a material critical of exposure errors, followed the luminous density curve quite closely over a range of solar altitudes from 7 to 80 degrees. Substantially the same camera exposure was required for all solar altitudes above about thirty degrees, whereas the illumination on a horizontal plane is about twice as great at 80 degrees as at 30 degrees. On the other hand, it must be admitted that the exposure for reversal materials tends to be judged by the average or maximum scene brightness rather than the minimum brightness, and it does not follow that exposures on negative material would give the same results. Jones and Condit lay some stress on the value of luminous density as an indication of the minimum scene brightness, but apparently find it necessary to introduce a somewhat complex system of correction factors, taking account of the direction of the incident light, in order to maintain this relationship. This appears to weaken the argument for luminous density, but it must again be emphasised that the " horizontal surface illumination " is not being defended as the guide to camera exposure in ground photography. Whatever system is ultimately found to be the best, and no simple system is likely to be universally correct, it seems certain that the illumination on a horizontal surface will have to be abandoned as the criterion of scene brightness.

For vertical air photography, on the other hand, the evidence does not appear to the author to be sufficient to justify the abandonment of the older exposure tables, which are based on the illumination on a horizontal surface, using in some cases the accurate measurements of Elvegard and Sjostedt. In obliques and ground photographs there is no principal or representative plane, but in vertical photography the mean ground plane is horizontal. It is true that individual areas such as the sides of hills depart from the horizontal plane, but these different inclinations probably average out. On the other hand, it can be argued that no ground except a smooth snowfield or flat desert is anything like a flat horizontal area, such things as trees and grass being made up of planes inclined at all angles, of which the horizontal is merely a special case. Furthermore, the brightness in the vertical direction of any horizontal surface will only vary in direct proportion to the illumination on that surface if it is a perfect diffuser, which is rarely the case. We may therefore conceive of the ground as a series of planes set at all angles and reflecting light in all directions, so that on the average the brightness in any direction is likely to be dependent on the luminous density rather than on the illumination on the somewhat arbitrary horizontal plane.

The luminous density argument may also be looked at in a different way. We have seen in a previous section that the minimum density in high-altitude negatives is determined by the brightness of the haze rather than the minimum brightness of the scene at ground level. (In a typical high-altitude view the haze brightness is of the order of four times that of the darkest shadow in the scene at ground level.) Now the haze brightness in the vertical direction will vary in a complicated way with the solar altitude, but we should expect it to be determined by the luminous density rather than the illumination on some arbitrary plane such as the horizontal. Therefore we might expect the camera exposure required for a constant minimum density under constant haze conditions to vary with the solar altitude in the same way as the luminous density. In examining an admittedly limited number of high-altitude negatives from this point of view the author found that the camera exposure followed a curve intermediate between the curves for luminous density and for illumination on a horizontal surface, so that the evidence is again inconclusive.

On the whole, the theoretical evidence seems to favour the luminous density relationship for the brightness of areas in sunlight. We cannot, however, accept the luminous density theory *in toto*, for it indicates that the brightness of any area becomes less when it passes into cloud shadow or when haze diffuses the sunlight, which can be very easily shown to be false by direct photometry or photography, either from the air or at ground level (see Appendix).

It does not seem likely that either the luminous density or the horizontal plane illumination relationships will be found completely satisfactory, but until more evidence is forthcoming judgment must be deferred.

Effect of Aircraft Altitude.—The camera exposure depends on the aircraft altitude because of two quite separate effects, one due to haze and the other to scale. With increasing altitude the camera looks through longer columns of haze and the shadows accordingly become lighter, irrespective of the scale. With reduced scale the mean brightness of the image tends to rise irrespective of any increase of haze, because many of the smaller shadows tend to vanish and within larger shadowed areas the reduction of scale produces an averaged brightness which is greater than that of the lowest brightness seen at the larger scale. This effect may, however, be regarded as similar to the haze effect and no special allowance should be made for it.

Low-altitude vertical subjects vary greatly in their brightness scale and in the camera exposure required, because there is no haze to level up the minimum brightnesses, and with the larger scale it is natural to look for detail in the darker shadows of relatively small area which would be passed over in the high-altitude photograph. There can be no easy guide to camera exposure in such circumstances, and the most that can be done is to explain some of the factors involved, leaving the user to work out the application to his own particular problems. The discussion in this section is offered to that end, and it is not pretended that it covers all practical cases, though reasonably typical examples are dealt with.

So far as the haze effect is concerned, it might be thought that the same arguments could be applied as when considering different degrees of haze in high-altitude photography, *i.e.*, that by suitable setting of the basic exposure both low and high altitude scenes, which in effect correspond to less and greater amounts of haze, could be accommodated on the best parts of the characteristic curve without any change of camera exposure. In principle this is true, but it would mean carrying the argument too far, because the high-altitude negative would have to be given an unnecessarily great exposure in order to cater for the much lower minimum brightnesses of the low-altitude scene. This may be demonstrated by a practical example. Vertical photographs were taken over a certain area from 1000 ft. and from 12,000 ft. within a short enough time for the illumination to be sensibly constant. The air was clear, with no obvious break in the haze as sometimes occurs at an altitude of a few thousand feet. The negatives were given the same camera exposure behind a Minus Blue filter on the same roll of film and the processing was the same for both. Density measurements were made on a large shadowed area (shadow in a railway cutting) and on a large area of light gravel, the positions of these densities being marked on the emulsion characteristic curve in Fig. 61. Point $D^H_{L\,max.}$ on the curve is the density of the light area, which was the same in both negatives, $D^L_{min.}$ is the density of the shadow in the 1000 ft. negative, and $D^H_{min.}$ its density in the 12,000 ft. negative. Perpendiculars dropped to the log E axis define the log brightness scales in the camera, BS^H and BS^L, at the high and low altitudes respectively. Readings taken off the log E scale indicate that the shadow was effectively about three times as bright when seen from the moderate altitude of 12,000 ft. as it was from 1000 ft., while the highlight brightness was unaffected by altitude. (Strictly speaking, the increased shadow density in the 12,000 ft. negative was partly due to

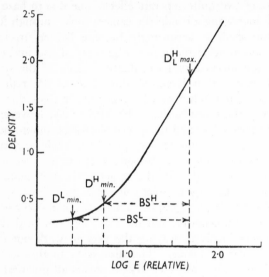

FIG. 61.—Effect of altitude on exposure and brightness scale.

increased camera flare, because the mean brightness of the scene was some-what greater when seen from the higher altitude. This does not affect the argument, however.) The effective brightness scale of the scene from 12,000 ft. was 1·0 ; if we allow a further contraction from the lower end so that it becomes about 0·75 at, say, 20,000 ft., the minimum density would rise to about 0·7, which is close to the optimum for high-altitude work. The minimum density is too low in the low-altitude negative, however, for the gradient at the extreme shadow end is of the order of 0·1, about 0·1 of the average gradient over the part of the characteristic curve used in the negative. Doubling the camera exposure improves the low-altitude negative, giving it a minimum gradient approximately 0·3 of the average gradient, but raises the minimum density of the high-altitude negative to about 1·1, which is undesirably high.

The same point is further illustrated by another example of similar type, the difference from the first being that the camera exposure was greater, and although the scene was again a country town the air was noticeably hazy. The placing of some salient densities on the characteristic curve is illustrated in Fig. 62. Point $D^{L}_{min.}$ is the density of a large shadowed area in the 1000 ft. negative, and $D^{H}_{min.}$ its density in the 12,000 ft. negative, while $D^{H}_{L\,max.}$ is the density of a large light area, which again was the same in both negatives. It will be noticed that all the densities are higher than in the first pair of negatives, due partly to the greater camera exposure, while the brightness scales are shorter, due to the hazy atmosphere. The minimum density of the low-altitude negative is now close to the bottom of the straight-line part of the characteristic curve, while that of the high-altitude negative, due to the greater shadow brightness, has risen above

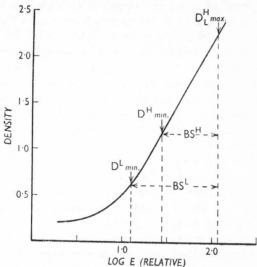

FIG. 62.—Effect of altitude on exposure and brightness scale.

the optimum value. The relative positions of the lower ends of the log brightness scales indicate that the minimum scene brightness was about two and a half times as great at 12,000 ft. as at 1000 ft. Plate 11 shows prints from the negatives, made with exactly the same exposure time on the same paper ; these may serve to illustrate how the same area seen from different altitudes can vary in the characteristics of brightness and brightness distribution, which are of importance in the estimation of camera exposure.

It will be clear from these examples that it would not be practicable to give the same camera exposure for high and low altitude photography, because the range of brightnesses is too great for any single exposure to span in a satisfactory way. At the same time, it is not desirable to aim at the same minimum density in low-altitude negatives as we have seen to be desirable for high-altitude work. The reasons for this may be explained by further reference to Fig. 61. It will be noticed that if the low-altitude scene had been recorded entirely on the straight-line part of the characteristic curve, with its gamma of 1·7, the negative density range would have been

2·2, which means that it would not have printed satisfactorily on the softest bromide paper available. The usually advocated remedy for excessive contrast, a reduction in the negative development time, would not be admissible, because the speed would then fall off more rapidly than the contrast, and for this type of subject we require all possible speed. This difficulty can only be solved in a fully satisfactory way by using a negative material which is of inherently low contrast and will give a gamma lower than unity even when developed for full speed. As an alternative the all-metol developer (formula ID15) can be tried, but it is not always the complete solution. A practical solution to the problem of excessive density range, which is usually imposed in any case by the sheer lack of exposure at the shutter time required to arrest movement, is to allow the lower densities to run down on to the toe of the characteristic curve, so that the effective average gradient is less than the gamma. The use of the toe must not, of course, be overdone or shadow detail will be lost ; the minimum density should not be less than about 0·1 above fog for safety. This practice means that an appreciable part of the brightness range of the subject is being recorded well away from the maximum of the resolving power curve, but this cannot be regarded as a very serious matter, because the resolution in low-altitude photography is determined by the image movement rather than the emulsion characteristics.

A rule which the author has found to work fairly well is that the exposure known to be correct for work at high altitudes (*circa* 20,000 ft.) should be doubled below 5000 ft. and doubled again below 1000 ft. Some or all of this adjustment can often be made by removing the Minus Blue filter, which is not needed for haze cutting below 1000 ft.

Low-altitude vertical photographs are sometimes taken under cloud for the sake of avoiding shadows, and the camera exposure should then be increased over that necessary when the sun is shining on the ground. The amount of the increase will depend on the kind of clouds, unless the weather is excessively dull a factor of two will be sufficient. The increased camera exposure is not required because the darker parts of the subject are necessarily any darker than under a clear blue sky, but because the brightness scale of the subject is shorter in absence of shadow and it is then desirable to work further up the characteristic curve for increased contrast (see also Appendix). This situation may again demand a compromise exposure in view of the need for stopping movement ; and with increasing aircraft speeds it is becoming increasingly difficult to obtain adequate exposure in low-altitude verticals without some form of movement compensation.

Obliques.—High-altitude obliques are equivalent to verticals taken from the same camera station under heavier haze conditions, and can therefore be given the same camera exposure or less if convenient, according to the haze. In general no great loss of quality will result if they are always given the same camera exposure as verticals. Obliques at low altitudes may require more camera exposure than high-altitude verticals because the subject-matter is often quite close to the camera and in the foreground at least there is no haze. When the nearest important objects are less than 1000 ft. from the camera the setting should be calculated as for low-altitude verticals, while at greater distances it may be reduced, and at 5000 ft. or more may be the same as for high-altitude verticals. If operating under cloud the camera exposure should be increased as for low-altitude obliques and for the same reason.

All of these remarks are, of course, to be read in the understanding that they are true only in a general sense and that some degree of personal judgment is quite unavoidable in any system where exposure estimation is not based on brightness measurements.

Nature of the Terrain

Most photographic exposure tables classify subjects according to the relative amount of shadow and the proportion of light or dark toned surfaces as " light," " average," " dark," etc., and indicate an appropriate change in camera exposure, but so far we have made little explicit reference to the lightness or darkness of the terrain being photographed. It is right to lay less emphasis on the subject reflectance in air photography, since with its comprehensive viewpoint any one picture is likely to include a variety of surfaces of different tone, all of which must be correctly exposed ; if the average camera exposure gets good results on, say, dark woods and light concrete, which are respectively about the darkest and the lightest things encountered in air photography, it is arguable that the same camera setting should be satisfactory when the picture contains all light or all dark surfaces. The correct view, however, is that the average exposure has to be a compromise and is usually set to give the best possible results at the middle of the tone scale ; given a subject which is predominantly in one tone it is only reasonable to adjust the camera exposure accordingly. This is the more desirable because in scenes which have little variety of tone there is naturally little contrast to convey information about the nature of the ground, and the user of the photographs requires the best possible reproduction of what little detail there is. Adjusting the camera exposure so that the subject is recorded on the best part of the characteristic curve ensures that the negative has the optimum contrast without excessive density, and incidentally the printer has an easier task when all his negatives require a similar printing exposure.

There is a tendency to exaggerate the differences of tone between the commonly encountered surfaces, possibly because the eye over-emphasises any change in the rather flat and featureless prospect seen from an aircraft. It should be remembered that even good white blotting-paper reflects only about twenty times as much light as black photographic wrapping-paper, and white paper is a great deal lighter than the lightest surfaces commonly seen from the air, so that the total range can never be very great. In European conditions at least there is usually an appreciable amount of haze which tends to restrict the range by making the darkest areas look lighter. The relative brightness of some typical surfaces seen from the air is illustrated by the figures in Table 6, which were measured with a telephotometer at 15,000 ft. over South and East England, at a solar altitude of about fifty-four degrees, with slight haze.

TABLE 6

Surface.	Brightness (Foot-lamberts).	Relative Brightness.
Light yellowish sand	2400	100
Brown soil	1100	45
Pasture grass	700	30
Streets and roofs of a non-industrial town	700	30
Deciduous woods (summer) . . .	600	25
Dark-green crops	560	23
Dark pine woods	300	12

These figures would hardly justify changing the normal camera exposure by a greater factor than two to one to cope with subjects which were all dark woods or all light sand. Needless to say, land under complete snow cover would be lighter than the highest figure in Table 6, probably about three times lighter, but few scenes consist of snow alone. It is also conceivable that in very clear air wooded subjects which contain a great deal of shadow might be relatively darker than the figures in the table would suggest. Occasionally in undeveloped countries large areas of grassland are burnt, and the black ash can have a very low reflectance, being sometimes as dark in sunshine as normal grass in cloud shadow; somewhat greater allowances might be made for these exceptional cases.

The figures in Table 6 were measured with a telephotometer covering a very small angle of view, and refer to small areas picked out of the general landscape; in most air photography over England or Europe, at least from high altitudes, the terrain is a mosaic of such small areas, so that the camera exposure can only be set to an average value. In less developed countries it is not unusual to work over large areas where negative after negative shows nothing but forest or grassland or sandy desert, so that the reading even of an integrating type of photo-electric exposure meter shows considerable variation according to the type of ground below the aircraft. The readings in Table 7, which are typical of this kind of effect, were obtained with a standard Weston exposure meter having an angle of acceptance of about seventy degrees, the aircraft being at about 10,000 ft., solar altitude about eighty degrees, atmosphere very clear.

TABLE 7

Type of Terrain (East Africa).	Weston Reading.	Brightness (Foot-lamberts).	Relative Brightness.
Very light whitish sand (desert area)	560	1760	100
Open green grassland . . .	200	630	36
Barren grass area, brown and withered	220	690	39
Fairly open tree cover . . .	200	630	36
Rich green grass near water . .	180	560	32
Dark-green woods . . .	100	314	18

There is a general similarity between these figures and those of Table 6, indicating that even under tropical conditions there is no need for very drastic changes of camera exposure when photographing different types of terrain. It is interesting to note that to the eye the brightness variations appeared quite marked; on entering the desert area from grass cover, in particular, the increase of brightness seemed quite dramatic, and an observer relying on his visual impressions would probably have deduced the need for a much greater change of camera exposure than the factor of 2·8, which the brightness measurements showed to be the maximum justifiable. It is also of some interest to observe that the general level of brightness is much the same in Africa with a solar altitude of 80 degrees as in England with a solar altitude of 54 degrees; protagonists of the luminous density theory could cite these figures in support of their case, but over this range of altitudes the illumination on a horizontal plane shows a log difference of only about 0·1, so that the data are not of any great significance in this particular connection.

While these brightness figures are before the reader it may be of interest to calculate the order of camera exposure required for emulsions whose sensitivity is known in sensitometric terms. From the figures, it follows that a representative figure for the brightness of average grass-covered terrain would be about 630 foot-lamberts, say, 200 candles per sq. ft. or 2222 candles per sq. metre. Assuming a lens aperture of $f/11$ and a lens transmission of 60 per cent., the illumination on the focal plane is given by

$$I = \frac{\pi.2222.0\cdot6}{4\cdot11^2} = 8\cdot6 \text{ metre-candle.}$$

A typical fast panchromatic emulsion requires an exposure of 0·01 metre-candle second for a density of 1·0. Allowing a factor of 2·5 for a Minus Blue filter, the time of exposure at an intensity of 0·86 metre-candle becomes 0·0029 sec., say, 1/340 sec., which is very close to the time of exposure actually given in air photography at $f/11$ on the same type of emulsion.

Exposure Meters

Exposure meters have not been widely used in air photography partly because a camera operator is not always available and partly because their indications cannot always be accepted without reserve. Only two types merit consideration, the " integrating " photo-electric and the visual photometer.

The photo-electric meters used in general photography contain a self-generating cell with suitable baffles to restrict the field of view to approximately the same as the average camera, and a galvanometer calibrated to read average brightnesses in arbitrary units or in candles per square foot. The spectral sensitivity of the cells is different from that of the eye or a panchromatic film, but can be brought into approximate agreement with the effective sensitivity of the film as used in air photography by fixing a piece of Minus Blue filter over the cell aperture. The colours in air views, however, are not saturated enough for this to be really necessary. For use in high-altitude air photography, the angle of view of these meters need not be altered ; the ground brightness does not change rapidly enough for exact matching to the camera angle to be essential.

The assumption underlying the use of the photo-electric meter in ground photography is that the average scene brightness bears a constant relation to the minimum scene brightness for a wide variety of scenes, so that the camera exposure based on the average brightness will always be adequate for the minimum brightness. This assumption is by no means true, and some skill is needed to use these meters and to apply the appropriate correction factors where necessary. In high-altitude air photography, however, the average scene brightness is quite a good guide to the camera exposure, because of the short brightness scale, and the photo-electric meter can be quite a useful piece of equipment. It must nevertheless be handled with discretion and is no substitute for thought. The photographer must always be certain that no clouds are in the field of view of the instrument when he takes readings, for white clouds are some ten times brighter than the sunlit ground, and even a small cloud will have a large effect on the indicated average brightness. With changing terrain it is best to make frequent checks of the ground brightness. If this is not done and the camera exposure is set for, say, a light sandy area, and then left alone, under-exposure will result on passing to a dark forest area. If the meter cannot be watched continuously the camera should be set to a mean exposure for the darkest area, but this procedure removes much of the value of having a meter at all.

The calibrating of the integrating meter for high-altitude air photography consists of finding the constant relationship between the average brightness reading on the meter scale and the camera exposure required to put the subject on the best part of the characteristic curve with the emulsion and filter, etc., in use. This relation is easily determined by a few trials, and once found need not be changed so long as the subject brightness range remains the same or gets shorter, as with increasing haze. If it becomes much longer, however, as when working at a low altitude, a different relation will probably be needed, for the same average brightness reading may then be obtained with a lower minimum brightness, or, more probably, the average brightness reading will be somewhat lower, but will not indicate a sufficient increase of camera exposure to cope with the much darker shadows. This is due to the fact that the meter reading is mainly influenced by the brighter parts of the scene. Suppose, for example, that a high-altitude scene consists of one part of shadow, brightness 1, and nine parts of sunlit ground, brightness 4 ; the mean brightness is 3·7. On descending to, say, 500 ft. the scene might consist of one part of shadow, brightness 0·25, and nine parts of sunlit ground, brightness again 4 ; the mean brightness is now 3·6, very much the same as before, yet the camera exposure ought to be increased four times to cope with the darker shadows. The same sort of error may arise in a different way ; at low altitudes shadows will be passed over very quickly and the mean reading is more likely to be representative of the light areas. The reading on a Weston exposure meter for the scene shown in Plate 11 (A) was 21, and 37 for that shown in Plate 11 (B); the meter has indicated more camera exposure for the low-altitude scene, but the increase would not have been sufficient, and this is quite typical of what generally happens. As explained on page 179, the camera exposure need not necessarily be increased in the same ratio as the shadow brightness decreases, but it would be wise to give, say, double the indicated exposure below about 2000 ft. if the meter has been calibrated for high-altitude work. The exposure meter is more likely to be used for low-altitude obliques than low-altitude verticals, and here it is necessary to avoid the disturbing influence of the sky brightness. The sky causes little trouble when using the meter for high-altitude obliques, because it is not relatively so much brighter than the ground, especially when clear and blue. White clouds, however, must be watched carefully and the meter pointed away from them unless they form the subject.

The photo-electric meters sold for ground photography are quite satisfactory for use in the air, provided they are handled with reasonable care, but the film speeds issued with the instrument may have to be changed to take account of the different conditions of exposure and development. Thus the fast panchromatic film used for air photography, if normally developed to a low gamma, would be rated at about Weston 100, but when fully developed in D19b this speed would be approximately doubled. On the other hand, use of a Minus Blue filter would halve it again, while the loss of light in a wide-angle survey camera would be equivalent to a further reduction to one-quarter, so that the final speed number would be about Weston 24. These figures only indicate the order of things, and final calibration should be done by air trials. A rough preliminary calibration may be obtained by exposing on a uniformly bright surface, such as a wall, whose brightness is measured with the meter, and choosing the speed setting which gives a negative density of about 1·3.

The telephotometer type of meter has not been available long enough for its practical value to be properly assessed. In principle it is good, giving unambiguous readings of the brightness of selected parts of a scene, the angle of view being of the order of a degree and satisfactorily small for ground photography. In air photography, however, the angle is still much too large to allow individual shadows to be measured ; moreover, if the angle were small enough for this purpose photometric matching would not be possible on the rapidly moving image of the ground. For the same reason this type of meter would be of little use in low-altitude photography, unless perhaps from a helicopter. In high and medium altitude photography the best method of working would probably be to measure the brightness of a large dark area such as a cloud shadow. The theoretical advantage of this type of meter is that the user can be quite sure of what he is measuring, with no chance of unobserved clouds giving a false reading, but this advantage is largely illusory if in fact it is not possible to measure the particular spot desired. Moreover, the field brightness is often too low for accurate matching when the eye is adapted to the high general level of illumination prevailing out of doors,

With all their disadvantages exposure meters should in the long run raise the standard of air photography, because the user can base his camera setting on a positive reading of ground brightness instead of relying on the mixture of faith, hope, and prophecy to which exposure tables ultimately reduce. The danger is that he may become mesmerised by the figures on the scale and forget the essential condition for success, which is that the reading is a basis for thought and not a substitute for it.

REFERENCES

1. JONES, L. A., and CONDIT, H. R. "Sunlight and Skylight as Determinants of Photographic Exposure. Part I. Luminous Density as determined by Solar Altitude and Atmospheric Conditions," *Journ. Opt. Soc. Amer.*, **38**, February 1948.
2. Hurter and Driffield Memorial Volume. Royal Photographic Society, London.
3. BERG., W. "Exposure Tables," *Photo. Journ.*, **82**, 107, 1942.
4. ELVEGARD, E., and SJOSTEDT, G. "The Calculation of Illumination from Sun and Sky," *Illuminating Engineering*, April 1940.
5. SELWYN, E. W., and PITT, F. H. G. "Colour of Outdoor Photographic Subjects," *Photo. Journ.*, **78**, March 1938.
6. MOON, P. "Proposed Standard Solar Radiation Curves for Engineering Use," *Journ. Frank. Inst.*, pp. 230, 583, 1940.
7. KUNERTH, W., and MILLER, R. D. "Variations of Intensities of the Visible and Ultra-violet in Sunlight and in Skylight," *Trans. Illumin. Eng. Soc.*, **27**, 82, 1932. "Visible and Ultra-violet in the Light obtained from the Sun," *Trans. Illumin. Eng. Soc.*, **28**, 347, 1933.
8. ELVEGARD, E., and SJOSTEDT, G. *Photo. Journ.*, **86-B**, No. 4, 1946.

APPENDIX

(To be read in conjunction with Chapter Ten)

On the Photographic Exposure for Clear and Dull Weather

In Chapter Ten the view is advanced that the camera exposure should remain constant in high-altitude air photography at a given solar altitude, irrespective of any variations in the amount of cloud or haze. It is suggested that the negative density variations which will occur when following this method will in general be in the right direction to give the best possible negative, and that better results will be had than by any attempts at altering the camera exposure in accordance with personal estimates of the scene brightness, which are liable to be seriously in error.

The argument is based on the experimental fact that in the progressive growth of cloud cover from a perfectly clear blue sky to the completely overcast condition the illumination or brightness of an area in shadow does not vary very much. In general, any kind of broken cloud slightly increases shadow illumination, at least up to the point where all blue sky is obscured. Continuous sheets of cloud also increase the shadow illumination up to a point ; the precise state at which the thickness becomes so great that the illumination begins to fall off is rather indefinite, but the increase persists at least up to the point where the sun's disc is no longer visible and shadows have faded out. States beyond this are of little interest except for low-altitude photography.

These remarks are mainly based on the data of Elvegard and Sjostedt, supplemented by personal observations which, however, are not nearly so comprehensive. Numerous observations have also been made over a period of years at the National Physical Laboratory, Teddington, London, and are available in an H.M.S.O. publication. While one could hardly expect any precise agreement between these data and the equations of Elvegard and Sjostedt, seeing that the National Physical Laboratory figures refer to a rather dirty atmosphere near London, and the Scandinavian data to " relatively clear and translucent air," the general conclusions are very much the same. Thus from a study of the National Physical Laboratory report one could draw the conclusions that, considering the whole sky hemisphere, blue skies give less illumination than skies with haze, thin clouds, or groups of white clouds. Overcast and cloudy skies have a more variable effect, sometimes giving less illumination than the blue sky, but never very much less. In one case the sky illumination during rain was only slightly less than under a blue sky. Bearing in mind the National Physical Laboratory definition of " overcast " as " the entire sky covered by a continuous layer of cloud," without any specification of its density or thickness, there seems to be a very reasonable agreement with Elvegard and Sjostedt's equations, plotted in Fig. 58 of Chapter Ten. From the point of view of air photography one of the more important deductions is that the illumination in cloud shadows cannot be any less than in shadows of terrestrial objects and hence no increase of camera exposure need be made when clouds are about but the sun still uncovered. The reader may feel that this point is being laboured, but the contrary argument is made so frequently that the effort is felt to be justified.

Now if the illumination in shadows is indeed the same or greater when clouds cover the blue sky, why is it that photographic exposure tables, which purport to give camera exposures based on the *minimum* scene brightness, always indicate a considerable increase when the scene is taken in " dull " light ? (" Dull," for any particular part of the landscape, meaning that it is in cloud shadow, or that the sun is not shining on it, although the sky may be clear at some distance.) The order of disagreement may be seen from Table 8. The column headed Exposure Ratios shows from left to right the relative camera exposures indicated by the older B.S.I. table (1940 issue), the A.S.A. or new B.S.I. table, Elvegard and Sjostedt's equations for 60 and for 10 degrees solar altitude. Reading down the table the weather conditions correspond to those described in the older B.S.I. table, which seem easier to understand than the later version, and the factors which appear to be equivalent have been selected from the A.S.A. descriptions. The words in brackets in lines four and five are Elvegard and Sjostedt's weather descriptions. The main point of interest in the table is the twofold to fivefold increase of camera exposure advised by the exposure tables in passing from the clear to the " dull " weather

TABLE 8

Weather Condition.	Exposure Ratios.			
	B.S.I.	A.S.A.	E. and S., 60° Sun.	E. and S., 10° Sun.
1. Blue sky, no clouds　.　　.　　.	1·6	1·0	1·5	1·1
2. Blue sky, white clouds, sun shining.	1·0	1·0	1·0	1·0
3. Sun slightly overcast, weak shadows (thin film of cloud over sun)　.	2·0	2·0-3·0	0·5	1·0
4. Dull, no shadows (clouded sky)　.	4·0	5·0	0·75	1·5

condition, in contrast to the reduction or very small increase deduced from the Elvegard and Sjostedt figures. Camera exposures are normally supposed to be based on the *minimum* scene brightness, which in general must lie in a shadowed area. The *average* scene brightness will certainly fall when clouds pass over the sun, but the minimum will not, if it depends on the illumination on a horizontal surface. On the other hand, the minimum brightness will fall if it depends on the luminous density. It is difficult to see why the minimum brightness should depend on the luminous density, which is determined mainly by the luminous energy in the sunlight on occasions when the sun is shining, unless we assume that a high proportion of the total light falling on the areas of minimum brightness comes via reflection from other objects. It may be arguable whether this is so for ground photography, but in vertical air photography it seems fairly certain that most of the light falling on a shadowed area comes from the sky.

The validity of the luminous density theory can apparently be checked by direct experiment, *e.g.*, by photometric measurement or by taking photographs under appropriate conditions, but such tests are difficult to arrange in a convincing way, partly because the required weather may only occur at long intervals of time and not necessarily with the sun always in the same place. This may be overcome by taking very large numbers of photographs, but the effort required for such an undertaking is very great. However, the author has had the opportunity of carrying out one test in which a useful sequence of weather occurred within twenty-four hours with the sun at exactly the same altitude and approximately the same azimuth for all exposures. The results were in agreement with Elvegard and Sjostedt, and disagreed with the exposure tables and the luminous density theory, and the details are worth quoting on that account.

An outdoor scene was photographed four times in succession from a high building at noon and at 14.00 hours B.S.T. on 25th and 26th November 1943, these times being chosen so that the sun would be at the same altitude, 18 degrees, in all cases. All exposures were on the same length of a standard panchromatic film as used for air photography, an Ilford " Gamma " filter was on the lens, the camera exposure was constant at 1/150 sec. at $f/5\cdot6$, and the development conditions were standardised. Readings of the mean brightness of a large shadowed area were taken with a Weston exposure meter, and the following details about the weather and sky conditions were noted :—

Exposure 1.—Noon, 25/11/43. Sun shining in a perfectly cloudless blue sky, with very little haze and extremely good visibility. The scene as a whole conveyed an impression of quite exceptional brilliance for the time of year.

Exposure 2.—14.00 hours, 25/11/43. Slight haze, with a few thin white clouds, much lower visibility than at the first exposure, the whole scene appearing much softer, " yellower," and less brilliant than before, although the sun was still shining.

Exposure 3.—Noon, 26/11/43. High thin cloud present at about 14,000 ft., so that the shadows were weak, much mist and poor visibility. The general brightness of the scene appeared very much lower than on the previous day.

Exposure 4.—14.00 hours, 26/11/43. The whole sky was covered with medium grey clouds at about 14,000 ft., so that the sun was quite obscured and there were no shadows. Much mist was present with poor visibility, and the scene as a whole could only be classified as " dull."

On inspecting the developed negatives it was apparent that while the *general* density of No. 1 was by far the highest, yet if judgment were restricted to areas which had been in shadow while the sun was shining, No. 3 had received most exposure, followed in order by 2, 1 and 4.

In Fig. 63 the characteristic curve for the panchromatic emulsion is drawn, and the maximum and minimum density for each exposure are located in correct position on the curve. From each of the minimum densities lines are drawn out parallel to the log E axis to meet perpendiculars dropped from the corresponding maximum densities, so that the lengths of the lines correspond to the image brightness scales in the camera under

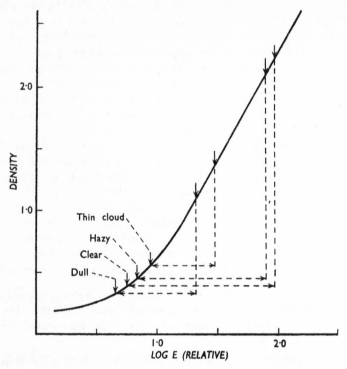

Fig. 63.—Exposure and brightness scale under various weather conditions.

the different weather conditions. The maximum density was measured on a patch of light concrete and the minimum on a patch of dark earth which was in shadow when the sun was shining. We can now visualise what happens as the light changes from brilliant through hazy to dull. With haze the maximum brightness falls and the minimum rises due to scattering of additional light into the shadows. Thin clouds over the sun further increase the shadow illumination and reduce the direct sunlight ; shadow has almost vanished and the brightness scale is now only one-third of that in the clear condition. Thicker clouds covering the whole sky reduce the general illumination by about 50 per cent., but cannot make much further difference to the brightness scale.

Table 9 shows the relative exposures which should have been given under the different weather conditions : (a) according to the Weston readings ;

(*b*) according to the exposure tables ; (*c*) according to Elvegard and Sjostedt ; (*d*) according to the densities shown in Fig. 63, *i.e.*, the relative camera exposures which would have given identical densities on the image of the patch of earth.

TABLE 9

Exposure required under different Weather Conditions

	Weather Condition.			
	1.	2.	3.	4.
Weston reading on shadow	1·0	0·9	0·7	0·9
Exposure tables	1·0	1·0 to 2·0	2·0	4·0
Elvegard and Sjostedt	1·0	1·0	0·7	1·5
From negatives	1·0	0·8	0·7	1·1

The density values in Fig. 63 and the relative exposures in Table 9 show that there is reasonable agreement between the Weston readings, the illuminations predicted by Elvegard and Sjostedt, and the camera exposures found by experiment, while the exposure tables indicate an unnecessary increase of camera exposure in the hazy and dull conditions. Now although the subject of the exposures was taken with a downward view, it was quite typical of the subjects taken by photographers in general, being, in fact, an open space some 50 yds. square surrounded by buildings about 50 ft. high. How then are we to reconcile the experimental results with the indications of the exposure tables, which are similar in this respect to tables which have presumably been used successfully for many years ? Either the increase of camera exposure given by photographers in dull weather is unnecessary (by no means an impossible supposition) or the tables, which purport to be based on the minimum scene brightness, are not drawn up on this basis at all. One possible explanation may be devised on the following lines.

We have proceeded throughout on the assumption that if camera exposure is based on minimum scene brightness it is with the purpose of making negatives with a constant minimum density whatever the lighting conditions on the subject. An alternative possibility is that the tables recognise that most photographs are taken partly on the toe of the characteristic curve, and that the increase of camera exposure in dull weather is for the purpose of having a more nearly constant negative density range for all types of subject, and hence easing the task of the printer. In this connection it should be pointed out that the negatives illustrated by the characteristic curve of Fig. 63 were of very different density range, though of similar minimum density, and that they required printing papers of very different contrasts to yield prints including the full paper range from white to black in all cases. Fig. 64 is an attempt to illustrate the argument. The characteristic curve is that of a well-known emulsion used for ground photography, developed to a gamma of 0·8. Hypothetical exposures in " clear " and " dull " weather corresponding approximately to those in Fig. 63 have been laid off from the foot of the curve along the log E scale. The minimum densities are in their correct relative positions as modified by the smaller slope of the curve in Fig. 64. The density ranges in the negatives are 0·93 for the " clear " condition and 0·34 for the " dull " condition. Although the lowest brightnesses of the scene are only slightly different under the two conditions, the greater brightness of the highlights when the sun is shining has caused the maximum density to run well up on to the straight line, assuming equal camera exposure for the two conditions. But if the

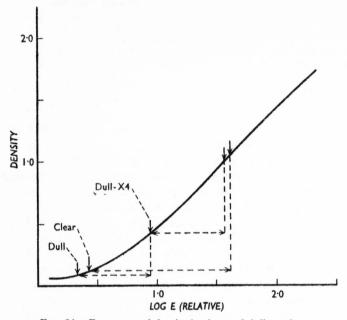

Fig. 64.—Exposure and density in clear and dull weather.

camera exposure is quadrupled in the " dull " condition the densities move up from the toe to a region of greater slope and the density range becomes 0·6, which will not look so flat and will be easier to print.

This is one possible explanation ; we are not greatly concerned about its correctness, because in high-altitude air photography the correct practice is to expose well up on to the straight line, with the minimum densities at a level of the order of 0·5 above fog. If this practice is followed the negative density range will vary according to the brightness scale of the subject, but the best resolving power will always be obtained. The only way in which exposure tables drawn up for ground photography have any impact on air photography is through their suggestion that the brightness of cloud shadows is less than the brightness of the shadows of terrestrial objects under a cloudless blue sky. We have seen, by considering (a) illumination measurements made by the National Physical Laboratory in England ; (b) illumination measurements made in Scandinavia ; (c) direct experimental check ; (d) the examination of the densities in air negatives, that this implication is not correct.

Chapter Eleven

ATMOSPHERIC HAZE

IT is probable that the optical properties of the atmosphere play a relatively insignificant part in the average person's awareness of the world around him. The influence of the atmosphere on light which passes through it is not always evident in straightforward and easily appreciated effects, and most of the experiences of daily life are consistent with an outlook in which the air is assumed to be perfectly transparent. In fact the air is a turbid medium, and the turbidity, though usually very slight, is quite sufficient to allow of measurement by direct methods. Living inside the medium, which is normally under substantially uniform illumination, we are not always aware of the turbidity as such. In indoor experience the optical phenomena due to atmospheric turbidity are usually insignificant, because the light paths involved are only of the order of a few feet. If, however, the illumination is markedly non-uniform, as when sunbeams or the rays from a lantern cross a darkened room, the turbidity becomes very obvious, especially in air which is dusty or laden with tobacco smoke. Out of doors the atmosphere is nearly always under uniform illumination, and we are apt to make a mental distinction between foggy days, when visibility may be restricted to a few score feet, and " clear " days, when we can see to the limit of our horizon, say a mile or so. In general, we pay much less attention to the state of clarity of the atmosphere when visibility is greater than a mile or two than we do when it is small enough to hinder locomotion. Aviators and others whose range of unobstructed vision extends much farther than that of a man standing at ground level and hemmed around by various objects in the landscape have a much more direct awareness that the turbidity of the air varies very greatly even on days without obvious fog. When the line of sight passes through miles of atmosphere, exposed to the full daylight illumination, effects which are quite negligible at close range assume great and sometimes dominating importance. In most air photography the light reaching the camera from the ground passes through some thousands of feet of air and the resultant effects cannot be ignored.

Out of doors in daylight, the atmosphere, as a turbid medium, scatters in all directions some of the light which falls on it from the sun and sky ; a fraction of this light enters the eye of the observer. It also scatters some of the light proceeding to the observer's eye from objects in the landscape, lowering their effective brightness. The combination of these effects tends to replace the differential brightnesses by which we see things with a uniform brightness, *i.e.*, the brightness of the atmosphere in the direction of sight. The light scattered towards the observer by the illuminated atmosphere is graphically described in German as *Luftlicht*, " air light." We are not normally conscious of the existence of the air light as such, but rather by way of its manifestation as " aerial perspective." Looking out on a landscape, we see the tones and colours of nearby objects in their full contrast and saturation, but as our eye moves to more distant objects, looking through longer columns of illuminated atmosphere, the contrasts are lowered and the colours diluted by the increasing air light. We are so accustomed, however, to judge distances by the relative lightness of similar objects that we have come to associate the air light with the distant object rather than with the intervening atmosphere. Looking at a nearby and a distant clump of dark trees, for example, our minds translate the physical facts into the subjective impression of similar things at different distances, and only with great difficulty can we " see " that due to the added air light the distant trees are nearly as light as the horizon sky. The dependence upon the observer's normal environment of this mental translation of lightness into distance may be realised from the under-estimation of distances invariably made by travellers new to polar or mountainous regions where the air is of unusual clarity.

Since the air light can be so useful as a subjective measure of distance, it must obviously modify the brightness characteristics of distant scenes in ways important for photography. In ordinary photography the modification is manifested as an increase in brightness and a reduction of the brightness scale ; distant planes are lighter and of lower contrast. Pictorial photographers value such effects as a means of conveying depth and distance to their pictures, but in air photography they are a serious handicap, since there is no foreground and the details of interest which ought to be shown with the greatest possible clarity are all behind the illuminated atmosphere.

The Causes of Atmospheric Turbidity

All the particles in the atmosphere contribute in greater or less degree to the scattering of light, but in absolutely pure air containing only gases and water vapour the amount of scattering is very small indeed. The gas and vapour molecules are of the order of 10^{-4} micron in diameter, and in each cubic centimetre of air at normal temperature and pressure their number is of the order of 10^{20}, but in spite of this inconceivably great number of particles, the molecular scattering only accounts for a small part of the total atmospheric scatter even in air normally considered " clean." Molecular scattering can be demonstrated in the laboratory, as was first shown by Lord Rayleigh.

In thinking about the atmosphere from the present point of view, most people would probably distinguish between " clean " and " dusty " air, the underlying assumption being that there is a sharp distinction between the two and that dusty air would become clean if allowed to stand quietly for a long time, by the settling out of the solid particles. No such sharp distinction exists, however. If dusty air is allowed to stand the grosser particles do indeed settle out, but other particles covering a wide range of size remain in suspension for very long periods and may never settle in natural air which is always in movement, while still smaller particles never settle even in still air, but remain suspended, buoyed up and kept in " Brownian motion " by the constant bombardment of the gas molecules. We are irresistibly reminded of a colloidal solution in which solid substance such as gold, if sufficiently finely divided, will remain in permanent suspension in a liquid. This parallelism is reflected in the collective name of " aerosols," given by meteorologists to the suspended solid and liquid particles of the atmosphere.

The aerosols cover a very wide range of sizes and are of a very diverse nature. General products of disintegration, such as minute fragments of sand and organic matter, ash from fires and volcanoes, spores and bacteria, minute crystals of salts derived from the sea, etc., can all remain suspended for long periods. Volcanic dust and other more or less inert disintegration products are commonly of the order of 1 micron in diameter, while the salts may be as small as $0\cdot1$ micron and combustion products smaller still.

" Haze " sometimes consists of inert solid particles, as when a dry wind blows from a desert area, and the " haze horizon " has been found to consist of blown sand in some parts of India, for example. Soluble matter, however, is of much greater general importance, because small particles of soluble substances can initiate condensation of water in drops from unsaturated atmospheres, whereas soot and other inert nuclei cannot do this. One important class of soluble condensation nuclei is provided by products of combustion, especially of sulphur-containing materials such as coal. Sulphur trioxide, which is extremely hygroscopic, can be formed from the combustion products of coal, and is said to play a large part in the development of haze over cities. It is also considered, however, that very active and widespread condensation nuclei are derived from salt spray. It is well known that the vapour pressure over a salt solution is less than that over pure water at the same temperature. Any sub-microscopic drops accidentally formed on salt crystals will therefore be less likely to evaporate, and may grow in size, depending on the humidity and the nature of the salt. Soluble crystalline matter can in fact be extracted from the air in various haze conditions, and is found to behave in ways characteristic of mixtures of common salts such as sodium and magnesium chlorides. Owens (1) found crystalline matter, deliquescing at relative humidities of 60 to 70 per cent., in air samples taken at Cheam, Surrey, when the wind was blowing from London; also on the south coast of England, the coast of Portugal, and the mouth of the St Lawrence River. On the St Lawrence the air contained nothing but crystalline matter, but in the other cases there was a mixture of crystals and inert dust.

H. L. Wright (2) has deduced the size of combustion and sea-salt nuclei as a function of relative humidity, and finds a continuous increase from the lowest humidities upwards. The rate of growth is slow up to about 75 per cent. relative humidity, but increases rapidly thereafter. Sea-salt nuclei increase from about $0\cdot1$ micron at zero humidity to about $0\cdot2$ micron at 75 per cent. and $0\cdot7$ micron at 100 per cent. relative humidity. Wright concludes that sea-salt nuclei, though not always the most numerous, are the most effective agents in causing haze. He shows on theoretical grounds that a concentration of 1000 such nuclei per cubic centimetre subjected to the full range of possible humidities could account for almost the entire observed range of visibility conditions.

We may therefore picture haze as a mixture of dust particles and droplets of salt solution. Under some conditions, and especially in dry air, the solid particles may be the chief cause of the air light, but in general the liquid droplets are responsible, though inert dust is nearly always present.

The number of dust and salt nuclei present in each cubic centimetre of air varies enormously. Owens, working in a dense fog in January, found 21,750 particles per cubic centimetre, while in clear, dry, sunny weather the number was 200. In densely populated cities the weight of suspended matter may be as great as 5 mg. per cubic metre of air, but in relatively clean air from the polar regions the quantity may be only one-thousandth as great.

It will be appreciated that since the aerosols are small enough to remain in suspension for long periods or for ever they will move about over the earth's surface with the wind. For example, a salt particle of density 2·0 and radius 0·2 micron would fall in still air at a rate equivalent to 300 ft. in 125 days. In air of normal turbulence such a particle would not fall, but would travel with the air currents in a three-dimensional way, so that sea-salt nuclei are by no means restricted to the immediate neighbourhood of the oceans. The clarity of the air at a given place therefore varies with the direction of the wind, and the dust and smoke of cities, as well as the salt spray of the sea, can influence visibility at far distant places. In a small town in Scotland the visibility was nine times greater when the wind blew from the sparsely inhabited mountain regions than when it came from the industrial areas ; in dry weather, with a psychrometric difference of 8 degrees, it was four times as great as in damp weather with a difference of only 2 degrees (3). Middleton (2) points out that in Canada the visual range may be 100 km. when the wind brings air from the polar regions, but as little as 5 km. when the wind blows up from the Gulf of Mexico. Flying south from the North of Scotland, in a northerly wind, the writer has been impressed with the marked deterioration in atmospheric clarity, even over open country and mountainous areas, beginning near Glasgow and extending all the way south. In the East African Highlands, where there are no industrial cities to provide combustion nuclei, the visibility is often quite remarkable by English standards, high mountains being visible for at least 120 miles. The classic case of the migration of atmospheric dust is the Krakatoa eruption in Malaya, when dust from the volcano affected the sunset colours in England and is said to have travelled several times round the world. In general, air coming from the polar regions is the clearest, while that from tropical areas or from the direction of towns and cities is laden with dust or condensation nuclei and is liable to be hazy. Atmospheric phenomena are very complex, however, and more precise rules than these can hardly be drawn up in the present state of knowledge.

The sizes of the scattering particles in the atmosphere are summarised in Table 10. It will be seen that while the gas molecules are much smaller than the mean wavelength of visible light, the dust particles and the salt nuclei which have collected water are of comparable size. The size of the particles in relation to the wave length has important consequences in connection with the relative amount of scattering at different wave lengths.

TABLE 10

Orders of Size of Atmospheric Particles

Gas molecules	10^{-4} micron
Combustion nuclei (little water) . . .	10^{-2} ,,
Sea-salt nuclei (little water) . . .	10^{-1} ,,
Sea-salt nuclei (humid air)	1 ,,
Fog, cloud	1 to 100 microns
Dust	1 micron
Wavelength of green light	0·5 ,,

ABSORPTION AND SCATTERING OF LIGHT IN THE ATMOSPHERE

When light falls on a turbid medium such as the atmosphere it is partially deflected from its original path and redistributed in all directions. This is given the general name of " scattering," although in the case of the larger fog particles reflection and refraction may play a more important part. However, in most conditions suitable for air photography the particles concerned are small enough for " scattering " to be a sufficiently precise term. In heavy industrial hazes some of the light is absorbed by material such as larger dust particles or flakes of soot and is converted into heat energy, being thus lost as luminous flux. True absorption, however, is generally taken to be negligible in ordinary clean air. Light is, of course, weakened in passing through the cleanest air, but this is due to attenuation by scattering away from the beam, and overall there is no loss of luminous energy.

We are not here concerned with the physical mechanism of scattering, but with its photometric effects, which are of importance in air photography.

A beam of light passing through the atmosphere suffers a certain attenuation by the loss of the scattered radiation. In general the attenuation will be greater for longer paths and higher concentration of scattering particles. With no absorption there is no loss of energy, and all the scattered light reappears after repeated rescattering as a general diffuse illumination of the medium. In photographing over long ranges or from great altitudes the light reaching the camera from the ground is appreciably attenuated. Even more important is the effect of the light scattered upwards from the haze, as this plays no part in image formation and merely lowers the contrast of the scene. Suppose we have two objects on the ground, of different brightnesses, B_1 and B_2. Their contrast is expressed by B_1/B_2. Both suffer the same proportional reduction A in brightness when seen through the haze, and the same amount of general light h is added to each. The apparent brightness ratio when viewed through the haze is therefore $A.B_1 + h/A.B_2 + h$. So long as any light is scattered upwards, this expression will be smaller than B_1/B_2, and it tends to unity, *i.e.*, to zero contrast, with increasing scatter.

Attenuation and Transmission Coefficients.—The scattering properties of the atmosphere can be given mathematical expression and determined in quantitative photometric ways.

Consider a beam of light passing through turbid air, which scatters without absorbing. In traversing unit length of air the initial flux F_o is reduced to tF_o. After x units of length the flux is $F_o t^x$. Thus t is defined as the transmission coefficient per unit length. We may also speak of the " transmission " through a given length of air, *i.e.*, the ratio of the final to the initial flux. Transmissions are generally expressed as so much per kilometre or per thousand yards, since the attenuation over shorter distances is very small in clean air.

Alternatively, we may think in terms of the rate at which light is scattered away from the main beam, which is, of course, the same as the rate of attenuation. This is measured by the " scatter coefficient " or " attenuation coefficient." The scatter coefficient, generally written σ, is the fraction of flux lost in traversing unit length of air. In traversing a length x, the initial flux F_o is reduced to F, where $F = F_o e^{-\sigma x}$. This is mathematically equivalent to

$$\sigma = -\frac{1}{F} \cdot \frac{dF}{dx}.$$

For unit length of air we have

$$F = F_o e^{-\sigma}$$
$$F = F_o t,$$

whence $t = e^{-\sigma}$.

σ is generally expressed as so much per foot.

Scatter coefficients are exceedingly small for clean atmospheres in good visibility. In pure dry air at sea level σ is approximately $0\cdot4 \times 10^{-2}$ per foot. Middleton (2) reports a value as low as 6×10^{-5} per foot for polar-Pacific air at Ontario, Canada. In conditions described by meteorologists as " good visibility. In pure dry air at sea level σ is approximately 4×10^{-6} per foot. Middleton (2) reports a value as low as 6×10^{-6} per foot for polar-Pacific air at Ontario, Canada. In conditions described by meteorologists as "good visibility " σ is about 8×10^{-5} per foot. A beam of light passing through direction under the clearest observed conditions is approximately 80 per cent.

The scatter coefficient is obviously related to the " visibility." As defined by meteorologists, " visibility " or " visual range " refers to horizontal observation, and is the distance at which a perfectly black body subtending at least $0\cdot5$ degree at the eye of the observer just becomes invisible against the horizon sky. This is another way of saying that the visual range is the distance at which the airlight equals the brightness of the horizon sky within the 2 per cent. which is the least brightness difference perceptible by the human eye in daylight. It is assumed that the air between the black object and the observer is homogeneous and uniformly illuminated. Calling the least perceptible brightness ratio E, and the visual range x, it can be shown that $E = e^{-\sigma x}$. This relationship is known as " Koschmieder's law," and it is found to hold approximately in practice. It follows that the visual range is the length of the atmosphere through which the transmission is 2 per cent.

If we assume a homogeneous atmosphere under uniform illumination, it follows from what has been said that we can deduce the visual range from the scattering coefficient, or vice versa. Fig. 65 (4) is an application of this principle, showing the relationship between scatter coefficient and atmospheric transmission for a scattering, non-absorbing atmosphere. The ordinates are percentage transmissions and the abcissæ are ranges in yards. Each curve expresses the relation between transmission and range for a given

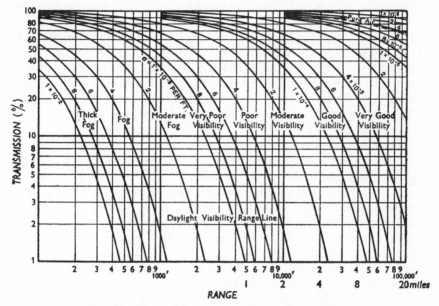

FIG. 65.—Transmission, range, and scattering coefficient.
(*Redrawn from Waldram*, "*Trans. Illum. Eng. Soc. (London)*," *Vol. X.*)

scatter coefficient. The horizontal line marked " Daylight Visual Range " is drawn at an ordinate value of 2 per cent. ; its intersection with the curves therefore defines the range of visibility corresponding to each scatter coefficient. Against the curves are written words descriptive in meteorological terms of the " visibility " corresponding to the appropriate visual range. Thus when σ is 10^{-3} per foot the visual range is theoretically 4000 ft., a state of affairs described by meteorologists as " very poor visibility."

A study of Fig. 65 will illustrate how a small change of scatter coefficient can make little difference to the transmission over short ranges, but a much greater difference over long ranges. Thus in changing from " pure air " to " good visibility " the change in transmission over 1000 ft. is only from approximately 100 to 90 per cent., but over a range of 30,000 ft. the change is from 85 to 5 per cent. As Waldram (4) points out, in very clean air the transmission over short ranges is so high that it is very difficult to measure with any accuracy, and measurements over short ranges are not a reliable means of predicting the transmission over long ranges, or of determining scatter coefficients. Assuming a homogeneous atmosphere, it may be more accurate to calculate the transmission from a measurement of the scatter coefficient.

A glance at Fig. 65 shows that molecular scattering accounts for but a small part of the atmospheric turbidity under normal conditions, for even in " very good visibility " with a visual range of 20 miles, the scatter coefficient is ten times that in pure air.

Fig. 65 does not refer directly to the conditions of air photography, since it applies only to horizontal vision through a homogeneous atmosphere. Nevertheless, it deals with closely analogous matters and provides a graphic illustration of the amount of light which can get through different lengths of atmosphere under various haze conditions. In conjunction with the data on the variation of scatter coefficient with altitude it enables us to make an approximate estimate of the transmission vertically or obliquely. In the case of obliques from moderate altitudes we can assume that the air is approximately homogeneous ; in such a case, with " very good visibility " the light reaching the camera from objects 10 miles away suffers nearly 90 per cent. attenuation.

Polar Distribution of the scattered Light.—Haze in general does not scatter the incident light equally in all directions. We can see the importance of scatter as a function of angle by considering the results of some imaginary polar distributions. If all the sunlight were scattered backwards along its original path no light would ever reach shadows, and hazy days would be dull days. If all the scatter were concentrated in a narrow zone around, say, 135 degrees, then with a solar altitude of 45 degrees air photography might well be impossible, for the brightness of the haze in the vertical direction might be greater than that of the ground seen through the haze and contrast would be exceedingly low.

The polar distribution of the scattered light is in fact a very complicated matter, and no hard and fast rules can be laid down. It varies among other things with the size of the scattering particles, and since at any given time the atmosphere holds particles of many sizes there must be as many modes of scatter. At the same time the available evidence does suggest that any particular time one type of scatter will always be predominant. Until fairly recently there seem to have been comparatively few measurements on polar scatter functions. Rocard (5) gave data for the distribution of light scattered by the atmosphere at ground level, and later measurements of Hulburt (6) on the brightness of the horizon sky and on a vertical searchlight beam produced results substantially in agreement with Rocard's. The form of scatter function as found by these investigators is generally similar to Fig. 67 (*a*), curve 1, page 203. The important characteristic is the preponderance of forward scatter, with a minimum at about a hundred degrees. It was at one time believed that the Rocard type of scatter was fairly general for the larger particles found in the air near ground level. More recent work suggests that this is not altogether true, but in any case we would wish, in the present connection, to know the types of distribution found at various altitudes at least up to 30,000 ft. Formerly, it might have been predicted that somewhere

above the top of the layer of " dust haze " that is commonly observed
on fine days in summer the Rocard type of scatter would begin to give place
to a more uniform polar distribution characteristic of very small particles.
In the clear air of high altitudes this more uniform distribution might have
been expected as a general occurrence, though abnormal scatter or diffraction
by ice crystals is sometimes observed.   The recent work of Waldram,
however, (4) indicates that scatter functions of very different types can be
found at all altitudes.

    Waldram's paper is of peculiar interest in that it describes direct measure-
ments of the turbidity of the air in an aeroplane flying at altitudes up to
30,000 ft.   In the instrument employed, the " polar nephelometer," a beam
of light from a powerful illuminating system is passed through a dark enclosure
and viewed against the perfectly black background of a light trap, as in
Lord Rayleigh's experiments on the scatter of dust-free air.   In the polar

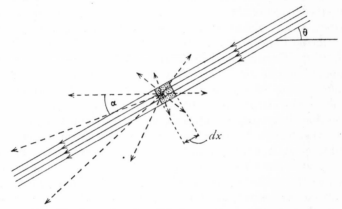

FIG. 66.—Scattering of sunlight by an element of atmosphere.

nephelometer the photometer head moves around an axis perpendicular to
the beam so that brightness can be measured in different directions, thus
enabling a curve to be drawn for the polar scatter function, from which the
scatter coefficient can be derived by integration.   The brightness of the beam
is of course extremely small in clean air, but the apparatus was sensitive
enough to measure the scatter coefficient of pure air.   In Fig. 66 (modified
from a diagram of Waldram's) a beam of sunlight at an angle θ to the horizon
passes through an element of atmosphere of length dx and passes on after
weakening by scatter.   The scattered light is distributed with different
intensity in different directions, the intensity in any direction at an angle α
to the incident beam being indicated by the length of the broken lines in
the figure.   (In Waldram's account the scatter angle is measured in the opposite
sense to that shown in Fig. 66 and his angles are therefore supplementary to
any quoted in this chapter.   The convention used here is felt to be better, as
it appears to be more natural to consider *forward* scatter as scatter at a *small*
angle to the incident light, and vice versa.)   In any direction α the element,
though not self-luminous, may be considered to have a " candle-power " $i\alpha$.

The values of $i\alpha$ are symmetrical about the axis of the incident beam ; in other words, the function of α which determines $i\alpha$ in the plane of the paper also determines it for any similar plane passing through the element of atmosphere. The polar scatter index is defined as the " candle-power " in a given direction of an element of atmosphere of unit length which receives unit incident flux ; it can be expressed as " candles per foot per lumen incident," or in " candles per foot cube per foot candle incident." Regarding the scattering element as a source of illumination, the polar scatter index is analogous to the candle-power in a stated direction, while the scatter coefficient corresponds to the total flux emitted. Given the polar scatter index, the scatter coefficient can therefore be derived by integration.

Waldram gives curves of polar scatter index obtained in clean atmospheres (*i.e.*, free from industrial contamination) on eleven different occasions. The flights were all made in England, some in spring, some in autumn or early winter. Over the whole range of experiments, covering altitudes up to 30,000 ft., the shapes of the curves varied very greatly, from those in which the distribution was almost uniform with angle, through other examples where the forward and back scatters were almost equal with a well-marked minimum, to the Rocard type, with a ratio of the order of 100 to 1 between maximum and minimum. The most general form of curve exhibits a minimum at 120 to 90 degrees to the incident beam, but occasionally the scatter increased steadily from 180 (back scatter) to 0 degrees. The curves showing little change with angle were all obtained at high altitudes, but on the other hand well-marked minima were also obtained up to 30,000 ft. At ground level and at the lower altitudes the Rocard type was very frequent, but Rocard scatter did not always coincide with heavy haze. The symmetrical type of curve, with nearly equal forward and back scatter and a minimum between 60 and 90 degrees, was found at ground level in " poor " visibility ($\sigma = 34 \times 10^{-5}$), but also up to 30,000 ft. ($\sigma = 0.4 \times 10^{-2}$). An interesting series of readings made in a clearing mist showed no great change in curve shape during a change from " poor " to " very good " visibility, *i.e.*, $\sigma = 32 \times 10^{-5}$ to $\sigma = 2.2 \times 10^{-5}$. No correlation could be found between the shape of the polar curves and the height, and little with the total scatter. A few of Waldram's results are shown in Fig. 67, the examples selected including the Rocard type, the symmetrical type, and the type showing little variation with angle.

The curves given in Fig. 68 illustrate typical changes of scatter coefficient with altitude, the dotted line at the left of the diagram indicating the theoretical scatter in pure air at different densities corresponding to the altitudes. There is a slight general tendency for the observed curves to follow this line, but numerous deviations can be seen. In some cases the scatter increased with height, and there was evidence of stratification in the haze. On the whole it may be said that while the total scatter varied with height, the variation was less regular than might have been expected. One case will be noted where the scatter coefficient actually increased from ground level up to 30,000 ft. It should be remembered that in all these cases the air was reasonably clear and free from contamination at ground level.

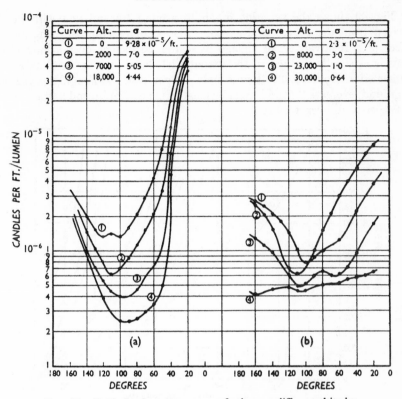

FIG. 67.—Typical polar scatter curves for haze at different altitudes.
(After Waldram.)

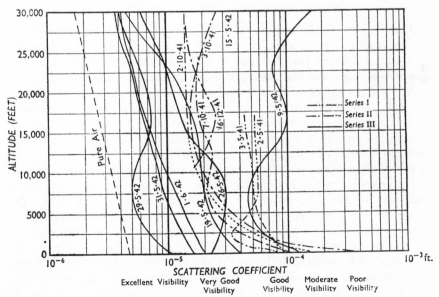

FIG. 68.—Variation of scattering coefficient with height.
(Redrawn from Waldram, "Trans. Illum. Eng. Soc. (London)," Vol. X.)

Fig. 69 shows the variation of air to ground transmission with height, derived from the curves in Fig. 68. These curves emphasise the marked effect of a relatively small change in scatter coefficient over a long range. This is especially marked in the extreme left-hand curve; in this case the transmission from 30,000 ft. was only 10 per cent., although the visibility at ground level was " good " with a visual range of 8 miles and a transmission of 90 per cent. over 1000 ft.

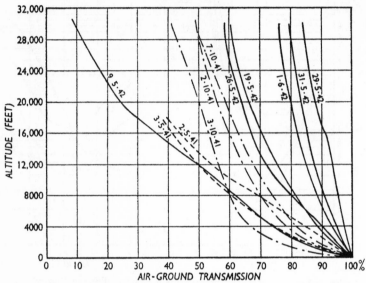

FIG. 69.—Variation of air to ground transmission with altitude (clean air).
(*Redrawn from Waldram,* " *Trans. Illum. Eng. Soc. (London),*" *Vol. X.*)

Practical Interpretation of Polar Scatter Curves.—It is theoretically possible to work out the effects of haze on the contrast of a scene, given the polar scatter function and the solar altitude, and making certain simplifying assumptions, *e.g.*, that the atmosphere is homogeneous and that the polar scatter function remains the same at all altitudes even if the scatter coefficient does not. These calculations have little practical application to air photography, however, in view of the great variations in polar scatter function encountered on different days and at different altitudes on the same day, but a few observations of a very general nature can be made.

In air photography the light scattered upwards and so into the camera is of primary interest. The scatter angles which are of importance in this connection lie mainly between 180 and 90 degrees to the incident light, though at very low solar altitudes and with a wide-angle camera, scatter angles rather less than 90 degrees may be concerned. In Fig. 70 the camera embraces an angle 2β, the solar altitude is θ, and the scatter angle is α for an element of haze vertically below the camera. At the edge of the picture remote from the sun the scatter angle is $\alpha_1 = 90 + \beta + \theta$, and at the edge nearest the sun it is $\alpha_2 = 90 - \beta + \theta$. In a typical case where 2β is, say, 60 degrees and θ is 45 degrees, α_1 is 165 degrees and α_2 is 105 degrees. Reference to Fig. 67 shows that for either the Rocard or " symmetrical" types of scatter function the haze effect must be greater at the side of the picture remote from the sun. This effect can sometimes be observed in air photographs or by looking down from an aeroplane, when the ground appears clearer at one side than at the other. The opposite effect is produced by the same types of haze for an observer looking upwards or horizontally, when the haze effect is much stronger " up sun " than " down sun." It is also clear from Fig. 70 that as θ declines from 90 to 0 degrees, α will vary from 180 to 90 degrees, and the amount of light scattered vertically upwards will in

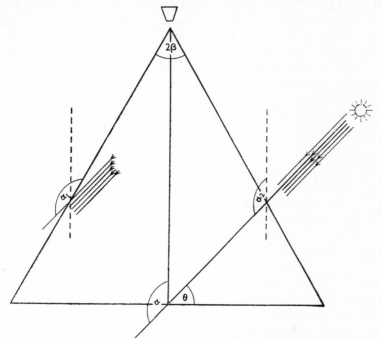

FIG. 70.—Scatter by haze into a vertical air camera.

general diminish to an extent depending on the shape of the polar scatter curve in the region between the minimum and the " back scatter " at 180 degrees. The ground brightness will fall off roughly as sin θ but always more rapidly, and probably much more rapidly in heavy haze. Between θ = 60 and 30 degrees, for example, the ground brightness is roughly halved, while from curve 1 in Fig. 67 (a) the haze brightness is not quite halved between 150 and 120 degrees, so that one would expect a small increase in the haze effect. On the other hand, the ground brightness will not change much between θ = 60 and 80 degrees but the vertical scatter will be approximately doubled between 150 and 170 degrees. We may note the fortunate circumstance that heavy haze with a high scatter coefficient seems in general to be associated with high forward scatter in the region 0 to 50 degrees, which is harmless in vertical air photography. This may be seen from the examples in Fig. 67, e.g., comparing curves 2 (a) and 2 (b), where the scatters are rather similar between 180 and 100 degrees, but curve 2 (*a*) associated with a scatter coefficient nearly twice as great as 2 (*b*) shows much higher scatter from 0 to 40 degrees. Curve 4 (*b*) has a very low scatter coefficient mainly due to the lack of forward scatter as compared with say 4 (*a*). This simple discussion has taken no account of the attenuation of light in the haze nor the variation of polar scatter function with altitude, and the subject is too complex for any further generalization to be made on these lines. Detailed mathematical analyses are to be found in papers by Duntley (9), Hulburt (6), Harrison (8), and others.

Plate 3 (A) shows a rather unusual example of strongly marked back-scatter. The illustration is part of a Colonial Survey air photograph taken in Nigeria on latitude 10° N. ; aircraft altitude, 16,500 ft. ; solar altitude, 72°. The lens focal length was 6 in. and the full size of the original photograph was 9 × 9 in. Higher solar altitude and wide angle of view have brought the back-scatter maximum well within the picture, and the low contrast of the detail in the bush country helps to show the variation of brightness determined by the polar scatter function of the haze. The point of maximum brightness corresponds to the maximum back-scatter at 180 degrees to the incident sunlight ; its angular distance from the plumb-point is 90 degrees minus the solar altitude ; a reflection of the sun, *e.g.*, in water, would appear at the same angle on the opposite side of the plumb-point.

Haze Factors.—For quantitative study of the photographic effects of haze, *e.g.*, in comparing the haze-cutting properties of different filters, it would be necessary to express the magnitude of the haze light in terms of some particular brightness of the ground. Sometimes the haze brightness is expressed as a fraction of the " average " ground brightness, but the " haze factor " is more usually defined for photographic applications as the ratio of the haze brightness to the brightness of a white object on the ground seen through the haze. The haze factor as defined by the latter method can be measured by photographing black and white areas from various altitudes and determining their relative brightness by photographic photometry. Thus if the brightness-ratio in absence of haze is C, and at any altitude is K, it can be shown (7) that the haze factor H is given by

$$H = \frac{C - K}{C(K - 1)}.$$

Photography of black and white areas can also be used to find the atmospheric transmission. Let the brightness of the white and black areas at ground level be B_1 and B_2 respectively, and as seen through a certain thickness of haze B_1' and B_2'. The original brightnesses are reduced by a factor t due to attenuation in the haze, and are supplemented by the haze brightness h. Thus we have

$$B_1' = tB_1 + h,$$
$$B_2' = tB_2 + h,$$

whence t and h can be determined in terms of the measured brightnesses.

In principle these methods of determining haze factors are fairly simple, but in practice many experimental difficulties are encountered. It is necessary to provide black and white patches of large area, nothing less than about 100 × 100 ft. giving a large enough image for accurate densitometry when photographed from say 20,000 ft. on a scale of 1 in 10,000. Each patch must be of uniform reflectance, perfectly flat so that it will not collect rain and with a rough matt surface so that it will act approximately as a perfect diffuser. The reflectance must be permanent under exposure to all weather conditions. When these and other requirements are taken into account it is found that a permanent concrete installation of prohibitive expense is required for accurate working. On the photographic side all the usual precautions of photographic photometry have to be observed under rather difficult conditions, and the flying has its own problems. Perhaps these difficulties account for the fact that although much has been written about the determination of haze factors by air photography, few if any results have been published. There is no mass of recorded observations at different altitudes under different weather conditions, and current practices in the use of filters, etc., are based on practical experience rather than physical measurement. Little is lost by this lack of precise data, because whatever the magnitude of the haze effects, no more can be done to overcome it than the use of the longest practicable wavelengths of light. On the other hand, it would be of considerable theoretical interest to have more information on the distribution of haze at different altitudes. Waldram's curves (Figs. 68 and 69) provide a useful contribution but it is curious that they show little evidence of the stratification of haze at low altitudes. It is very common, when climbing to altitude, to experience the sensation of " coming out of the haze " at some moderate altitude such as 7,000 ft. This is associated with a temperature inversion, and the demarcation between hazy and clear air is often very marked. A typical case is illustrated in Plate 1 (C), an oblique infra-red photograph taken on a hazy summer day from about 5000 ft. There is a marked " top " to the haze ; below this top the scatter is evidently due to fairly large particles which scatter quite strongly even in the infra-red, while above the top there is practically no scatter. It is of interest to point out that the haze is the brightest part of the picture after the white cloud, though to the eye it looked a very dark grey.

Without performing any experiments it is possible to make approximate estimates of haze factors from the known brightness ranges of air photographs. The effect of the haze light is to shorten the brightness scale for a subject seen from any altitude, and if we can make an estimate of its value at ground level we have all that is required to determine the haze factor. Now it is known from density measurements on large numbers of negatives that the average brightness scale for high altitude views is about 5·5 to 1, including any flare light in the camera. The brightness scale so found is derived from the highest and lowest densities found in the negatives, the highest corresponding to large light areas such as concrete roads and the lowest to shadowed areas, all of which have much the same density, the differences which are apparent at ground level being ironed out by the haze. Now at ground level the subject brightness scale from sunlit concrete of reflection factor say 40 per cent. to shadowed dark earth would probably be about

20 to 1 on a clear day. The haze light is therefore sufficient to reduce a scale of 20 to 1 to 5·5 to 1, whence the haze factor (including flare) is approximately 20 per cent., or about 8 per cent. if referred to a perfectly white object instead of concrete. Similarly the haze factor is about 5 per cent. when the brightness scale is 10 to 1 and 90 per cent. in extremely hazy conditions when it is only 2 to 1. Figures such as these are only approximate, but are sufficiently typical to be used in working out the tone reproduction in air photographs under different conditions. The effects of haze on tone reproduction are considered in Chapter Twelve.

SCATTER AS A FUNCTION OF WAVELENGTH

In this chapter the subject of scattering has so far been treated as though the scatter coefficient were independent of the wavelength of the light. In general this is not true, and scatter as a rule is some function of wavelength. Nevertheless the general relationships which have been discussed will always hold good provided that the scatter coefficient appropriate to the medium and the wavelength is used. The coefficients mentioned already refer to visual observation but are approximately correct for photography with a panchromatic emulsion and yellow filter ; with such an emulsion and filter the visual range is an approximate guide to the photographic range. In order to appreciate the possibilities of " haze penetration " at their true worth it is necessary to pay some attention to the dependence of scatter coefficients on wavelength.

Scatter in Pure Air.—In a mathematical investigation of the mechanism of scattering, Lord Rayleigh showed that for an atmosphere consisting of particles such as air molecules which are very small compared to the wavelength of light the scatter coefficient for any wavelength λ could be written as

$$\sigma = \frac{32\pi^3(\mu_\lambda - 1)^2}{3n\lambda^4}$$

where n is the number of particles per cubic centimetre, and μ_λ is the refractive index of the atmosphere for the wavelength λ. In the present application the simpler form $\sigma = A\lambda^{-4}$, where A is a constant factor, is adequate. This indicates that for violet light of wavelength 0·4 micron the scatter coefficient will be five times as great as for orange light of wavelength 0·6 micron and sixteen times as great as for infra-red light of wavelength 1·0 micron. If all the atmospheric scatter took place according to the Rayleigh law it would clearly be advantageous to take air photographs by light of the longest possible wavelength, other things being equal. However, in air photography in general, the veiling light is not entirely or even mainly scattered by air molecules, and the gain to be anticipated from the use of say infra-red light is correspondingly less spectacular. The likely orders of magnitude here may be seen from the following simple considerations. Assuming a homogeneous atmosphere, Fig. 65 shows that under conditions of " good visibility " the visually effective scatter due to the air molecules is approximately one-tenth of the total scatter. If the scatter from the aerosols were found to be quite independent of wavelength it would clearly make little difference to the total veiling light if the molecular scatter were effectively eliminated by working at a long wavelength. On the other hand, by using a non-colour sensitised emulsion responding mainly to blue-violet light, the effect of the molecular scatter would be increased some four or five times and it would become comparable to that from the aerosols.

Effects due to the Rayleigh scatter of the air, which are generally insignificant at short ranges, develop much greater importance when the light travels a long distance through the atmosphere. The extreme example of this is the blue colour of the sky, which according to Rayleigh is entirely due to scatter from the molecules. Although the scatter coefficient for pure air is so small, the total light scattered by the entire depth of the atmosphere adds up to an appreciable brightness, and since the air is relatively clean above the lowest few thousand feet the preferential scatter of the shorter wavelengths develops the magnificent hue familiar to us in clear and cloudless weather. Rayleigh was able to show in his laboratory that the light scattered from pure air is much richer than the incident light in the short-wave components. There is little doubt that the colour of the sky is indeed due to molecular scattering, and with few reservations the Rayleigh theory is generally accepted (3).   The blue sky colour is only seen in its full glory when the air is very clean, as in the high mountains or when flying high above the earth's surface, where the dusty air scatters all wavelengths more or less equally and dilutes the saturated blue with white.   It is interesting to note, as pointed out by Minnaert (3), that with a sufficient depth of air the scattered light must appear white, since for a non-absorbing atmosphere all the light which enters must eventually re-emerge.   On this assumption the sky should get whiter towards the horizon, as indeed it appears to do even in clear weather, but it is difficult to say how much of this effect is due to aerosols which do not show such a marked selective scatter as the air molecules. A similar effect can be observed in the cloud of smoke from a bonfire, which is blue at the edges but white in the denser parts of the cloud.

Inasmuch as the light scattered by small particles is blue, the transmitted light must be lacking in blue, *i.e.*, orange-red. When the sun is high this effect is not significant, but towards sunrise and sunset the rays have to traverse a much greater length of atmosphere and the sunlight appears red or orange, at least on clear days when a high proportion of the total scatter is due to the air molecules. It should be pointed out, however, that the colour of the general illumination near sunset or sunrise is not redder but bluer than at midday ; although the sunlight is redder it is so much weaker that the blue sky contributes a greater proportion of light to the total illumination.

Scatter by the Aerosols.—Rayleigh's law for scatter only holds good for particles much smaller than the wavelength of the light, and for particles larger than about 10^{-3} microns some other relationship must be sought. A great deal of work has been done on this subject without establishing any precise and universally applicable relationships between particle size and type of scatter. In a very general way, however, it does appear that with increasing size, from molecules up to something of the order of 1 micron, the preferential scatter of the shorter wavelengths progressively diminishes. Middleton (2) gives a good account of work on this subject. From the point of view of air photography the interesting aspect of such investigations is the possibility of a relationship between the scatter as a function of wavelength and the state of visibility in the atmosphere at the time.

In general terms, if scatter is a function of wavelength we can write

$$\sigma = F\lambda.$$

For pure air, as we have seen, $F(\lambda) = A\lambda^{-4}$. For the atmosphere in general at least one other term will have to be introduced to take account of the scatter from the aerosols, which will not obey the Rayleigh law. Neglecting absorption, since we will generally be working in clean air, the more general expression for atmospheric scatter will be $\sigma = A\lambda^{-4} + Cf\lambda$ where C is another constant and represents the behaviour of the aerosols. The nature of $f\lambda$ will in general be different for different atmospheric conditions. It is important to remember that $A\lambda^{-4}$ will be negligible relative to $f\lambda$ for photography behind a yellow filter unless the visibility is quite exceptionally good.

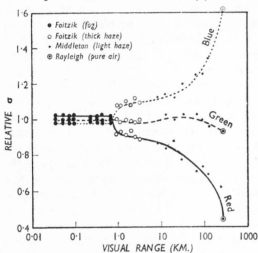

Fig. 71.—The ratio of σ for each of three colours (red, green, and blue) to the mean σ for the three wavelengths, plotted against log (visual range, kilometres).

(*Redrawn from Harrison, "Photographic Journal," Vol. LXXXV-*b.)

While the precise expression of $f\lambda$ for any atmospheric condition must be extremely complicated, various investigators have found simple functions which gave an approximately correct representation of the scatter as a function of wavelength for certain visibility conditions. Rocard and de Rothschild, working when visibility was about 12 miles ($\sigma = 6\cdot7 \times 10^{-5}$ per foot) found that $f\lambda = k\lambda^{-2}$ was in approximate agreement with their observations. Middleton (2) describes measurements of his own and of Foitzik covering visual ranges from 0·06 to 200 km. (about 60 yds. to 120 miles), *i.e.*, from thick fog to an exceptionally clean atmosphere. The results are expressed by Middleton as the ratio of σ for red, green, and blue light to the mean σ for the three wavelengths. The ratios were plotted against visual range, giving the curves shown in Fig. 71. From the present point of view it is of great interest to note the very rapid change of relative σ with wavelength above a visual range of about 50 km. For the visual ranges corresponding to the commonly experienced " good " or " very good " visibility the scatter coefficient for red light is not very much less than that for blue light, and only above some 50 km. range does the difference between red and blue become really marked. At a visual range of about 0·8 km. (say one third of a mile) the curves meet at a ratio of 1·0, indicating that scatter is quite independent of wavelength. Thus in " moderate fog " the incident and scattered light have the same colour and there is no advantage to be gained from the use of any kind of light filters. Below 0·8 km. the curves cross over, so that heavier fog is somewhat more transparent to blue light than to red. However, Middleton stresses the danger of applying these conclusions too literally to air likely to be polluted by dust storms or by human agency.

Middleton also shows the correspondence between visibility and the dependence of scatter on wavelength in a different way. Writing $\sigma = A\lambda^{-a}$ he plots — a against log σ for his own data obtained in clean country air. The curve is shown in Fig. 72 with a point which has been added for Rayleigh scatter. The range of visibilities covered is from " moderate " to " exceptionally good." In passing from the pure air condition there is at first a rapid drop in the value of a, followed by an almost linear relation

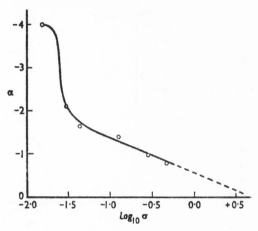

FIG. 72.—Relation between the exponent a and log σ for country air.

(*Redrawn from Harrison, " Photographic Journal," Vol. LXXXV*-B.)

between a and log σ. The extrapolation of the curve indicated by the broken line cuts the log σ axis at a point approximately equivalent to the visual range at which other investigators have found scatter to be independent of wavelength.

These results do therefore support the idea of a correspondence between visual range and the dependence of scatter on the colour of the light, and provide us with approximate values for the exponent in the scatter function at any range.

Harrison has made a very interesting use of the conception that for any condition of visibility the scatter coefficient will be expressible as a known function of wavelength (8). He first develops a method of calculating the visual range in pure air, assuming Rayleigh scatter and a homogeneous uniformly illuminated atmosphere, and taking into account the relative sensitivity of the eye at different wavelengths. The visual range so calculated is found to be 280 miles. The range is then calculated for monochromatic light of various wavelengths, enabling the curve shown in Fig. 73 to be drawn. This curve shows the superior " penetration " of the longer wavelengths in pure air when the visibility is extremely good, but the results have no application in practice since the photography at ranges greater than 100 miles is limited by other factors than atmospheric scatter.

In Fig. 73 the visual range of 280 miles corresponds to an " effective wavelength " of monochromatic light of 0·575 micron, and Harrison takes

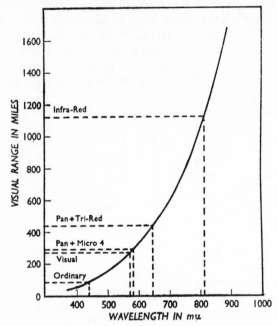

FIG. 73.—Range beyond which the contrast of a black body against the horizon sky is reduced to 0·02 plotted against wavelength, using the Rayleigh scatter function.

(*Redrawn from Harrison, " Photographic Journal," Vol. LXXXV-*B.)

this as the " effective " wavelength of the eye. Effective wavelengths for a number of different photographic materials and filters are then assumed and give the corresponding ranges shown on the ordinate scale of the figure and in column two of Table 11.

TABLE 11 (From Harrison, p. 61)

Visual and Photographic Ranges

	Effective Wavelength.	Range in Miles when scattering Coefficient varies as :—				
	Micron	λ^{-4}	λ^{-2}	λ^{-1}	$\lambda^{-\frac{1}{2}}$	—
Visual . . .	0·575	280	85	8	1·9	0·3
Non colour-sensitive .	0·420	100	50	6	1·7	0·3
Panchromatic + Minus Blue	0·580	290	85	8	1·9	0·3
Panchromatic + Tricolour Red	0·650	440	105	9	2·0	0·3
Infra-red + 207 . . .	0·810	1,120	160	11	2·2	0·3
Ratio infra-red λ visual .	...	4	1·9	1·4	1·18	1·0

From Middleton's curve (Fig. 72), values of σ are next found which are proportional to λ^{-2}, λ^{-1}, $\lambda^{-\frac{1}{2}}$, and independent of λ. Since these values of σ have been determined visually they are assumed to correspond to a wave-length of 0·575 micron so that the scatter coefficient associated with any other wavelength can also be found for each visibility condition, and the ranges can be determined as before. Harrison's results are given in columns one to six of Table 11, and have been plotted in Fig. 74 as the ratio of visual to photographic range against the log of the visual range for a number of wavelengths. The wavelength of 0·420 micron corresponds to the use of a non-colour sensitised photo-graphic emulsion, 0·580

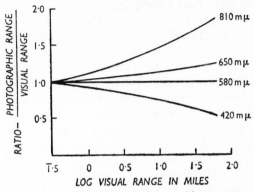

Fig. 74.—Dependence of photographic range on wavelength.

micron to a panchromatic emulsion with Minus Blue filter and approximately to the human eye, 0·650 micron to a panchromatic emulsion used with a red filter, and 0·810 micron to the common type of infra-red emulsion used with an infra-red filter. The eye and the panchromatic emulsion with yellow filter are approximately equal in haze penetrating power and possesses a marked advantage over the purely blue-sensitive emulsion. The further step of using a red filter does not yield quite such a big improvement, but infra-red material appears to afford an even greater improvement over panchromatic than the latter does over the non-sensitised emulsion. It will be noticed, however, that all the differences become much smaller as the haze density increases and the visual range decreases.

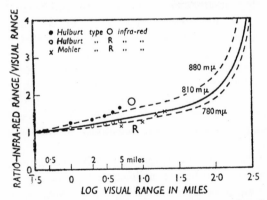

Fig. 75.—The ratio infra-red range/visual range plotted against visual range for three types of infra-red sensitive material, showing experimental points obtained from data of Hulburt and Mohler.

(*Redrawn from Harrison, " Photographic Journal," Vol. LXXXV-*B.)

Harrison points out that his calculations are in reasonable agreement with experimental work of Hugon, Mohler, and Hulburt. In Fig. 75 the full line gives the ratio of the infra-red to the visual range as calculated for 0·810 micron ; the upper broken line is drawn to fit points derived from figures found by Hulburt with type Q infra-red material sensitive mainly to 0·880 micron, the lower line correspondingly expresses results of Hulburt and Mohler for type R infra-red sensitive to 0·780 micron. It will be observed that the experimental points for 0·880 micron lie above the theoretical curve for 0·810 micron and the points for 0·780 micron lie below it, in remarkable agreement with the general theory of atmospheric scattering.

These calculations and observations have important consequences for air photography. They show in the first place that there is no hope of penetrating fog or dense haze by use of infra-red emulsions, because under such conditions the scatter is almost independent of wavelength. For example, if the visual range is 1 mile, infra-red photography will only increase it to about 1·1 miles, whereas an increase to about 8 miles would be necessary to show the scene as it would appear in conditions of " good visibility." In clearer air the increase of range is more marked, but infra-red does not double the visual range until the latter is of the order of 80 miles, which is quite exceptional visibility at least for Western Europe at sea level. For long oblique views when the light passes mainly through clean air infra-red does indeed increase the visual range, and this has been very effectively used in special work, e.g., the high-altitude obliques taken by Col. Stevens from the stratosphere balloon, Explorer II (7), where it was important to show the horizon and distant objects of very large size, such as ranges of mountains. In general air photography, however, where it is important to show objects of normal size, the range tends to be limited in ordinary clear air by the resolving-power rather than by atmospheric haze. Thus an angular resolution of 1 in 10,000 is about the highest normally available, which means that no low-contrast detail smaller than about 5 ft. can be distinguished beyond a range of 10 miles, while the " visual range " might easily be 50 miles. This is not to say that infra-red photography is useless, but merely that it will not increase to any striking extent the range at which average-sized objects as distinct from natural features can be recorded. In practice there is always *some* gain in clarity by using light of longer wavelength, even in heavy industrial haze, but it is not spectacular, and has to be balanced against the lower resolution due to larger lens apertures and/or slower shutter speeds necessitated by the deeper filter or by the lower sensitivity of infra-red film.

The order of difference between different wavelengths over a relatively short range in different atmospheric conditions is illustrated pictorially by the comparative vertical photographs of Plates 12 to 15. In taking these photographs simultaneous exposures were made from 10,000 ft. in matched cameras all using a standard type of panchromatic air film but fitted with different filters, viz., a normal Minus Blue, a Tricolour Blue and a Tricolour Red. The examples illustrated in Plates 12 and 13 were taken over a small town in fairly clear conditions, while those of Plates 14 and 15 were taken over an industrial area under extreme conditions of haze and smoke. Plate 13 was printed on a soft bromide paper from the Tricolour Blue negative, and is obviously less contrasty than 12 (A) which was printed on the same paper from the Minus Blue negative. It might be argued that the difference is due to the lower negative gamma normally associated with the use of a Tricolour Blue filter, and to counter this example 12 (B) was printed on a contrasty bromide paper. Its contrast now equals 12 (A) in the sense that the print has a similar density-range, but the tone reproduction is different and 12 (B) is altogether inferior to 12 (A) in clarity of detail. The main result of increasing the printing contrast has been to emphasise the negative graininess, and although the details already visible in 13 have been made clearer, no new details have been revealed.

In Plates 14 and 15 the prints were all made on contrasty bromide paper. Example 15 is from the Tricolour Blue negative, and it shows no significant detail. Example 14 (B) is from the Minus Blue negative and 14 (A) from the Tricolour Red negative. The Tricolour Red result is slightly better than the Minus Blue, but the difference is negligible compared with the difference between either example and the kind of photograph that could be had under clear conditions. Thus we can see that the panchromatic emulsion with Minus Blue filter represents a great advance from the unsensitised emulsion which responds to blue only, but the use of a red filter does not offer much further improvement, and is hardly worth while, especially in view of the extra-camera-exposure required.

Plate 16 shows a comparison between panchromatic film with Minus Blue filter and infra-red film with Tricolour Red filter, the effective response of the latter being largely in the infra-red region with a sensitivity peak at about 0·8 micron. The comparative exposures were made from 18,000 ft. over a large city, with heavy haze, but the conditions were not so extreme as those in Plate 15. The use of the infra-red film has given a clearer picture, but the improvement again falls far short of the quality which could be obtained on panchromatic film in clear weather. The loss of resolution on infra-red film, moreover, is much more serious than that due to the use of the red filter with panchromatic film. Like so many other things in air photography, the choice of emulsion and filter for haze penetration must be a compromise. The longer the wavelength that can be used, the clearer will the picture be, but the greater is the camera-exposure that must be given and hence the worse the resolution for fine detail. If conditions are very bad it may be worth while using a red filter or infra-red to get a result of some kind even at the expense of the finer details, but only practical experience and a first-hand knowledge of the kind of result that will be acceptable will enable a decision to be made.

Effect of Haze on Definition.—It is often supposed that haze affects the definition of photographs by diffusing the outlines of objects as distinct from lowering their contrast. This is a natural misconception, because it is so easy to confuse lack of contrast in small details with lack of sharpness. To some extent, of course, the contrast and the sharpness of photographs are interlinked because a contrasty reproduction will have a steeper density-gradient at the boundary of any image, but apart from this it has been shown experimentally that a reduction of contrast under conditions which cannot possibly affect definition always conveys the impression of a reduction in sharpness. It has also been shown experimentally that haze does not affect sharpness of definition in the true sense (4), (9).

REFERENCES

1. OWENS, J. S. " Condensation of Water from the Atmosphere upon Hygroscopic Crystals," *Proc. Roy. Soc.*, (A) **110,** 738, 1926.
2. MIDDLETON, W. E. K. Summarised in " Visibility in Meteorology." A valuable account of the subject, with a very extensive bibliography. University of Toronto Press.
3. MINNAERT, M. " Light and Colour in the Open Air." C. Bell & Sons, London.
4. WALDRAM, J. M. " Measurement of the Photometric Properties of the Upper Atmosphere," *Trans. Illum. Eng. Soc.* (London), **10,** No. 8, August 1945.
5. ROCARD, Y. *Revue d'Optique*, **2,** 193, 1932.
6. HULBURT, E. O. *Journ. Opt. Soc. Amer.*, **31,** 7, 1941.
7. CLARK, W. " Infra-red Photography," Chapman & Hall.
8. HARRISON, G. B. *Photo. Journ.*, **85-B,** No. 3, May-June, 1945.
9. DUNTLEY, S. " Reduction of Apparent Contrast by the Atmosphere," *Journ. Opt. Soc. Amer.*, **38,** February 1948.

Chapter Twelve

EFFECTS OF HAZE LIGHT ON THE REPRODUCTION OF BRIGHTNESS AND DETAIL

EVERY effort is made to minimise haze in air photography, but complete elimination is not possible, and even when deep yellow filters are used its effects are not negligible except in verticals taken from very low altitudes. The general result is a loss of contrast, *i.e.*, a reduction of the effective brightness range of the subject, which not only makes the larger details difficult to see but inevitably lowers the resolving power and makes some details disappear altogether. Both of these effects are relatively more serious in the darker tones of the subject, and although the loss of contrast can be offset by appropriate photographic techniques, nothing can be done about the lowered resolving power. The influence of these effects on the nature of the high-altitude air photograph is discussed in this chapter.

BRIGHTNESS REPRODUCTION

Suppose that the original subject has a brightness range of a, *i.e.*, the brightest highlight has a brightness of 1 and the deepest shadow has a brightness of $\frac{1}{a}$. Now let haze light be added uniformly all over the subject, and let the brightness of the haze be $\frac{x.1}{100}$. The new brightness range, a', is then

$$\frac{1 + \dfrac{x}{100}}{\dfrac{1}{a} + \dfrac{x}{100}},$$

and its value can readily be calculated for any values of x and a. It follows from this way of defining the haze brightness in terms of the maximum subject brightness that the effect of a given percentage of haze light will be relatively greater for a long original brightness range than for a short one. This is quite reasonably in accordance with reality, however, for the highest possible brightness in any outdoor scene (excluding specular reflections) is that of a perfectly white diffusing surface exposed to sunlight; although white is relatively rare, it is readily definable and hence suitable for a "key" brightness, and the brightness scale can only extend downwards from it. For the present purpose it is convenient to regard the maximum brightness as unity, no matter how much haze light has been added, and this can be done without altering the value of a' by multiplying all the brightnesses by

$$\frac{1}{1 + \dfrac{x}{100}}.$$

Figures calculated in this way for original brightness ranges from 1 to 1000 and haze brightnesses of 5, 20, and 100 per cent. are given in Table 12, and these figures have been plotted in Fig. 76 as log brightness scale without haze against log brightness scale in the same subject after addition of the different amounts of haze. With original brightness ranges of 10 or more the contraction of the range and the distortion of relative brightness values are obviously very serious for the amounts of haze shown. With 5 per cent. haze the maximum possible range is about 20 to 1, whatever the original range, and there is practically no differentiation between the tones which are 1/100

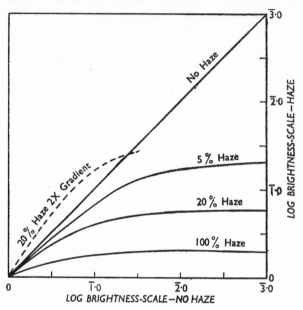

FIG. 76.—Effect of haze light on subject brightness range.

and 1/1000 of the greatest brightness. With 100 per cent. haze the maximum possible range is 2 to 1 and there is extreme distortion of all dark tones. In practice, haze reduces all the subject brightnesses by a constant factor, but since this has no effect on the *relative* brightnesses it will be ignored and only the consequences of the added light will be considered.

How far is the reproduction of brightnesses in air photography influenced by effects such as these? To answer this question we must first know what order of haze light is representative. Obviously the haze is a very variable factor, and it has already been mentioned in Chapter Eleven that there are no adequate figures based on direct measurement. It is known, however, from density measurements on large numbers of high altitude negatives that the brightness range in the camera for scenes taken in fairly clear weather from about 20,000 ft. is approximately 5 to 1. This figure is derived from measurements on areas of density corresponding to large uniformly bright areas on the ground, so that the reduction of brightness range may be regarded as due solely to haze and free from any effects due to reduction of scale. There is not sufficient information about the brightness ranges of the corresponding types of scenes in absence of haze, but from general knowledge of the photometric characteristics of outdoor scenes in clear sunny weather we can say that their brightness ranges are usually greater than 20 to 1. A glance at Fig. 76 shows that for hazes of 20 per cent. the brightness range in the camera is between 5 and 6 to 1 for any original brightness range greater than 30 to 1, so that it is a reasonable approximation to take 20 per cent. as a representative average haze figure for high altitude views in normal clear weather. It will be appreciated that the 20 per cent. refers to the lightest object in each photograph that was measured, and that these objects were not necessarily perfectly white but had some lower reflectance value, probably about 30 to 40 per cent. in most cases. This fact, however, does not affect the argument, because the same off-white objects would be used in determining the brightness range at ground level. The haze figure also includes the effect of any flare in the camera, but this is not normally more than 5 per cent. of the average field brightness, and hence much less than 5 per cent. of the brightness of the brightest object in the field of view of an air camera. For the present purpose it is quite satisfactory to take the haze and flare together and regard them as one.

In the haziest air in which high altitude vertical photographs are normally taken, *i.e.*, over industrial cities, the brightness range in the camera may be of the order of 2 to 1, and Fig. 76 shows that the corresponding haze is about 100 per cent.

Distortion caused by the Haze Light.—We may now consider more closely the effect of the haze light on brightness reproduction. In the first place it is necessary to define the kind of reproduction that is regarded as ideal. This has always been a question of quite fundamental importance in general photographic theory, and an immense amount of research has been devoted to it (1). For some decades after Hurter and Driffield's classical investigations attention was devoted to purely physical aspects of the subject, and the ideal held up to photographers was a linear unit slope relation between the log of the subject brightness and the log of the reproduction brightness. For various reasons it was not possible to fulfil the requirement with any accuracy, but in recent years it has become widely recognised that physically perfect reproduction does not necessarily give the most realistic pictures, because of the curious psychological mechanisms which come into play when viewing scenes not under uniform illumination (2), (3), (4). The study of these problems, though of great fascination, has no direct application to air photography, though it may be noted that for outdoor scenes under uniform illumination a physically perfect reproduction is judged to be the most satisfactory by a majority of observers (5).

Strictly speaking the air photograph does not and need not set out to be a " true representation " or a realistic picture. In principle there is no need for it to " look like " the original scene, and usually a photograph which did so would fail in its true purpose. The extreme example of this is found in the use of infra-red photography, where the tones of the subject are deliberately distorted to reveal details which would otherwise be invisible.

Even when the spectral sensitivity of the emulsion is the same as that of the eye, however, the air photograph should not set out to produce a linear unit-slope record of the tones of the subject *as it appears from the air*. A reproduction of this kind would be more or less lacking in contrast depending on the amount of haze, and however faithfully it might convey the appearance of the scene from the air it would inevitably lose much of the low-contrast detail on the ground.

The nature of the ideal reproduction for air photographs is not at all obvious, and any assumed standard is bound to be rather arbitrary, but it does not seem unreasonable to postulate that there should be a linear unit-slope relation between the logs of the reproduction brightnesses and the logs of the brightnesses in the original subject *as seen at ground level in absence of haze*. This involves the further assumption that there is an equal probability of finding detail of importance at any point in the brightness scale of the original subject. This is not necessarily true, but no other assumption seems possible. It will be clear that in the presence of 20 per cent. haze the reproduction is likely to depart very appreciably from the postulated ideal. Assuming that the photography is arranged to give a linear unit-slope reproduction of the subject as imaged in the camera, then the 20 per cent. haze line in Fig. 76 gives the reproduction in terms of the subject without haze, and there is obviously a marked distortion, especially in the reproduction of the darker tones. Just how serious we consider the distortion to be depends on the brightness range of the scene without haze. Jones (6) found that the average brightness range for outdoor scenes of the kind taken by amateur and professional photographers was 160 to 1, and for ranges of this order the distortion is very serious indeed. However, it is not considered that Jones' figures are representative for air photography, since he appears to have measured the maximum brightness range in his scenes including very small areas of brightness such as small shadows receiving light from a very restricted part of the sky. For the purposes of air photography there is no point in considering the reproduction of things which are of negligibly small size or are unimportant for other reasons. The darkest shadows appearing in vertical photographs, for example, are those between walls which are very close together, or otherwise screened from the sky in such a way that any detail within them must be very small. The brightness range could be made infinitely long by considering the shadow within a very tall chimney, but no one would expect to find detail in such a place. Again, pure white objects are rare and it is not usually necessary to find detail within their areas, so that they also can be ignored. From such considerations and a knowledge of the average ratio of sun to shadow illumination at ground level it is concluded that a reasonably representative figure for the brightness range of sunlit scenes observed from vertically above in complete absence of haze is 32 to 1.

Referring again to Fig. 76 and confining our attention to the 20 per cent. haze curve, we see that the log brightness scale of a 32 to 1 original subject contracts from 1·5 to 0·77 after addition of the haze, while the extreme shadow gradient has fallen from the correct value of 1·0 to 0·125. The obvious approach is to increase the contrast in the photographic reproduction, as by using a negative material of high gamma. The effect of doing this, while still retaining a linear reproduction, has been indicated by the dotted line in Fig. 76 which corresponds to 20 per cent. haze with an overall gamma of 2·0 in the reproduction. The log brightness range of the reproduction has now been restored to that of the original scene without haze, but the tonal distortion is unaffected, the gradient at the shadow end of the curve still being only one-eighth of that at the highlight end. To obtain full compensation for the effects of the haze light it is necessary to introduce non-linearity into the reproduction as well as increasing the overall contrast.

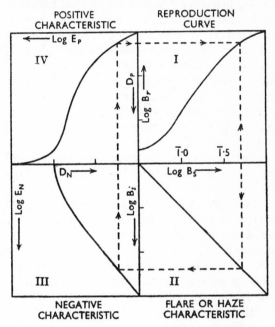

Fig. 77.—Typical tone-reproduction diagram.

Problems such as this are best studied with the aid of a four-quadrant tone-reproduction diagram adapted from that of Jones (6).

Tone-reproduction Diagrams.—Fig. 77 is a typical tone-reproduction diagram, used in this example to find the reproduction for a low-altitude view of brightness range 32 to 1, or 1·5 on the log scale. We start at the log brightness scale of the subject, log B_s, in quadrant I, and proceed clockwise around the diagram. Quadrant II is used to introduce any differences between the log brightness scale of subject and image caused by haze or by flare light in the camera. In this instance there is no haze and flare is neglected, so that the log B_s scale is transferred unchanged via the straight line at 45 degrees to form the log image brightness scale, log B_i. The log B_i scale now becomes the log exposure scale, log E_n, for the negative characteristic curve, which is drawn, rotated through 90 degrees from its normal position, in quadrant III. The negative densities produced by the projection of the log En scale on to the characteristic curve are now projected upwards to form the log exposure scale, log Ep, for the printing paper characteristic curve, which is drawn in quadrant IV inverted from its normal orientation. The resultant reflection densities may be regarded as the negative logs of the reproduction brightnesses, log Br, and are projected across into quadrant I to meet perpendiculars erected from the appropriate points on the log Bs scale, their intersections giving points on the final reproduction curve. The effect of variations in negative or printing exposure can of course be simulated by moving the characteristic curves bodily along their respective log exposure axes.

In Fig. 77 the log brightness range of the original subject is I·5, and this is transferred unchanged to a negative characteristic curve of mean slope 0·66, a considerable part of the curved foot being in use, so that the negative gradient is much lower in the shadows than in the highlights. On transferring to the paper characteristic curve, however, the shadow tones are recorded on a steeper gradient than the highlights, and a partial compensation for the shape of the negative characteristic is introduced. The full density range of the paper has not been used, so that the final reproduction has a shorter brightness range than the original, with a marked compression of the extreme shadow tones. Over most of the brightness scale, however, the reproduction curve does not depart very seriously from the ideal straight line of unit slope, and the reproduction would probably be considered quite reasonable by most people.

The negative and paper characteristic curves used in Fig. 77 do not relate to any particular emulsions but are similar to the curves of emulsions which might well be used for a photographic task of the kind described. The use of part of the curved foot of the negative characteristic and the compensation by the roughly reciprocal shape of the paper curve are representative of a common occurrence in general photography, and also serve to demonstrate the use of the tone-reproduction diagram.

We may now study the application of the same kind of graphical construction to the problem of tone-reproduction in presence of haze. In Fig. 78 the " flare or haze " characteristic drawn as the curved line in quadrant II is the " 20 per cent. haze " typical for high altitude verticals, and is drawn from the figures given in Table 12. The log Bi scale is now very different from the log Bs scale, and if quadrant II is followed by straight line unit slope characteristics in quadrants III and IV, or by any combination of characteristics which together yield a straight line of unit slope, the final reproduction will be given by the curved line in quadrant I, which indicates a great reduction in brightness range and a serious distortion in the lower brightnesses. The problem is to find the shape of negative characteristic curve, or the combination of negative and positive characteristics, which will lead to linear reproduction in quadrant I, and two possibilities are shown in the diagram. Quadrants III and IV each have two " characteristic curves," one of each pair being the straight line at unit slope and the other being simply the " haze and flare " curve transferred from quadrant II and suitably orientated. Taking the negative stage first, it will be clear from a study of the diagram that any point on the log Bs scale leads to the same negative density whether it is followed round by way of the straight lines or the curved lines in quadrants III and II. In other words, the negative densities will be a linear representation of the log brightnesses in the original subject if the negative characteristic curve has the same shape as the haze characteristic. This negative printed on a paper having a straight-line characteristic will then reproduce the log brightnesses of the

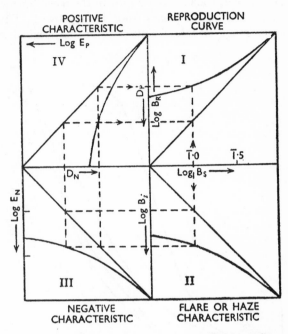

Fig. 78.—Tone-reproduction diagram including haze effect.

original subject on the ideal straight line. Similarly, it can be seen that if the haze characteristic is followed by a straight line of unit slope as the negative characteristic in quadrant III, the tonal distortion will be offset if the paper has the characteristic curve shown in quadrant IV, which is again the haze characteristic. A straight-line negative of less or greater than unit slope should be followed by a paper characteristic of basically similar shape but with the slope at each point multiplied or divided by an appropriate factor. For any different haze percentage an appropriate haze characteristic would be applied.

Desirable Negative and Paper Characteristic Curves.—The negative characteristic curve shown in Fig. 78 as compensating for haze distortion is not like the characteristic curve of any real negative material, though a curve resembling it could be isolated from the characteristic curve of a rather contrasty negative emulsion having a tendency to " shoulder off " at the higher densities. The inverted haze characteristic, on the other hand, is reminiscent of the general shape of bromide and more particularly of chloro-bromide paper characteristics, most of which are steeper at the higher densities and decline fairly rapidly to much lower gradients as the highlight end of the curve is approached. This leads us to conclude that it would be more practical to consider reproduction in terms of straight-line negative materials, which are a common type, used in conjunction with various bromide papers. Some examples have been worked out along these lines, adopting the restriction that the print densities should not exceed 1·3 nor be less than 0·1, thus conforming with the usual practice of avoiding very high or low densities in prints from air negatives. This means that the print density range is 1·3, against 1·5 for the original scene without

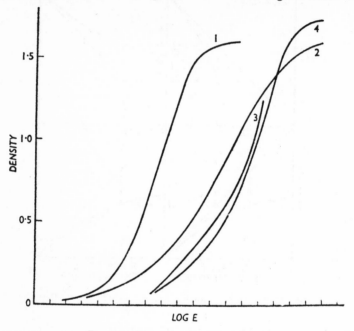

Fig. 79.—Paper characteristic curves.

haze, but the reproduction gradient is still much greater than unity referred to the subject as seen through the haze.

Fig. 79 shows characteristic curves for some representative types of bromide and chloride papers ; curve 1 is a " contrasty " grade commonly used for printing air negatives, while 2 is a corresponding medium grade ; curve 4 is a commercial chloride paper and 3 is the hypothetical curve required to give correct reproduction with a straight-line negative of gamma 1·3. The match of curves 4 and 3 is remarkably close, and the others exhibit the general tendency for higher gradients at higher densities already referred to. It is easy to derive by graphical means the negative characteristic curves which would give perfect reproduction with the paper curves 1 and 2, but they are of very irregular shape and could not be imitated in any practicable negative emulsions. It is of greater value to derive overall reproduction curves for these papers used with standard types of negative emulsions, and some examples are shown in Fig. 80. Ideal reproduction in this figure would be given by a straight line at a slope of 0·8, because of the restricted density range assumed for the print. Curve 1 shows the reproduction obtained when the log brightness range of the image is accommodated entirely on the straight line portion of the characteristic curve of a negative emulsion such as " Super XX Aero " developed to a gamma of 1·3. The negative is printed on the medium paper shown as curve 2 in Fig. 79. The extreme shadow gradient is decidedly less than the average slope, but it is clear that there has been some compensation for the flattening effect of the haze in the lower brightnesses, and the overall reproduction is quite reasonable, with

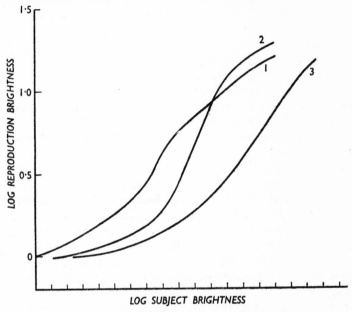

FIG. 80.—Overall reproduction curves.

some tone-separation at all parts of the scale. Curve 2 in Fig. 80 illustrates the effect of under-exposing the same negative emulsion to a degree represented by a minimum density of 0·05 above fog ; thus using an appreciable part of the foot of the characteristic curve. The negative density range is thereby reduced and the contrasty paper shown as curve 1 in Fig. 79 is the most suitable, though its exposure scale is slightly too short and the print has slightly lower densities than is normally considered desirable. There is a marked departure from linear reproduction and the gradient in the shadows is much less than in the middle tones. The low shadow gradient is due to the combined effect of haze light and exposing on to the toe of the negative characteristic curve. If the negative had been of uniform low gradient throughout it could in principle have been printed on a harder paper and would then have given better reproduction, but when the shadows are on the toe and the lighter tones on the straight line the difference in gradient is too great to be reconciled in normal printing. If for any reason the shadow details are of no special interest then the type of reproduction given by curve 2 is not inferior to that of curve 1. Curve 3 illustrates the use of " Panatomic X," a " long-toe " emulsion which has sometimes been used for air photography. In this case the minimum density is assumed to be 0·1 above fog and the negative is printed on the medium paper shown as curve 2 in Fig. 79. Here again the shadows are considerably flattened due to the use of the curved toe, but the transition from a low to a relatively high gradient is more gradual than in the case of curve 2, and the overall reproduction is better, though not so good as in curve 1.

Practical Considerations.—These studies in tone reproduction form a pleasant diversion and exercise for the student, but they have no direct application in practice. The discussions have been based on assumed average brightness ranges in subjects with and without haze. This was quite justifiable for demonstration purposes, but in practice real subjects will only rarely have exactly the average brightness range and the amount of haze will rarely be the average figure of 20 per cent. Thus the curve shapes required for tone compensation can never be exactly known, and if they were known the negative and printing exposures would have to be controlled with impracticably great accuracy to avoid introducing greater errors than it was hoped to correct. The only conclusion of a strictly practical nature which can be drawn from tone reproduction studies in air photography is that it is a good thing to work on a straight line negative characteristic, while it is a useful fact that paper characteristics are qualitatively of a desirable shape. As a side issue it may be pointed out that the best gamma for the negative characteristic is about 1·3 if it is desired to print the majority of negatives on bromide paper of medium contrast, which seems to be a reasonable thing to do. This follows from the fact that the average log brightness range of high-altitude views in the camera is 0·75 approximately, while the log exposure scale of medium bromide paper for density limits of 0·1 to 1·3 is approximately 0·95 ; 0·75 multiplied by the gamma figure of 1·3 is just over 0·95, so that the average negative will suit medium paper very well.

RESOLVING POWER

In the first section of this chapter we have considered the effect of haze light on tone reproduction and have seen how its differential lowering of contrast may be offset to some extent by appropriate photographic technique. This study relates only to the larger details and general appearance of air photographs rather than their small details. For most purposes, however, the resolution of fine detail is highly important, and it is now necessary to inquire how the negative resolution is affected by the haze light.

Since resolving power in a negative depends profoundly on the test-object contrast it follows that haze light lowers the resolution and lowers it more seriously in the darker tones of the subject. The variation of resolving power with test-object contrast has been briefly discussed in Chapter Six, where it was shown to be different for different lens and emulsion combinations. For the present purpose, however, it will be sufficient to consider one combination only, which is sufficiently representative of all combinations likely to be used in air photography. The chosen combination is the 8 in. Pentac lens used with Super XX film, and the data are taken from the work of Romer (7). In Fig. 81 the angular resolving power for this lens and film are plotted against the contrast of the test object (density difference), and it will be seen that below a density difference of 1·0 the resolution is beginning to fall away, while below 0·2 it falls away very rapidly indeed.

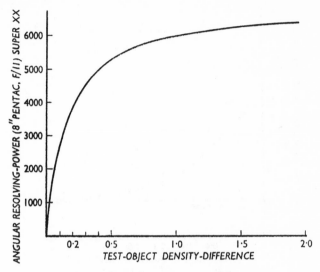

Fig. 81.—Effect of contrast on resolving power.

In order to study the effect of haze light on resolution at different parts of the subject brightness scale it will be convenient to assume a hypothetical subject having, in absence of haze, details of equal contrast spaced at equal intervals of log brightness. A convenient subject for this purpose would have groups of Cobb test objects arranged in steps of log brightness of 0·2, the contrast in each group also being 0·2. Thus the background of the first group would have a relative log brightness of 0 and the bars a relative log brightness of 0·2; in the second group the background would be 0·2 and the bars 0·4, and so on. With eight such groups the total log brightness scale of the subject would be 1·6. The assumption that details of equal contrast will be found at all subject brightness levels is somewhat arbitrary and not necessarily in accordance with reality, but it is the only possible assumption on which to base a simple treatment of the problem.

We next assume that our subject is seen through haze such that 20 per cent. of the maximum brightness is added to all brightnesses, as in the standard high-altitude scene assumed for the tone reproduction study ; the contraction of the total brightness scale and the new contrast of each group of test objects are then easily derived. The total scale contracts from

1·6 to 0·726; the contrast of the first step falls from 0·2 to 0·0274, while that of the eighth suffers a much smaller drop to 0·159. By applying these figures of contrast to the curve in Fig. 81 we can now obtain the resolving power for each step of the subject as seen through the haze, and this has been plotted in Fig. 82 where the ordinates give the resolution as modified by the haze for any point in the brightness scale of the subject without haze. For ease of comparison with actual air photography the ordinate scale has been given as feet resolved on the ground from 20,000 ft. altitude by the 8 in. Pentac lens on Super XX film.

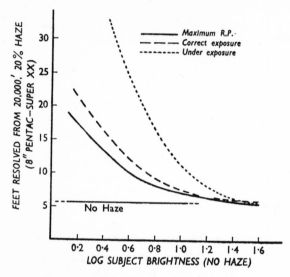

FIG. 82.—Effect of haze on resolving power.

The three curves in Fig. 82 represent different exposure conditions. With any emulsion the resolving power varies with exposure, rising rapidly to a maximum value from the under-exposure region and falling away again with over-exposure. Uniform resolution is not possible throughout any brightness scale of finite length, and the distribution of resolving power through the scale will vary according to the exposure level of the subject as a whole. The full curve in Fig. 82 represents a purely hypothetical case where each step of the subject is supposed to have been given the exposure for optimum resolution; this could be done in a laboratory test with several separate exposures, but not in actual air photography where the whole subject is necessarily exposed at once. This curve is of theoretical value, however, as it shows the unmodified effect of the haze on resolution through the tone scale. There is a most marked reduction of resolving power at the low brightness end of the scale; at the first step the ground resolution changes from 5 ft. without haze to 17 ft. with the haze, while at the highest brightness the change is negligible.

The broken curve in Fig. 82 shows the effect of the haze as modified by the shape of the emulsion resolving power/log exposure curve. The optimum exposure level is a somewhat arbitrary matter, but it seems reasonable to locate the middle of the subject brightness scale at the maximum of the resolving power curve, and the broken curve was drawn on this assumption. It was obtained from the first curve by multiplying each ordinate of the latter by a factor derived from the resolving power/log exposure curve for Super XX film. The correction for the emulsion characteristics has accentuated the upward trend of the first curve in the low brightness region, but the effect is small in relation to the effect of the haze acting alone.

The dotted curve in Fig. 82 illustrates the effect of giving under-exposure on the same emulsion, assuming a minimum density of 0·05 above fog. Here the lower brightnesses fall on the toe of the emulsion characteristic curve where the resolving power is falling away steeply, and this combined with the great loss of contrast due to the haze causes a very serious falling off in the ground resolution, detail being practically wiped out in the deepest shadows.

It will have been noticed that the correction of the full curve in Fig. 82 to produce the other two curves involves the assumption that the shape of the emulsion resolving power/log exposure curve is independent of the test-object contrast, at least for all contrasts below 0·2. There seems to be no *a priori* reason why this should be so, but Romer's investigations already mentioned suggest that the assumption was justified, since his curves for resolution against log exposure have practically the same shape for all contrasts of the test object.

Practical Consequences.—This subject has been discussed in terms of a hypothetical subject having details of equal contrast at all parts of its brightness scale, and it has been shown that when such a subject is seen through haze the size of ground detail resolved will be much larger at the low brightness end of the scale. The assumption of equal contrast at all points of the brightness scale was not strictly justified, because in real subjects the shadow details in general have much lower contrasts than those in sunshine. This is an inevitable consequence of the absence of directed lighting within shadowed areas ; indeed, much of the higher contrast detail in outdoor scenes is provided by the juxtaposition of sunlight and shadow. It follows that even in the complete absence of haze the shadow details would be the first to be lost with increasing altitude and decreasing scale. This tendency is accentuated by the haze effect and the result is the familiar " empty " shadows of the high-altitude photograph, which cannot be made to show more detail by any increase of camera exposure.

These facts obviously have a bearing on our views about the meaning of " correct exposure " in high-altitude air photography. Normally, correct exposure means just enough exposure to record detail in the darkest tones of interest, but Fig. 82 shows that even with the best possible exposure the smallest details in shadow must be very largely wiped out through sheer lack of contrast. " Under-exposure " in the sense of blank shadows loses most of its meaning. Is it best to give enough exposure to secure all possible shadow detail, or to give rather less exposure in the interests of somewhat better resolution in the middle and light tones, recognising that practically no shadow detail can be recorded in any case ? There is no unique solution to this problem, and the method to be adopted must remain a matter for personal preference. It is fortunate that very little resolution will be lost in the middle and light tones by giving enough exposure to ensure that the shadow details are reproduced under the best possible conditions.

We inevitably inquire how far these effects of haze on resolution are intensified or reduced in the printing operation. Unfortunately little work seems to have been done on the resolution of very low contrast detail in prints. On the one hand we have the positive fact that at the limit of negative resolution, when the contrast of the image becomes less than the random density fluctuations of the graininess pattern, no increase of printing contrast will separate details not resolved in the negative. On the other hand it has been stated that details of too small contrast to be seen in the negative can

TABLE 12

No Haze.		5% Haze.	20% Haze.	100% Haze.
$1/a$	Log $1/a$	Log $1/a$	Log $1/a$	Log $1/a$
1/2	$\bar{1}\cdot699$	$\bar{1}\cdot719$	$\bar{1}\cdot785$	$\bar{1}\cdot875$
1/3	$\bar{1}\cdot398$	$\bar{1}\cdot562$	$\bar{1}\cdot648$	$\bar{1}\cdot824$
1/4	$\bar{1}\cdot398$	$\bar{1}\cdot456$	$\bar{1}\cdot573$	$\bar{1}\cdot796$
1/5	$\bar{1}\cdot301$	$\bar{1}\cdot377$	$\bar{1}\cdot523$	$\bar{1}\cdot778$
1/8	$\bar{1}\cdot097$	$\bar{1}\cdot222$	$\bar{1}\cdot433$	$\bar{1}\cdot752$
1/10	$\bar{1}\cdot000$	$\bar{1}\cdot155$	$\bar{1}\cdot398$	$\bar{1}\cdot741$
1/16	$\bar{2}\cdot796$	$\bar{1}\cdot030$	$\bar{1}\cdot340$	$\bar{1}\cdot725$
1/20	$\bar{2}\cdot699$	$\bar{2}\cdot979$	$\bar{1}\cdot319$	$\bar{1}\cdot720$
1/32	$\bar{2}\cdot493$	$\bar{2}\cdot889$	$\bar{1}\cdot285$	$\bar{1}\cdot712$
1/100	$\bar{2}\cdot000$	$\bar{2}\cdot757$	$\bar{1}\cdot263$	$\bar{1}\cdot704$
1/1000	$\bar{3}\cdot000$	$\bar{2}\cdot686$	$\bar{1}\cdot224$	$\bar{1}\cdot700$

be seen in prints on contrasty papers (5) ; presumably these details were much larger than the limit of resolution. In the absence of systematic investigation one can only argue from analogy and general photographic experience, which indicates that printing on very contrasty papers does not reveal details not already visible in the negative, though it may improve the general appearance of a photograph and make it easier to interpret by increasing the contrast of the broader areas of tone. It may be assumed with some certainty that when ground resolution has been lowered by haze it cannot be restored by increased printing contrast and that the compensations obtainable in tone reproduction will not extend to the smaller details. Normally we find decidedly lower resolution at the ends of the tone scale in prints, but the available data only apply to details of contrast greater than 0·1, and there seems to be no information about the very low contrasts. However, it is not unreasonable to assume that a similar effect will be observed for all contrasts, at least to the extent that the shape of the print density/resolution curve is controlled by the slope of the paper characteristic curve.

If this is so we should have to make a correction to the curves in Fig. 82 in order to arrive at the final resolution throughout the tone scale of the print. In the absence of specific data it would hardly be justifiable to construct any corrected curves, but if the correction were applied it would have the effect of raising the curves still further at each end while leaving the middle part substantially unchanged. The greatest change would be about a 40 per cent. drop in resolution at the low brightness end of the scale.

REFERENCES

1. MEES, C. E. K. " Theory of the Photographic Process," chapter xx.
2. ARENS, H. " Über einige für die photographische Abbildung wichtige psychologische Phänomene," *Veröffentlichungen des Wissenschaftlichen Zentral-Laboratoriums der photographischen Abteilung Agfa,* **5,** 85,. 1937.
3. EVANS, R. M. " Brightness-constancy in Colour Photography," *Journ. Opt. Soc. Amer.,* **33,** 579, 1943.
4. EVANS, R. M., and KLUTE, J. " Brightness Constancy in Photographic Reproduction," *Journ. Opt. Soc. Amer.,* **34,** 533-40, 1944.
5. JONES, L. A. " The Evaluation of Negative Film Speeds in Terms of Print Quality," *Journ. Frank. Inst.,* **227,** 279 and 497, 1939.
6. JONES, L. A., and CONDIT, H. " The Brightness Scale of Exterior Scenes and the Computation of Photographic Exposure," *Journ. Opt. Soc. Amer.,* **31,** 651, 1941.
7. ROMER, W. " The Influence of the Contrast of the Test Object on the Resolving Power of the System ' Objective-Sensitive Layer,' " *Sci. & Ind. Photo.,* **18,** 193-200, July 1947.

Chapter Thirteen

COLOUR PHOTOGRAPHY

COLOUR photography has made considerable advances in recent years, and numerous processes are available for the production of transparencies and colour prints, with very satisfying accuracy of reproduction in the best cases. The application to air photography has been limited so far, although the prospects might at first sight appear to be very good.

Colour processes are very largely used for what might be somewhat loosely termed " artistic " reasons, most persons preferring to see pictorial or record photographs in colour because they are more pleasing and interesting than monochromes. A great part of one's pleasure in Nature is intimately associated with colour, and it is not surprising that the coloured record goes so much further than the black and white in recreating the experiences which prompted the taking of the photograph. Many air photographs taken in colour, generally low-altitude obliques, are included in this category. In contrast to these uses for colour photography there are numerous applications in scientific or technical fields where the accurate reproduction of coloured objects has a purely utilitarian purpose. Nevertheless, the love of colour is so deeply engrained in the human mind that there is often a confusion of motives when assessing the value of colour photography for a given technical purpose. It is only natural to prefer the colour photograph even if there is no clear technical reason for doing so. This warping of the judgment is quite liable to occur in the application of colour to serious air photography, *i.e.*, air photography carried out for military purposes or one of the numerous civil survey tasks. Air photographs in colour can be exceedingly attractive to look at, and their fascination is apt to obscure the fact that they may convey no more information than a good monochrome, and sometimes less. It is not suggested that there is no place for colour in air photography ; a really satisfactory process, giving paper prints in unlimited numbers with the same ease as black and white, and requiring the same camera exposure, would obviously be invaluable, but there is no such process as yet and no likelihood of one appearing. As things stand at present colour photography has definite disadvantages, and in general it can only be used for special tasks under favourable conditions.

Colour Processes.—Most colour photographs taken from the air have been made by the transparency processes such as Dufaycolor, Agfacolor, Aero Kodacolor, Anscocolor, and, at the lower altitudes, Kodachrome. Colour prints have been made in an experimental way both from transparency originals and via separation negatives taken in triple or beam-splitter cameras, but the latter method is hardly likely to come into regular use. Dufaycolor, being an additive process with a filter mosaic, has obvious limitations in resolving power, and is not likely to receive much further application except for low-altitude obliques, where it can be very satisfactory. Agfacolor seems to have been used experimentally by German air photographers, and is of interest in that it was applied as a negative-positive process giving either colour transparencies or colour prints from a colour negative taken in a normal camera. As yet, however, there are no signs of Agfacolor coming into regular use, and it is probable that most serious air photographs in colour will continue·to be taken on Aero Kodacolor for some time to come. This process has been used quite extensively for experimental purposes in applications such as forestry surveys in North America. It has mostly been employed in a reversal form yielding a positive transparency ; there is no fundamental reason why such a process should not be worked as negative-positive in the same way as Agfacolor, but there are doubtless many practical difficulties to be overcome. There is often a long interval between the production of a few specimens by a new colour technique and its final establishment on a firm basis. Positive transparencies are basically much easier to make than prints and have a much longer tradition of successful production behind them ; they represent an established method in which most of the difficulties have been shouldered by the manufacturer, but printing from negatives involves tricky problems of colour balance and will always be a more difficult and lengthy process.

General Characteristics of Aero Kodacolor.—Aero Kodacolor is a three-layer process in which the colour is produced by dye coupling. (In the second development in the reversal form of the process.) The colour formers are incorporated in a dispersed form in the emulsion layers and no very exact control is required during processing. There is no point in describing the details of the processing technique, which may well be liable to slight modifications from time to time and will always be fully covered by the manufacturer's instructions ; it is sufficient to say that there are twelve operations, taking some three hours for an average roll, and that satisfactory results can be obtained with the common type of spool developing tank. Needless to say, the operations are more complicated than black and white processing, but with reasonable care in following instructions no experienced photographer should have any difficulties.

Aero Kodacolor requires about six times the exposure of a fast panchromatic film exposed behind a Minus Blue filter. A typical camera exposure for high-altitude verticals is 1/200 sec. at $f/6\cdot3$ for a solar altitude of about forty-five degrees.

The slope of the characteristic curve is steeper than in the colour materials sold for ground photography, approximate figures being gamma $1\cdot8$ and mean slope $1\cdot4$ over a log E range of $1\cdot0$. This may be compared with an overall reproduction gradient of about $1\cdot8$ for a typical monochrome technique using medium bromide paper. The higher contrast necessarily means less exposure latitude than with other colour processes, such as Kodachrome, and errors greater than one stop either way cannot be tolerated.

Special gelatine filters are provided with each batch of film, one set to balance the colour rendering at ground level to an acceptable datum, and a set of " haze filters " to correct for the overall blueness of scenes viewed from high altitudes under various conditions of haze. This use of two or more gelatine filters is not good practice, but at present there seems to be no alternative unless the user carries a large stock of cemented filters. Even then it will always be necessary to use at least two filters, which would introduce peculiar problems of calibration if the material were ever used for accurate surveys.

Effects of Haze in Colour Photography.—In the ordinary way the aim of colour photography is to get a faithful reproduction of the colours of the scene. The precise definition of " correct colour reproduction " is somewhat elusive, but the general aim is clear enough in ground photography—the picture should look like the subject. Strictly speaking this implies correct tone reproduction at a gamma of 1·0, and neutral greys recorded as such throughout the tone scale, as well as the obvious need for accurate hue and saturation of colours. Errors in hue and saturation are unavoidable even in the best processes, but it is usually considered correct to produce a neutral grey scale as the foundation of all good colour photography.

In air photography the problem is complicated by haze, which dilutes all colours with bluish-white light and changes their hue. If the material is correctly balanced for use at ground level, the grey scale will be recorded with an overall bluish cast when seen from altitude through haze. The blue is partly correct, in the sense that it is a record of the scene as it would appear to the eye, but in the light scattered by the haze there is an increased proportion of ultra-violet, which does not affect the eye but affects the blue sensitive emulsion layer and records as excess blue. The first aim of the haze filter must therefore be the complete exclusion of ultra-violet, which is technically a fairly simple problem.

Having got rid of the ultra-violet, it is still necessary to correct for the overall blueness of the scene. If we know the scatter wavelength function for the prevailing haze we can derive the filter curve required to correct the energy distribution of the scattered light back to that in the incident light, *i.e.*, to correct the bluish haze light back to white sunlight. Unfortunately there is no simple relationship between the scatter and the wavelength, everything depending on the size of the particles in the haze. For pure air the scatter varies as the minus fourth power of the wavelength, but in normal " very clear " air it varies approximately as the minus second power, while in heavier hazes the dependence of scatter on wavelength becomes less and less. In general, if $E\lambda$ is the relative energy at any wavelength λ, we could write $E\lambda = A\lambda^{-4} + B\lambda^{-2} + C\lambda^{-1}$, etc., where the relative values of the constants would depend on the state of the atmosphere. For the clear conditions under which colour photography from the air is normally attempted it seems probable that the second term in the expression is predominant, but no single type of filter can be universally correct.

Assuming oblique photography through homogeneous clear air, then with increasing range to the ground the amount of haze light increases and we might expect to require filters of increasing strength but based on the same curve shape. With further increases of range and in going to very high altitude verticals, the relative effect of scatter from the air molecules becomes increasingly important, and the curve shape would require to be different. In heavier haze, again, the curve would have to be modified.

The subject is in an early stage of development and little if any work has been published on the theory of filtering to overcome the effects of haze. Middleton, however, (1) has made a mathematical investigation on the colours of distant objects, finding that hue as well as saturation can be profoundly altered by haze light, while all colours tend towards grey at the limit of the visual range. Experience with colour photography from the air suggests that filtering is only effective in very light haze, and that the loss of colour saturation, which is so evident to the eye under very heavy haze conditions, cannot be recovered by any photographic means. In principle it is possible to filter for a neutral balance with any haze, but this still leaves the colours more or less diluted with white light.

Aero Kodacolor has presumably been given a high contrast to offset the lowering of contrast due to the haze light. Its mean slope of about 1·4 is well suited to the clear conditions under which medium and high altitude vertical photographs are taken, though it is too high for low-altitude work, and too low for very heavy haze. Any higher contrast, however, would make the exposure latitude impracticably small, and the value of colour photography in such conditions is in any case doubtful. Strictly speaking, correct colour representation is not possible at a greater slope than 1·0, but so many other factors affect the issue in air photography that high contrast has a negligible influence. It does appear, however, to make the material very sensitive to slight changes in filtering.

The Kodacolor emulsion filter is determined by the manufacturer and does not concern the user, but the choice of the haze filter must ultimately lie with him. It is a somewhat arbitrary choice and must inevitably be made from experience.

The haze filters are naturally very different from the sharp-cut yellows and reds used in monochrome photography, since they have a progressively increasing absorption from the violet to the red. The amount of absorption is very slight, even in the strongest filters and at the blue end of the spectrum ; their transmissions are rather like those of the filters used for correcting colour temperatures.

Possible Uses for Colour Photography.—The use of colour photography for air survey or military reconnaissance would only be justified if it conveyed information not given by monochrome, or enabled things to be seen more easily than in monochrome. The first of these may be the more important, for once a skilled interpreter has picked out details they can always be shown to less skilled people ; on the other hand, where photographs have a wide circulation ease of seeing important features is an undeniable advantage. For colour to be useful from this point of view it is clear that there must be details in the scene which can only be recognised or distinguished by a characteristic colour. As examples, one can think of such things as tarmac roads running over grass ; the two may record in practically the same tone of grey and given heavy enough haze the difference may vanish altogether. Colour photography could be useful here by differentiating the two by colour differences when no tonal difference exists, but in practice it is found that colour is least useful under the hazy conditions when ordinary panchromatic photographs may fail. In this particular example infra-red is more likely to be useful. Colour could conceivably be much more valuable as an aid to identification of specific details under clear conditions ; for example, it might be important to know the colour of sea-bottoms in shore-line studies, to distinguish grass from sand, to record seasonal changes in the colours of vegetation, or to follow the outcropping of distinctively coloured geological formations. There appears to be great promise in such fields as these provided that great accuracy of hue-rendering is not essential.

It is sometimes suggested that colour photography might be useful for revealing camouflage in military reconnaissance, but it is not easy to see why this should be so, for if the camouflage colours match their surroundings to the eye, they should do so in a colour photograph also. However, errors in colour-rendering might lead to visually matching colours being differentiated in the photograph. The remarks about photographic detection of camouflage in Chapter Fourteen apply here.

The author's personal experience of colour photography from the air is somewhat limited but has covered most kinds of atmospheric conditions, and the broad conclusions are in agreement with the foregoing arguments. Colour photography was found to be at its best in very clear air, when its outstanding characteristic was the greater ease with which important features of the landscape could be picked up by unskilled observers. The ability to identify certain details by colour alone was also of great value in isolated cases. Under hazy conditions colour was inferior to comparative panchromatic and infra-red monochrome photographs.

In all cases the need for giving the colour film a greater camera exposure led to much lower resolution than the black and white comparison. Considered in conjunction with the difficulty of getting good duplicate copies even in monochrome and the high original cost of the material, this seems to rule out any prospect of using colour except for special purposes and in a separate camera, for the monochrome record will always be required.

Non-literal Colour Photography.—The arguments so far have assumed that colour photography always involves the attempt to show the colours of the scene as they would appear to the eye at ground level. The purposes of air photography, however, might sometimes be better served by making a different use of the different spectral reflectance characteristics of the various surfaces photographed. The " transparency " method of determining beach gradients and water-depths, developed by J. W. Moore, may be regarded as a special technique of this kind, although no colour process is used. The scene is photographed with red and green filters on the camera lens, and the water-depth and gradient of the sea-bottom are worked out from the density gradients on the two negatives, which differ because of the different absorption coefficients of sea-water for red and green light. (2) In this particular process colour is not involved at the printing stage, in fact the negatives need not be printed at all, but it is easy to imagine special colour processes where the scene is photographed through various filters and printed in different colours designed to throw up and exaggerate certain kinds of detail. For example, we could use a two-layer subtractive type of colour process, exposing by green and infra-red light and printing in magenta and green pigments. Suppose with such a process we photograph a system of creeks running through marshland. The green vegetation will record as " white " in the infra-red record and will print in magenta, while the water areas will be " black " to the infra-red emulsion and will print in green. All the creeks will therefore be shown up in excellent contrast as green on a magenta background, and their course will be followed with ease. More or less neutral objects such as houses and roads would be recorded in approximately neutral tones. Schemes such as these are obviously capable of considerable development ; wherever the subject details have strongly marked spectral reflectance characteristics they can be photographed in ways to take advantage of this and printed in colours to throw up the differences. It is rather doubtful, however, if the demand for such special processes would ever justify their development, and the future of colour photography would seem to lie with accurate rather than distorted reproductions.

REFERENCES

1. MIDDLETON, W. E. K. " Visibility in Meteorology." University of Toronto Press.
2. MOORE, J. W. G. *Phil. Trans. Roy. Soc.*, **240-A,** No. 816, 163-217, January 1947.

Chapter Fourteen

INFRA-RED PHOTOGRAPHY

IT was once said of infra-red in air photography that it is " too valuable to abandon but not good enough to use," which is perhaps an exaggeration but does express the position rather well. Infra-red has potential advantages for air photography, but they are only realised by sacrificing other desirable qualities, and the infra-red photograph can never replace the panchromatic for general use. Each has advantages and disadvantages and the combination is more useful than either alone, but if only one emulsion can be used then it must normally be panchromatic. Some of the drawbacks of infra-red photography are associated with the sensitive material or the lens and may in time be eliminated, but others are fundamental and will always be present.

INFRA-RED SENSITIVE EMULSIONS

The term " infra-red " is applied to the very wide range of wavelengths which extends from the limit of the visible red at about 0·75 micron to the shortest radio waves at about 100 microns. Photography as normally understood, *i.e.*, using silver halide emulsions, is confined to a relatively narrow region between the end of the visible red and about 1·3 micron ; infra-red radiation of much longer wavelength can be detected and used to form images by other means, but air photography by these methods has not been accomplished. The fast and relatively stable infra-red emulsions used for air photography are not sensitive beyond about 0·9 micron, special emulsions sensitive to 1·2 micron are made for spectroscopic work, but they require very long exposures and are unstable, having to be stored at low temperatures until required for use. In so far as any " haze penetration " with infra-red photography is due to the use of longer wavelengths than are present in visible light, it would seem desirable to have emulsions sensitive as far into the infra-red region as possible, but, as Clark (1) points out, there are fundamental reasons why sensitising cannot be carried much further than at present. The thermal radiation from bodies at room temperature would obscure any differences in reflectance which they might exhibit if illuminated by very long wave infra-red, say 4 microns, while at wavelengths of the order of 2 microns the sensitising dyes could absorb enough energy from the thermal radiation to undergo spontaneous decomposition with fogging of the emulsions. Infra-red photography as now understood will therefore remain confined to the region adjacent to the visible spectrum.

The earlier materials used for infra-red photography were sensitised to a fairly narrow band of wavelengths, generally around 0·8 micron, with little or no sensitivity to any visible wavelength except in the blue-violet region common to all silver halide emulsions. At the present time practically all infra-red air photographs are taken on the emulsion made by Kodak Ltd., which still remains, as at the time when it was first introduced, much faster than anything else available. The spectral sensitivity of the Kodak infra-red film is shown in Fig. 83, and it will be seen that the added sensitivity extends from the yellow-green almost to 0·9 micron in the infra-red. With the older emulsions even a deep yellow filter such as Minus Blue was sufficient to cut out all effective visible light and give photographs by infra-red alone, but the Kodak film must be exposed behind a visually opaque filter if true infra-red photography is required. Nevertheless its sensitivity is much higher in the infra-red region than in any part of the visible spectrum except the blue-violet, as is shown in use by the fact that the well-known " chlorophyll effect " is strongly marked even in photographs taken with a Minus Blue

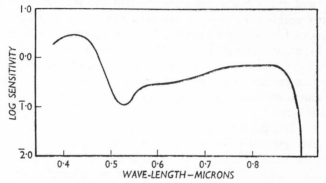

Fig. 83.—Spectral sensitivity of Kodak infra-red Aerographic film.
(*Redrawn from Clark,* " *Photography by Infra-Red,*" *by permission of Messrs Chapman & Hall, Ltd.*)

filter. The infra-red characteristics become more apparent as the filter cut is moved further down the spectrum, but at the same time the exposure has to be increased to make up for the loss of total energy utilised. If photographs are to be taken by infra-red light only, a suitable filter is the Ilford 207 or Wratten 88A ; due to the loss of visible red light the exposure is then doubled as compared with the usual compromise practice of using a Tricolour Red filter.

Infra-red film in general does not keep as well as panchromatic, especially at elevated temperatures, and it should be used within six months of coating for the best results. If possible the unexposed rolls should be stored in a refrigerator at a temperature of about 55° F. ; they should be removed from the store a day or so before use and allowed to warm up gradually so that condensation is avoided. However, it should also be stated that the modern Kodak emulsion seems to keep remarkably well, and the author has found that rolls stored in a fairly cool room without refrigeration were quite usable after two years, the speed having fallen to one-third its initial value with a negligible increase in fog.

Very stale film can sometimes be brought up to speed by hypersensitising, but this is a tedious process and is not normally recommended.

Sensitometry of Infra-red Emulsions.—Artificial " Mean Noon Sunlight " does not match real sunlight in the infra-red region and cannot be used for the sensitometry of infra-red materials. Filters are known which in combination with half-watt light give a spectral energy distribution over the photographic infra-red region closely matching that of real sunlight, but there is no internationally agreed standard. This is not a very serious matter, in view of the small quantity of infra-red film used and the limited number of sensitisings. Scientific users must in any case determine the working speed of the material under their own special conditions, while for general purposes the speed is expressed in terms of the exposure required under any given condition relative to that required for some standard panchromatic emulsion under the same conditions. This is not altogether satisfactory, because of the very unusual colour rendering given by infra-red emulsions, and the variable infra-red content of daylight, but no other course is practicable. The speeds and contrasts of different batches, or of different makes having approximately the same spectral sensitivity, can be compared by using half-watt light in the sensitometer and a step-wedge of the silver type, which is not transparent to infra-red light. In air photography satisfactory results are given by infra-red materials having a gamma of about 1·5 and a characteristic curve shape similar to that of the standard panchromatic types.

Exposure.—The exposure of infra-red film presents special problems for which no easy general solution exists, because the intensity of infra-red radiation at the earth's surface at any time is not necessarily proportional to the visual illumination. The infra-red content of sunlight is less scattered by haze than the visible light, but on the other hand it is much more strongly absorbed by water vapour or clouds. If infra-red exposures are calculated in the normal way for ground photography, under-exposure is likely to result on cloudy days and over-exposure when there is much haze. Harrison (2) has made records of the infra-red content of daylight with a recording photo-electric system sensitive to the photographic infra-red range, and his results show marked lack of correlation between the infra-red and visible radiation under different weather conditions. In the more restricted field of air photography the problems are less difficult, because infra-red photographs are nearly always taken when the sun is shining on the ground, so that absorption by the water in clouds causes no trouble. As a rule the effects of any difference in haze penetration can be neglected and the infra-red exposure calculated in a constant relation to the panchromatic. Exposure problems of a different kind are introduced by the special characteristics of infra-red photography, *e.g.*, the white rendering of green vegetation and the dark rendering of water, and the exposure has always to be calculated with the nature of the subject and the purpose of the operation in mind. When the sun is shining on the subject it is generally correct to give Kodak infra-red film used with a Tricolour Red filter four times the camera exposure required by fast panchromatic film used with a Minus Blue filter. This basic exposure may be halved if the subject is mainly grassland or other green vegetation having a higher infra-red than visual reflectance, and should be at least doubled if working over areas such as railway yards or leafless woods which reflect little infra-red light. Shadows may not be sufficiently exposed to show any detail, because they are often illuminated solely by light from the blue sky, which is lacking in infra-red, but haze or white clouds diffuse and reflect infra-red light and under some conditions well exposed shadow areas may be obtained. In general it is only practicable to expose for the sunlit areas and accept the loss of shadow detail when it occurs ; indeed, the emphasis of shadow is commonly held to be one of the merits of infra-red in air photography. Cloud shadows are also liable to be under-exposed but do not always show less detail than in panchromatic air photographs. If the air is clear and the clouds few and small their shadows will record quite black and devoid of detail, and it is said that on occasion they have been plotted as " lakes " when surveying new country, due to the difficulty of distinguishing them from water areas when both appear equally black. On the other hand, when there is haze and many large cumulus clouds the recording of cloud shadow detail may be superior in the infra-red photograph, because there is enough infra-red light reflected into the shadows and the superior haze penetration gives better contrast than in the panchromatic photograph. This may be especially marked if the terrain is well-grassed, which increases its apparent brightness in infra-red light.

Infra-red photographs are rarely taken under cloud, but in such conditions the rule given by Rawling (3) for ground photography in dull weather works quite well. Rawling says in effect that if the exposure for panchromatic emulsions has to be multiplied by four on dull days as compared with sunny days, then it should be multiplied by eight for infra-red emulsions. The thickness of cloud cover and hence the absorption of infra-red light will naturally vary very greatly on " dull " days, but on days when the sun is quite obscured but the weather is still good enough for flying, successful infra-red photographs have been taken by giving eight times the camera-exposure appropriate to panchromatic film.

At present there is no exposure meter on the market which measures the intensity of infra-red light ; the self-generating type of cell is not sensitive enough to give a direct reading in infra-red, and the vacuum cells require amplifiers which cannot be made up in a cheap and easily portable form.

Processing.—Infra-red air film can be processed in the same way as the standard panchromatic types, a typical development time being ten minutes at 20° C. in D19b, to give full speed and contrast. The details of processing treatment discussed in Chapter Four may be considered to apply equally to infra-red emulsions.

When it is important to get the utmost speed out of infra-red emulsions the R.A.F. Pyro-metol developer is worth trying ; it may give double the speed obtainable with D19b, but the gain may be erratic and fog may be high with some batches. There is also a tendency to produce small black spots.

The earlier infra-red emulsions, which had a very wide gap in the spectral sensitivity range, could be handled safely for processing under a relatively bright yellow safelight which absorbed infra-red, and it should perhaps be pointed out that the faster Kodak emulsion, which is sensitive to much of the visible spectrum, will fog at once if exposed to this kind of dark-room illumination. There is no difficulty in handling any kind of negative material in complete darkness, and when loading or processing infra-red material it is best to follow the same rule as with panchromatic and avoid the use of any kind of safelight.

Hypersensitising.—In normal circumstances hypersensitising is not advocated, but under special conditions or for experimental work it may be useful and a procedure which has been used successfully is therefore described. This technique was originally recommended by Kodak Ltd., but does not necessarily represent their official view at the present time. One advantage of hypersensitising is that old film which has lost a good deal of its speed seems to gain more than fresh film, so that within limits a more or less constant speed is obtained regardless of the age of the stock. It is important to observe great cleanliness at all stages of the process, to keep the dark room temperature reasonably low and to carry the whole operation through as quickly as possible. With due attention to chemical cleanliness the immersion in the hyper-sensitising bath can be carried out on the spool type of developing outfit.

The film is wound dry on to the spool unit, transferred without previous wetting into a 4 per cent. solution of 0·880 ammonia in distilled water and wound to and fro for three minutes. The spool unit is removed and drained, then transferred to a 1 in 25,000 solution of Kodak anti-fogging agent in 70 per cent. industrial methylated spirit and the winding continued for a further two minutes. The film is then fed on to a Smith type of dryer through a squeegee, dried by the air-blast without heat and reeled up for loading into the camera. Hypersensitised film should be used as soon as possible after treatment, if possible immediately afterwards, though it may keep for a few days in a refrigerator. This treatment followed by development in R.A.F. Pyro-metol has been found to give about three and a half times increase of speed, with film about six months old, over the untreated film developed in D19*b*.

DEFINITION IN THE INFRA-RED

Lens Focus.—Photographic lenses are nominally achromatic, *i.e.*, the position of best focus is supposed to be the same for all wavelengths of visible light. In lenses of normal construction, however, it is only possible to bring two wavelengths to exactly the same focus, and the chromatic errors are usually recorded in a diagram such as Fig. 84. In Fig. 84 the ordinates represent wavelength and the abscissæ position of focus along the optical axis. The broken portions of the curves are extrapolated. Curve 1 illustrates the performance of a 20 in. *f*/5·6 air camera lens designed and made in 1918 and representing the best practice of its time. The focal length is seen to be a minimum in the blue-green, with the same focus position for two wavelengths, one in the yellow and the other in the blue. This was the usual practice among photographic opticians in those days, the argument being that since the lens would be focused visually it would be set to give sharpest definition for yellow-green light, and that this focus setting would then be correct for the emulsion, which was predominantly sensitive to blue light. The argument was of course entirely fallacious, because the majority of air photographs were taken on panchromatic plates with yellow filters, even in 1918. Curve 1 shows that the position of focus changes very rapidly through the red and into the infra-red; the best focus for any emulsion sensitive to a wide range of wavelengths can only be a compromise, but it is obvious that the best infra-red focus must be at a much greater distance from the lens than the " panchromatic " focus. Curve 2 relates to a 20 in. lens of very high quality designed in 1944; its position of minimum focus lies further to the red and the achromatising is adjusted logically for red and green light. The slope of the focus curve is much less than that of the

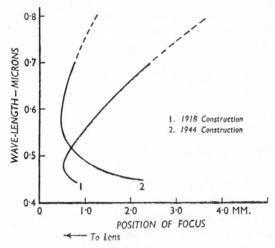

FIG. 84.—Chromatic aberration of two 20 in. lenses.

old lens in the red to infra-red region and there is less difference of focus between the visible and the infra-red, nevertheless an appreciable difference remains.

Some lenses sold for air photography are stated to require no change of focus when used with infra-red emulsions, but in the author's experience all lenses without exception require some change, even though it may be very small in certain cases. It does not necessarily follow that the general excellence of a lens is in inverse ratio to the change of focus required for infra-red photography, since definition is determined by many factors, of which longitudinal chromatic aberration is only one.

The magnitude of the focus shift for infra-red is best determined by making resolution tests with the collimator apparatus described in Chapter Five. A series of exposures is made on panchromatic film with the appropriate filter at different focus settings and the resolving power determined for each setting. Resolving power is then plotted against focus setting, giving a curve with a maximum as shown in Fig. 85, the maximum corresponding to the optimum focus position. The procedure is then repeated for the infra-red film, and the distance between the two focus maxima gives the change of focus for the infra-red emulsion in use. In carrying out tests of this kind it should be borne in mind that infra-red film is generally exposed at about two *f*/stops larger than panchromatic, and to avoid any trouble from spherical aberration in the lens the infra-red focus should be found for the aperture most likely to be used. It should also be remembered that Kodak infra-red film is sensitive to a very wide band of wavelengths, and with some lenses there may be an appreciable difference of focus according to the type of filter in use. The focus should therefore be determined with the filter which will actually be used.

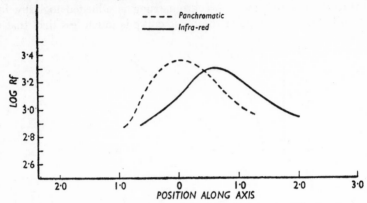

Fig. 85.—Determination of focus shift for the infra-red. (The lens is 8½ in. *f*/4 wide-angle type.)

The change of focus for a number of lenses used for air photography in England is given in Table 13; the change relates to the lens used with Kodak infra-red film and a Tricolour Red filter as compared with panchromatic film and a Minus Blue filter.

If a collimator apparatus is not available for testing the focus, a distant object such as a church spire a mile or so from the camera can be used as a target. In this case the results cannot be plotted as resolutions, and the best position must be judged from the definition in the photographs.

TABLE 13

Approximate focus shifts for lenses used in air photography when changing from panchromatic film to Kodak Infra-red film with Tricolour Red filter. For the most accurate work the user should determine the shift for his own lens.

Lens	Focus Shift (Thousandths of an Inch)
5 in. *f*/4 Ross W.A. Xpres (E.M.I.)	18
8 ,, *f*/2·9 Dallmeyer Pentac	18
8 ,, *f*/5·6 Cooke Aviar	9
14 ,, *f*/4·3 Dallmeyer Serrac	40
14 ,, *f*/5·6 T.T.H. Aviar	40
8¼ ,, *f*/4 Ross W.A. Xpres (E.M.I.)	22
20 ,, *f*/6·3 Ross Survey (serial numbers before 182310) .	64
20 ,, *f*/6·3 Ross Survey (serial numbers after 182310) .	28
20 ,, *f*/5·6 T.T.H. Aviar	64
36 ,, *f*/6·3 Dallmeyer telephoto	64
7 ,, *f*/2·5 Kodak Aero Ektar	18

Resolving Power.—The general literature on infra-red photography gives the impression that infra-red film requires a change of focus and that once this has been done the lens will perform as well as in the visible region. This is incorrect, and much of the difficulty in using infra-red film for air photography is due to the inferior lens performance. Aberrations in general are corrected as well as possible for some wavelength in the visible region, and even if the optimum infra-red focus is found the definition may be seriously affected by the change of wavelength, especially off axis. This trouble is accentuated by the low speed of infra-red emulsions which requires the use of the lens at two or more stops larger than with fast panchromatic film. When this is taken into account it is commonly found that the average resolving power over the field may be reduced by about 40 per cent. of its normal value. Theoretically the resolving power of the lens as such would be lower when using light of a longer wavelength, but the lens/film resolution is quite divorced from effects of this order and the reduction observed in photographic resolving power is entirely due to inferior correction for aberrations in the infra-red.

It is sometimes supposed that infra-red emulsions as such have lower resolving power than panchromatic, but while this may be true it is certainly a very minor factor in comparison with those already discussed. Figures published by Kodak Ltd. for their emulsions show that " Infra-red Aerographic " gives forty-five lines per millimetre under conditions in which Super XX gives fifty lines per millimetre.

One might expect to find inferior definition in infra-red photographs of subjects having a considerable range of brightness, because infra-red light probably penetrates the emulsion layer more effectively than visible light and may therefore be more liable to give halation effects with an unbacked film. Infra-red film certainly gives halation very easily on long-scale subjects, but no systematic investigation of such effects seems to have been made. There is no reason to anticipate any trouble from this cause in air photography, however, because over-exposure of infra-red film is most unlikely.

GENERAL CHARACTERISTICS OF INFRA-RED PHOTOGRAPHS

The value of infra-red for air photography depends on two characteristics, first and foremost the unusual tone rendering of scenes with green vegetation and water, and, much less important, the superior haze penetration. In the past, far too much prominence has been given to the second of these attributes, especially in the popular press, and the belief that infra-red can " photograph through fog " has become firmly implanted in the general mind. This belief has undoubtedly been fostered by the publication of numerous long-distance photographs, and especially by comparative pairs showing the relative penetration of haze by infra-red and " ordinary " plates. Too often the " ordinary " plate was ordinary in the photographer's sense that it was sensitive to blue-violet only, and a comparison with a filtered panchromatic plate would have been much less sensational, but this was not always made clear. It has been emphasised again and again in scientific publications, and notably by Dr Walter Clark, the foremost authority on the subject (1), that the haze penetrating power of infra-red is strictly limited, but there now seems to be little hope of destroying the legend. Nevertheless, the truth about this subject is so important in a work on air photography that further emphasis here may not be out of place.

Unusual Tone-rendering.—The most striking characteristic of infra-red photographs is the very light rendering of green vegetation, which always records much lighter than in panchromatic photographs and sometimes almost as light as snow. This effect is caused by the peculiar absorption

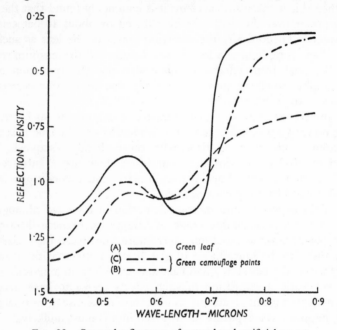

FIG. 86.—Spectral reflectance of natural and artificial greens.

spectrum of chlorophyll, the universal green colouring matter of nature, though strictly speaking the peculiarity is in the visible spectrum and not in the infra-red, where chlorophyll is transparent and " colourless."

The spectral reflectance curve of a green leaf is shown in Fig. 86 ; leaves of different trees and plants show detail differences from this typical curve, but all green vegetation shows the essential features of a maximum reflectance in the middle green region, a minimum in the red at about 0·66 micron, and a very rapid rise at the extreme red end to high reflectance in the infra-red. It should be especially noticed that the reflectance in the infra-red is much higher than at the highest point in the visible spectrum. Clark (1) gives several curves for leaves of different plants.

We are not accustomed to think of green leaves as particularly dark objects, yet most of them reflect less than 20 per cent. of the incident light even at the maximum in the middle green, and the average reflectance over the band of wavelengths used in panchromatic air photography with a yellow filter, say from 0·52 to 0·65 microns, is less than 10 per cent. Moreover, the peak of sensitivity of the modern panchromatic air emulsions usually falls at about 0·64 micron and they are generally more sensitive in the red than in the green. Green vegetation in general, therefore, tends to be reproduced in air photographs as quite a dark shade of grey. When we pass to the infra-red, however, the reflectance is very much higher, being of the same order as the lightest surfaces commonly seen from the air. The green leaf shown in Fig. 86, for example, reflects about 40 per cent. in the near infra-red, about the same as light concrete roadways or copings.

The light appearance of green vegetation in infra-red photographs is sometimes supposed to be due to fluorescence of the chlorophyll present in the plant cells. Clark (1) discusses this point and quotes evidence to show that the fluorescence is not a significant factor although it can be observed under favourable conditions. The fluorescence is confined to the red and very near infra-red, but foliage appears equally bright when photographed by any wavelength of infra-red, including longer wavelengths than those at which the fluorescence occurs. The bright appearance is simply due to the transparency of the chlorophyll in the infra-red, so that the mass of cellulosic tissue becomes effectively colourless and equivalent to cotton-wool, or as some workers have pointed out, to freshly fallen snow, the multitudes of cell fibres scattering light in all directions. Fresh green grass photographs very dark on panchromatic air film with a yellow filter, whereas withered grass or straw, containing only yellowish or brownish pigments, photographs in a light tone.* In the infra-red the green grass is as "colourless" as the withered grass in visible light and photographs as light or lighter.

It follows from this explanation that the tone in which green vegetation photographs must depend to a considerable extent on its physical condition as well as its spectral reflectance, while the result is also influenced by the texture and amount of "contained" shadow, or the amount of dark earth showing through. However, in any given circumstances these effects are much the same for visible or infra-red light and do not obscure the differences due to different spectral reflectance.

In general all the natural colouring matters as well as chlorophyll are transparent to infra-red, so that flowers and fruits photograph as light as grass and leaves. Coniferous trees are an exception, and photograph dark in infra-red light, due no doubt to the physical configuration of the needles.

Infra-red photographs are also characterised by a very dark rendering of water. Natural water areas in general tend to act as light traps, since the bottoms are mostly dark and the water is often slightly coloured by various impurities. Unless the water is clear and shallow over a light-coloured bottom or turbid with light-coloured matter, or sending strong surface reflections upwards into the camera, it usually records fairly dark in panchromatic photographs. Pure water begins to absorb quite appreciably at

* It should perhaps be pointed out that in many parts of the world grass is green for a much shorter period of the year than in Western Europe, and the comparative properties of panchromatic and infra-red photography will be modified accordingly.

the extreme red end of the visible spectrum, and by about 1·4 microns a centimetre or so gives practically complete absorption. Natural water areas, even ditches only a foot or so in depth, record quite black in infra-red air photographs. It will be clear that where there are areas of water and green vegetation in the same picture infra-red gives a great increase of contrast by extending the brightness scale at both ends.

Emphasis of shadow is another characteristic of infra-red which increases the effective contrast of the scene being photographed. The effect is most marked under a cloudless blue sky with no haze, so that the shadows are illuminated only by blue sky light which contains practically no infra-red. Needless to say, when conditions favour the emphasis of shadow they will also tend to prevent any detail being recorded within the shadowed area. At the opposite extreme from the very clear condition, in heavy haze, a great deal of infra-red light is scattered into the shadows but the light scattered upwards into the camera may mask the shadow detail. During the transition from the first condition to the second the rendering of shadow detail will at first improve, but will then deteriorate again. Much will depend on the polar scatter index, at least for the lighter hazes, as well as on the scatter as a function of wavelength, but prediction of results is hardly possible. At any haze condition the presence of white clouds will of course improve the shadow detail but reduce the emphasis of shadow ; in hazy conditions with much white cloud infra-red often shows more detail than panchromatic in cloud shadows on grass-covered terrain.

Most infra-red photographs lack shadow detail through sheer underexposure if there is little cloud or haze, though hypersensitised film can be given adequate exposure except under very clear conditions. With a natural green cover over most of the ground area shown in a photograph the greater part of a negative can have a density of about 1·0, and hence it will appear well-exposed though detail is lacking even in the larger shadowed areas where one might expect to find it in a panchromatic photograph. The same remarks apply to large dark areas such as railway yards which have no green cover, and to deciduous woods in winter. The dark areas as such stand out more clearly than in panchromatic photographs, but there will probably be less detail within them.

Plate 17 illustrates a laboratory demonstration of the special characteristics of infra-red which have been discussed in the preceding paragraphs. The objects were displayed on a white card and photographed from vertically above by Photoflood light. The panchromatic photograph was taken without filter and the infra-red with an Ilford 207 filter, which passes little visible light. The infra-red emulsion was the Kodak type sold for air photography. The prints were approximately matched for density and contrast on the grey scale. In the panchromatic photograph the grass and leaves are a rough match for the fourth step on the scale, which had a reflection density of 0·9, but in the infra-red they are lighter than the second step, density 0·3, and are not easily distinguished from the white background. The coke and dark humus-laden earth around the grass roots are about equally dark in both pictures, but the yellowish sandy soil on the underside of the turf is somewhat lighter in the infra-red. The glass cylinder held about eighteen inches depth of water ; it was covered with a sleeve of black paper over most of its length to minimise reflections. In the panchromatic photograph the bottom of the cylinder, backed up by the white card, is clearly visible through the water, but the latter has recorded almost black in the infra-red photograph.

It is interesting to observe that the seventh step on the grey scale records very dark in the panchromatic photograph but has an effective reflection density little greater than 0·3 in the infra-red. This step is made from black flock paper which has evidently been darkened with an infra-red transparent dye. The material would evidently be useless for lining the interior of cameras intended for infra-red photography.

Haze Penetration.—A general account of haze penetration by light of different wavelengths has been given in Chapter Eleven and there is no need to repeat the arguments here. It was shown that the extension of the visual range is relatively small except when the air is very clear with a visibility of some 30 miles or more. Now in air of this order of clarity the useful photographic range with panchromatic film is limited by scale rather than lack of contrast and improved haze penetration offers little or no improvement. The position is different if it is required to show only major geographical features such as mountain ranges or coastlines, but in most air photography the recording of individual objects on the ground is important. Thus there is no great scope for improved haze penetration at very long ranges in clear air ; a substantial improvement in hazy conditions with a visibility of a few miles would be more useful but it is just then that infra-red has least to offer.

The reader may find it difficult to reconcile these conclusions with the remarkable improvement in clarity shown by infra-red in some comparative photographs, but the discrepancy is readily explained. The visual range is defined as the vanishing range of a large black object seen against the horizon sky. The object vanishes because its contrast has fallen below the limit of visual perception, *i.e.*, its apparent brightness, due to the airlight, is equal to the sky brightness within less than 2 per cent. This is a good criterion so long as we are dealing with visual observation or photography with materials having roughly the same colour sensitivity as the human eye. The conditions are rather different in infra-red photography, however, because it can alter the apparent brightness characteristics of a scene so profoundly. Consider the case of a camera directed towards, say, a clump of leafless trees in open grassland. In a panchromatic photograph the wood and grass will reproduce as not very different densities, the wood reflecting little light of any colour and the grass having an effective photographic reflectance of the same low order due to the strong chlorophyll absorption in the red. They are both rather dark tones and seen from a long distance through haze the contrast between them may easily fall below the level at which they can be recorded as different densities in the panchromatic negative. In infra-red light, however, while the wood still reflects very little, the effective brightness of the grass is greatly increased and the contrast may be high enough for a clear photograph to be obtained. Suppose, for example, that in clear conditions the relative brightnesses of the wood and the grass are as 10 to 11 in the panchromatic range of wavelengths. Let haze light be added in the proportion of 50 units of brightness, which is not unrealistic for long-range obliques. The brightness ratio then changes from 1·100 to 1·016 and the wood will probably be indistinguishable from the grass, depending on the scale at which it is recorded. In infra-red light the wood may still be considered to have the same brightness of 10 units in absence of haze but the grass may be effectively raised to 40 ; when haze light of 50 units is added the brightness ratio becomes 1·5 and the contrast is more than adequate for the wood to be seen. It should be noted particularly that it is the increase of brightness of the grass which has done so much to offset the flattening effect of the haze. If the grass had remained at the same brightness while the wood fell to one-quarter of the original value, *i.e.*, to 2·5 units, the final brightness ratio would be 1·16, not nearly such a great improvement. In reality the haze would weaken the light reaching the camera from the ground as well as adding scattered light uniformly all over the picture, but this attenuation has no effect on brightness ratios and can be ignored in the argument. Apart from this, the figures used, though imaginary, are such as could well occur in practice, and we may conclude that the increase of contrast given by infra-red accounts for much of the improved clarity in infra-red photographs taken under hazy conditions, quite apart from any genuine haze penetration due to smaller scatter of the relatively long-wave light by the aerosols.

The same kind of reasoning can be applied with even greater force to the case of shore-lines, etc., for in the infra-red the water is darkened at the same time as the green vegetation on the land is lightened. Conversely, if there is no green vegetation or water there can be no increase of contrast other than that due to genuine haze penetration, and in actual air photographs this is found to be the case. In photographing a city, for example, infra-red may distinguish a park from a railway yard with remarkable clarity, but the improvement within the area of the railway yard is much less striking.

In general, then, the "haze penetration" of infra-red photography is most frequently due to enhanced contrast in the subject caused by the unusual rendering of water and green vegetation. The effect is no less useful for being spurious, but if it is not understood, the possibilities of infra-red cannot be appreciated at their true value. The greatest improvements in "haze penetration" are to be expected when photographing well-grassed terrain, especially in early summer when the green is at its brightest and most saturated. There is always some improvement even over completely built-up areas, but it is not possible to predict just what infra-red will do or when it will be worth using, since this is ultimately a matter of opinion and must be based on personal experience. The improvement over smoky industrial cities is sometimes rather greater than might be expected from the visibility, due possibly to small-sized combustion particles in the haze, but the photographs of such areas on infra-red film on a hazy day never approach in quality those taken on panchromatic film on clear days. If clear photographs are required of a hazy industrial area the best policy is to wait for clear weather and use panchromatic film. The clearest air is likely to be found on Sundays and probably in spring rather than any other season.

VALUE OF INFRA-RED TO THE INTERPRETER

The interpretation of air photographs is a highly specialised subject outside the scope of this book, but it will not be out of place to consider how the special properties of infra-red may influence the amount of information to be obtained from cover of different types of country. As we have already emphasised, it is desirable to forget haze penetration as a primary virtue of infra-red photography and to realise that its outstanding advantage is the power which it conveys of seeing the landscape quite literally in a new light, with a frequent reversal of the familiar tonal values. This applies only where there is green vegetation and water, because rock, sand, mud, heather, coniferous woods, and wholly built-up areas have similar reflectance character-istics in infra-red and in visible light. However, there are few areas of the earth's surface where there is no water or grass, and the special qualities of infra-red photography can be used to advantage in most parts of the world.

The first object of interpretation is the recognition of the objects shown in the photograph, and they cannot be seen at all unless they have some contrast with their background or with adjacent details. In the original scene the contrast may be in colour and in tone, but in the photograph we are restricted to shades of grey. The available contrasts will therefore depend to a considerable extent on the relative brightness with which different colours record, the relative brightness of any object shown in the picture depending on the hue and saturation of its colour and the colour sensitivity of the emulsion. It has already been shown how infra-red photography can extend the visual range by increasing the contrast of objects hidden by haze from normal observation, and the same argument can be applied to the case of details within a scene whose broad outlines are quite clear. In a typical panchromatic high altitude photograph before the writer the scene as a whole is clearly shown and most of the important details can be picked out by anyone familiar with the study of air photographs ; nevertheless these details have to be sought with close attention because their contrast with each other or with the general background is not very great, *e.g.*, a canal, a road, a cinder track, a railway yard, and the intermingled areas of grass are all reproduced in almost identical tones of grey. One useful feature of infra-red photography is its property of lifting vegetation in general to a much lighter level of tone against which the railways, the canals, and the " map detail " in general stands out with great clarity. Perhaps this does not give much help to the skilled interpreter because he can generally find all this information in the panchromatic photograph, but it does show up the general features of a tract of country in a broad and obvious way which may sometimes be very useful. There is a tendency to differentiate the varied objects of the landscape into natural vegetation, water, and things which are neither vegetation nor water, and this helps to lead the eye at once to features of interest.

Again, in high altitude vertical photographs taken under hazy conditions the contrast between some objects and their background may fall too low for them to be seen at all. In sharp large-scale photographs it is possible to distinguish between objects by differences of surface texture, especially with stereoscopic viewing, even though their tones may be a perfect match when seen in the mass. On a small scale, however, the textural details fall below the limit of resolution and only the broad tonal differences remain, so that when the tonal difference is nil the object will vanish in the photograph. Cinder or tarmac paths running across grass are examples of the kind of detail which tends to become lost in panchromatic photographs taken under hazy conditions; in infra-red the light rendering of the grass gives a clear differentiation from other things which are a tonal match in visible light.

A further advantage of infra-red, especially in small-scale photographs taken under hazy conditions, is that it sometimes helps in identifying objects which can just be seen in the panchromatic photograph but with insufficient detail for precise naming to be possible. For example, a heap of coke may be an almost perfect tonal match for adjacent green vegetation in the panchromatic photograph, and may even resemble it in surface texture, but in the infra-red photograph the vegetation records white and the coke black, so that confusion is impossible. Again, while vegetation and deciduous trees generally record white in infra-red, coniferous trees record dark. In panchromatic photographs the two types of tree may be confused, but in infra-red there is a clear differentiation of tone, which has some value in forestry studies.

The strong absorption of infra-red by water leads to a valuable application of infra-red photography in mapping the shallow water limit along shore-lines and revealing the position of navigable channels and the limits of sandbanks in river estuaries, etc. The emphasis of shadow by infra-red can be useful to the interpreter by revealing ditches and trenches and by showing up contours, apart from the more obvious cases of revealing objects by intensifying the shadowed outlines.

The light rendering of green vegetation which is so useful in showing up many of the darker features of the landscape has the reverse effect on light detail. Concrete roads, tracks worn down to sandy soil or chalk, quarries, cuttings in chalk or other light rock, are examples of light-toned detail which photographs more clearly in panchromatic than in infra-red, and the possible loss of such details must be balanced against the clearer rendering of water and communications and dark objects generally.

CAMOUFLAGE DETECTION

Infra-red air photography is popularly supposed to be used for camouflage detection in wartime, and enough information has been published to show that a good deal of thought must have been devoted to the subject, at least on the part of those who design camouflage and manufacture camouflage paints (1). Information is lacking, however, on the extent to which infra-red photography has actually been used for such purposes or whether it ever detected any camouflaged objects, and the military authorities who presumably have the relevant facts are not likely to divulge them. Nevertheless it is quite possible to make an intelligent appraisal of the situation in terms of material which has been published.

Under certain conditions infra-red photography might be expected to provide some help in detecting material camouflaged to match surrounding green vegetation. There is small prospect of it detecting things painted to match earth, sand, etc., since it is possible to use paint pigments of the same chemical nature as the surroundings and having the same spectral reflectance. In any case most of the common building materials and pigments which match earth, rock, etc., have no very strong absorption bands at any part of the visible or near infra-red spectrum.

Consider the spectral reflectance of green vegetation, which may be represented by the curve shown in Fig. 86. This curve may be regarded as representing green leaves in general, though any particular leaf will exhibit detail differences, e.g., in the height of the maximum and the depth of the minima, and to some extent in the position of the maximum. The important characteristics for the present purpose are the strong absorption of red light, shown by the minimum at about 0·68 micron, and the sharp rise to high reflectance at the edge of the infra-red. It is in this region that exact matching of the natural greens by the artificial paint colours is so difficult, though making a visual hue match is relatively easy. Colours may be a close visual match in apparent hue without necessarily having the same spectral reflectance curves, differences at one part of the spectrum being made to balance out against opposing differences at other parts. In Fig. 86, curve B, which does not represent any particular paint but may be taken as representative of one class of green camouflage paints, would be a good visual match for the green vegetation represented by curve A. Colour B reflects much less infra-red light than A, however, and an installation camouflaged with it would stand out black against the white of the green vegetation in an infra-red photograph. This paint would naturally be avoided by the camouflage designer. Curve C in Fig. 86 is typical of another class of camouflage paints which match the natural green very closely and also come nearer to it in infra-red reflectance. Straightforward infra-red photography with the usual rather wide range of wavelengths would not easily differentiate between natural greenery and an object painted with paint C. Needless to say, exact visual matching is never practicable where green vegetation is concerned, because the natural colour changes in hue and tone almost from day to day and the most that can be done is to ensure that the camouflage is a reasonable match for the average visual appearance of the surroundings. If the designer can also ensure that his effort will not look startlingly different in the infra-red little more can be expected of him. Paints such as C are reasonably satisfactory from this point of view and were used on a large scale during the late war.

" *Narrow Band* " *Techniques.*—Although there is little difference between the total light reflected by colours A and C in Fig. 86 over a wide band of wavelengths in the red and infra-red, there are appreciable differences at specific points, notably in the deep red at about 0·68 micron and 0·73 micron. Evidently paint C would show up light on a dark background of vegetation if photographed by a narrow band of wavelengths centred on 0·68 micron, and dark on a light ground if photographed by the band centred on 0·73 micron. This method seems to have been first suggested in England by Sir Thomas Merton, and it has been applied to air photography by use of suitable emulsion sensitisings and filters. In practice, however, it suffers from the severe limitation that a considerable increase of camera exposure is required, and this is an unavoidable shortcoming in view of the very narrow range of wavelengths which must be used. Regular infra-red photography which makes use of the available light-energy in a comparatively wide band of wavelengths is seriously handicapped by the need for greater camera exposure and hence lower resolution than panchromatic photography, but the difficulty is much more pronounced with narrow band methods, and it is unlikely that they will ever be used except for very special purposes. It is of interest to note, however, that visual observation of camouflage paints by a very narrow band of deep-red light gives a quick method of judging their suitability for use in a natural green environment. The easiest way of getting the required band of wavelengths is to view the samples in sunlight or arc light through a Wratten 89 infra-red filter which transmits enough of the red end of the visible spectrum to give what is required.

The reader will probably observe that narrow band methods could equally well be applied in the violet and green regions of the spectrum, where curve C of Fig. 86 departs appreciably from Curve A. In principle this is true, but in actual air photography it is desirable to work at the longest possible wavelengths in the interests of haze penetration. Admittedly there is no striking gain of haze penetration under many conditions, but to throw away the available advantage by working in violet light would be foolish when differences of spectral reflectance are present at the red end of the spectrum, especially since these special techniques are most likely to be useful under hazy conditions.

Practical Aspects of Camouflage Detection.—In considering the practical value of infra-red photography and the other methods just described as having potential value for camouflage detection it should be remembered that colour matching is only one aspect of the art of camouflage and sometimes a very minor part. There are some kinds of camouflage which photography cannot possibly break down, *e.g.*, a factory may be built underground or in a wood. Here the camouflage is genuinely a part of the natural surroundings and not an attempt to imitate them, and no kind of photography can reveal a difference that from the present point of view does not exist. It is generally accepted that camouflage of the larger objects such as factories or warships is impossible in the sense of hiding them from straightforward vertical photography with panchromatic film. The use of netting, disruptive painting, etc., may render the object less conspicuous, especially from a distance, and so may confuse the bomb-aimer working with his visual sight, but given a clear photograph and stereoscopic observation the interpreter will invariably spot differences from the environment which will arouse his suspicions. Many photographs, obviously not infra-red, were published by the Royal Air Force during the late war, with captions calling attention to the presence of camouflaged installations, battleships under netting, etc. The precise nature of the camouflaged objects may not always have been clear, but the point of the present argument is that the camouflage as such did not escape detection by panchromatic photography, and that infra-red would have conveyed no more information. (In many cases it would convey less on account of its inferior resolution.) Some exceptions to this general deduction might occur in very hazy weather, but there is no evidence available to show how important this might be.

Not all objects of military importance are large, however, and some are small enough to escape observation in small-scale panchromatic photographs, where there is no chance of picking them up by textural differences. In a marginal region of size infra-red might be expected to have a slight advantage over panchromatic, especially in hazy conditions; above this size panchromatic photographs would be as good as infra-red or better, in the region infra-red might reveal the presence of *something* by increased local contrast, below it the detail is lost again by inadequate resolution. Thus if we are photographing a row of tents painted to match their surroundings with a non-infra-red reflective paint, at progressively decreasing scales, the tents will at first be clearly shown in both panchromatic and infra-red photographs, then a point will be reached at which the contrast is too low in the panchromatic photographs for resolution of essential details and the tents will become confused with the surroundings; at this stage they may still show in the infra-red photograph as dark patches on the white background; at a still smaller scale they will not be shown even in the infra-red photograph. In this argument, however, we have assumed that the tents cast no shadow, which in practice would help to reveal their presence and would greatly narrow the margin between the panchromatic and infra-red results. Needless to say, the device of complete concealment applies with even greater force to the smaller objects which are so easily sited in woods or in other suitable surroundings. Since small-scale air photographs are almost devoid of shadow detail, siting in a shadow is practically equivalent to complete concealment against high altitude photography.

Broadly speaking, it appears that the larger objects cannot be hidden from normal air photography, while the smaller are easily hidden by proper siting, but if badly sited may be shown better by infra-red under a rather limited range of conditions. In view of this it does not seem likely that infra-red photography will ever be used to any great extent for the specific purpose of " detecting camouflage."

DESIRABLE SPECTRAL SENSITIVITY FOR AIR PHOTOGRAPHY

The discussions in this chapter will have made it clear that neither panchromatic nor infra-red emulsions have ideal spectral sensitivities, infra-red revealing some kinds of detail more clearly by making the general background of green vegetation appear very light, while panchromatic makes it darker and is better for other kinds of detail. In general, no single type of sensitising can be universally satisfactory, but there would be advantages in using both panchromatic and infra-red emulsions on all occasions. The object of this would be to record green vegetation as light as possible in one photograph and as dark as possible in the other, and from this point of view it would be desirable to have the panchromatic emulsion sensitised further out into the red than at present in order to take fuller advantage of the chlorophyll absorption band.* Dual operation, however, is normally out of the question and one is led to speculate on the ideal sensitising for use when only one photograph can be taken of each subject.

In developing panchromatic sensitisings for general photography one of the primary aims has been a spectral sensitivity approximately the same as that of the human eye, using filters on the lens if necessary. Matching the eye sensitivity is not necessarily ideal on every occasion but is probably the best practice for photography on the whole. One may sometimes find two colours, say a red and a blue, which are sharply differentiated in nature by their hue difference while photographing in the same shade of grey, but such cases are rare enough to count for little against the positive advantages of the panchromatic emulsion in other cases of importance to all photographers, e.g., the ability to record white clouds against a blue sky. There is no need for the eye sensitivity to be matched with any great precision, but marked differences are undesirable ; thus in portrait photography excessive blue sensitivity, as in an " ordinary " emulsion, exaggerates freckles, while sensitivity extending too far into the red gives the featureless " bladder of lard " appearance to faces photographed under tungsten light. Broadly speaking, if the effective emulsion sensitivity is greatest in the middle of the spectrum, avoiding high sensitivity at either end, pleasing reproduction is obtained, and the present types of sensitising have no doubt been developed with such considerations in view.

When we turn to air photography, however, we are not bound by the same requirements. It is not an *a priori* necessity for the emulsion to simulate the eye sensitivity, because the purpose of the air photograph is not to look like the original scene but to convey information about it. These two ends may well be served by the same means, but they remain distinct and one should not be allowed to confuse the other. In practice the air photographer at present makes no attempt to simulate eye sensitivity but exposes behind a deep yellow filter in the interests of haze penetration, thus giving his emulsion a relatively higher red sensitivity than the eye and making the blues and greens record unnaturally dark. The distortion of blues, or indeed of any non-natural colours, is of little significance, but green vegetation occupies so high a proportion of the area of most air photographs and is the background for so much ground detail that special thought should be given to its reproduction in monochrome. It has already been shown in this chapter that the usual dark rendering of green vegetation often leads to confusion of dark details such as water areas, tarmac, etc., with their surroundings, especially under hazy conditions when all dark tones tend to be com-

---

* *I.e.*, to peak at about 0.66 micron.

pressed together. A lighter rendering of natural greens would avoid much of this confusion, though admittedly it would lessen the contrast between the general background and the lighter details such as sandy tracks, concrete roads, etc. However, a compromise between the dark panchromatic and the light infra-red renderings would appear to have possibilities. All renderings must inevitably be unsuitable for some kinds of details, but any rendering which helps to differentiate between natural vegetation and things which are not natural vegetation, while avoiding obvious disadvantages, should be useful. In visual reconnaissance of a tract of country the eye scans the area and dwells for a further inspection on things which are not green ; in monochrome photography this can be simulated by making the natural greens record either very light or very dark. The " dark greens " method does not appear to be very promising, since it could only be accomplished to a sufficient extent by using a narrow band of wavelengths around 0·66 micron, and this would be impracticable for reasons already discussed. Moreover, when haze is present and all dark tones get crowded together the advantage of a dark background would be much less. The " light greens " method is developed to its logical conclusion in infra-red photography, but appears to go too far in view of the loss of the lighter details. A rendering between that of infra-red and the usual panchromatic rendering would appear to be ideal, since it would differentiate the greens from important details of dark tone and by its slightly " unnatural " appearance would help to isolate natural greenery from other things. It may appear that the choice of renderings for natural greens is purely arbitrary, and no doubt there are no startling improvements to be made by changing from the spectral sensitivity of the present panchromatic emulsions, but inspection of numerous air photographs over a number of years has convinced the writer that the present panchromatic rendering is not the best possible.

It would be possible to get a slightly lighter rendering of natural greens by using an orthochromatic emulsion, but the change would be relatively slight and in view of the inferior haze penetration there might on balance be a loss of clarity. It would be much better to work in a band of wavelengths extending approximately from 0·6 to 0·8 micron, with a peak at about 0·7 micron. This would make use of the rising chlorophyll characteristic at the extreme red end of the spectrum, and by suitable choice of sensitisers to give the right balance against the red absorption the desired rendering could be obtained. This " deep red " sensitising would have the advantage of somewhat improved haze penetration.

It may be wondered why the film manufacturers have not already developed sensitisings of this type if they really have the advantages now claimed for them, and various speculations can be made on this point. In the first place, film manufacturers naturally devote most research to the needs of their biggest markets, and air photography is not one of these. Again, there is not an unlimited choice of sensitisers, and few dyes give a useful combination of sensitivity to the desired spectral region and high working speed. It seems to be difficult to obtain high speed as one moves towards the longer wavelengths, and it may be intrinsically impossible to make an emulsion having the desired spectral sensitivity and as fast as the Super XX panchromatic type. Moreover, the energy in daylight decreases as one moves to longer wavelengths, which would be a further difficulty in the way of achieving high effective speed. It is to be hoped, nevertheless, that we may eventually see an emulsion in use whose spectral sensitivity is based on the requirements of air photography rather than on those of photography in general.

COMPARATIVE PHOTOGRAPHS

In Plates 18 to 29 a number of comparative pairs of infra-red and panchromatic photographs are displayed. They were taken by simultaneous exposure in two cameras held in double mountings and the lenses were matched for resolving power (on panchromatic film) so that the experimental conditions were identical for both members of each pair, enabling a just comparison to be made between the panchromatic and infra-red results. A number of areas have been marked on each photograph showing typical examples of the advantages and disadvantages of infra-red, as discussed earlier in this chapter. These points are explained by captions accompanying the photographs. Needless to say, each pair of photographs contains many more points of difference than have been marked.

REFERENCES

1. CLARK, W. "Photography by Infra-red." Chapman & Hall, London. This is the standard reference work for the subject.
2. HARRISON, G. B. "The Infra-red Content of Daylight," *Photo. Journ.*, 73, 1933. *Sci. Tech. Suppl.*, pp. 1-3.
3. RAWLING, S. O. "Infra-red Photography," Second edition. Blackie, London.

Chapter Fifteen

SOME FINAL REMARKS ON GRAININESS
AND RELATED FACTORS

THIS book is largely built up around a constantly recurring theme—the need for the highest possible resolution of ground detail in air photography. It has been emphasised that all the conditions of operation make fulfilment of this need very difficult, for the camera is on an unsteady and rapidly moving platform, lenses and emulsions have limited resolving power, and the subject details are a long way off behind a veil of haze. The usual techniques are adapted to deal with this situation, *e.g.*, we use the fastest shutter and the smallest lens aperture that conditions allow, and the emulsion and development which give the best balance between speed and graininess. The haze, however, is a variable quite beyond our control; in its unforeseeable fluctuations it affects the subject contrast and hence the resolving power. From another point of view we may consider that the effective graininess of the emulsion increases with the haze, because the end result is that the brightness differences in the image become smaller relative to the random density fluctuations of the graininess in the developed negative. If the photographer is not alive to the importance of these facts he is liable to blame his emulsion or processing technique for " increased graininess " when the real fault is in the atmospheric conditions. This is no hypothetical case; again and again the author has seen flat-looking negatives and heard complaints that the emulsion has deteriorated, or that a fine-grain developer would give better results, or that a miniature camera would produce sharper pictures, or that the negatives are under-exposed (in such cases they are usually over-exposed) or under-developed or over-developed. In all cases the only cause of failure has been the haziness of the atmosphere at the time of exposure. Graininess as related to emulsion, development, and atmospheric conditions is so much misunderstood that it seemed worth while to devote a final chapter to special consideration of this subject.

Some examples have already been shown in which, by comparative air tests, the effect of haze on apparent graininess, and other aspects of graininess, were demonstrated. Air tests, however, sometimes lack the conviction of a carefully controlled laboratory experiment, because it is not normally possible to show comparisons of the same scene under different haze conditions with all other possible variables held constant. For this reason the tests illustrated in this chapter are presented; they were carried out with the controlled precision possible in the laboratory, but by their pictorial nature may be more convincing than figures or diagrams.

A LABORATORY SUBJECT FOR DEMONSTRATION PURPOSES

In these tests the basic subject was an illuminated transparency made from a low-altitude air negative, and by photographing it at a suitable reduction and flooding it with "haze" light the conditions of high-altitude photography could be simulated. Different photographic techniques could then be compared on a subject which had all the appearance of a high-altitude scene but whose brightness characteristics could be held absolutely constant in any chosen condition. The set-up is shown diagrammatically in Fig. 87 The transparency T is illuminated by the illuminating box B_1, with lamp and opal glass O_1. It is photographed through the plate-glass sheet P inclined at an angle of 45 degrees to the optical axis. P is illuminated to any desired brightness by varying the illumination given by a second lamp in the box B_2 with opal glass O_2. For same size copies the camera is close to the plate glass,

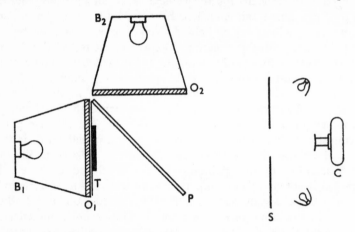

FIG. 87.—Set-up for simulating the haze in air photography.

while for "high altitude" reduced copies a 35 mm. camera is located at a suitable distance, as shown at C. In this relatively remote condition the illuminated transparency occupies only a small part of the total field of view of the camera, and to keep the flare conditions the same as in the larger copies, a white screen S, with a hole just big enough for T to be seen unobstructed, is illuminated to the mean brightness of T by the shielded lamps shown.

    The negative from which the transparency was made had been taken with a moving film camera from 200 ft. at a scale of 1 in 450; it was quite sharp and showed ground details of the order of 1 in. in size. There was no haze of any significance in the original scene. The brightness range of the transparency, without any added haze light, as mounted on the opal and viewed from a short distance in front, was 40 to 1 measured from the white washing on the lawn to the dark shadow adjacent to the upper chimney on the house, and 25 to 1 measured from the large highlight on the house roof to the same shadow. These brightness ranges are probably close to those in the original scene; they are certainly of the right order for such scenes, which is all that is necessary for this experiment.

    The transparency was therefore a reasonably faithful monochrome reproduction of the scene as it appeared from 200 ft., and by adding suitable amounts of haze light it could be given the shorter brightness ranges typical of high-altitude subjects.

Effect of Haze alone.—Plate 30 shows the effect of haze acting in isolation, which is not normally observed in practice, but the demonstration is probably the more valuable on that account.

Example (A) is from a direct print from the original air negative ; since the transparency cannot be shown it may be regarded as the nearest possible equivalent to the transparency or to the original scene that can be shown in a half-tone illustration. It is naturally inferior to the transparency in tone reproduction, especially in the highlights and shadows, but will serve as a reference standard. The other examples will be judged according to the closeness with which they approach this standard.

Example (B) is from a 1 to 1 copy negative of the transparency, haze having been added to bring the brightness range down to 6 to 1, which is fairly close to the average value for subjects seen from 20,000 ft. in average clear weather. The transparency naturally looked much flatter behind the veil of haze, but the photographic conditions were adjusted, as they would be in actual air photography, so that the contrast between the darkest shadow and the brightest highlight in the picture was brought back to approximately the original value. The overall contrast is the same as in absence of haze, but the tone reproduction is quite different, and in particular the low contrast shadow detail has been largely wiped out. This is, of course, due to the fact that although the overall slope is greater than 1·0 in terms of the subject brightnesses seen through the haze, it is less than 1·0, and in the shadows very much less than 1·0, in terms of the original scene. Thus the haze has changed the brightness characteristics of the scene in a way which we can do very little to counter.

Example (C) corresponds to (B) except that the brightness range was brought down to 2 to 1, corresponding to very heavy haze in a high-altitude view. It exhibits the same characteristics as (B) to a greater degree ; although printed on a more contrasty paper this has not been sufficient to overcome the flattening effect of the additional haze.

It is probable that in the reproduction example (B) will not look very different from (A) ; it should then be remembered that (B) and (C) differ from (A) in the same way but to different degrees.

The reader will observe that examples (B) and (C) look very like prints on contrasty paper from badly under-exposed negatives, and it should be particularly stressed that in both cases the negatives were fully exposed, all densities being well up on the straight line portion of the characteristic curve. Haze and under-exposure are in fact very similar in their effects, both losing shadow detail by lack of sufficient gradient. The high-altitude negative can therefore never be made as good as the low-altitude one, however excellent the resolution may be for details which are not in shadow.

Combined Effects of Haze and Scale Reduction.—Plate 31 contains examples of scale reduction without haze and scale reduction combined with haze, the latter simulating the conditions of high-altitude air photography. All the examples are from negatives made from the transparency at a twenty times reduction in a miniature camera fitted with a 2 in. " Summitar " lens, used throughout at $f/6\cdot3$. The definition given by this lens is probably better than that given by most of the lenses used in air photography, though it is very little better than that of the best aircraft lenses. As it was used always at the same aperture and all the pictures were taken in the same part of its field it is a constant factor and need not be considered any further. The densities of the negatives referred to in this plate and Plate 32 were all $0\cdot85\pm0\cdot05$, measured on the patch of lawn at the right of the picture. This constancy of density was essential in making comparisons of graininess. The only exceptions to this statement will be referred to when considering the effect of exposure on graininess. The twenty times reduction is equivalent to photographing the original scene at a scale of 1 : 9000, a rather large scale for high-altitude work. The negatives were all enlarged twenty times for ready comparison of the ground detail with that shown in the original scene. Viewing from different distances will simulate the effect of viewing the negatives at smaller degrees of enlargement.

Example (A) was taken on a standard type of fast panchromatic film as used for air photography. No haze light was present, and it was therefore developed to a gamma less than unity in D76, and enlarged on a soft bromide paper. There is, of course, a great loss of detail compared with the original scene (cf. (A) in Plate 30) and the loss is most serious for the details of lowest contrast, e.g., in the shadows.

Example (B) was taken with sufficient haze, as in example 30 (B), to bring the brightness range down to 6 to 1. As would happen in actual air photography of a scene with such a brightness range, it was developed in D19b for maximum speed and a gamma of more than unity. It was then enlarged on a medium contrast bromide paper, so that the overall black to white contrast is much the same as in example (A). The tone reproduction must differ from (A) in the same way as (B) differs from (A) in Plate 30 but the differences are less obvious in this case because the shadow details have been largely obscured by the graininess even in the example without haze.

Example (C) corresponds to (B) except that the brightness scale was brought down to 2 to 1 by adding more haze light, as for (C) in Plate 30. The negative was then enlarged on to a contrasty bromide paper, but even this has not brought the brightness range of the print back to match (B), while the increase of graininess and loss of detail are very serious. In making this negative the exposure was adjusted so that the density on the patch of grass was $0\cdot95$; in actual air photography under such hazy conditions as those simulated here the increase of density might be greater and the graininess correspondingly worse.

Effect of Negative Over-exposure.—Example (D) in Plate 31 corresponds to (B) in all respects except that its negative exposure was much greater, yielding a negative density of $2\cdot1$ on the grass patch. The catastrophic effect of over-exposure on graininess and resolution of ground detail is sufficiently obvious to need no comment.

Comparison of Different Developers and Emulsions.—Plate 32 illustrates the kind of graininess difference and the effect on ground detail produced by use of fine-grain developers and different emulsions. It may help to put the " fine-grain " case in better perspective. All the examples were taken on the scale of 1 : 9,000 and enlarged twenty times, and the brightness scale was 6 to 1 in each case.

Example (A) was on fast panchromatic film fully developed in D19b ; (B) was on the same emulsion developed in DK20 for the highest practicable speed, which was about one-third of the speed in D19b. The graininess is slightly lower than (A), but the difference is not great enough for a significant increase of detail to be seen. In actual air photography the lens would have had to be used at one to two stops larger, and overall there would have been a loss of detail.

Example (C) was on Panatomic X fully developed in D19b. The graininess and detail are similar to (B) ; in practice the lower speed of Panatomic X would again result in an admittedly less grainy picture but no significant change in detail resolved.

It will be noticed that the graininess difference between (A), (B), and (C) is less than the difference caused by over-exposure on the fast emulsion (*cf*. Plate 31).

Example (D) was taken on Microfile film developed in metol to a gamma of 1·4. Its graininess is very much less than the other three, and it shows much more detail. Example (D) in Plate 32 is in fact very little inferior in any respect to the full-size copy (B) in Plate 30.

Thus we see that for a really substantial reduction in emulsion graininess we have to go to an extremely slow film such as Microfile, which requires about eighty times the exposure of the standard fast film. It is not, of course, practicable to use Microfile for actual air photography.

CONCLUSION

We have ended this book as we began it, with a reference to the limitations of the photographic process even in one of its most characteristic attributes, the reproduction of fine detail. Such limitations are often imposed by the difficult nature of the subjects which are encountered in air photography, above all the uncontrollable factor of atmospheric haze. The need for brief exposure times and the smallest practicable lens aperture generally prevents us using the most desirable photographic techniques, and with the compromise methods that must be adopted it is all the more important to avoid those errors which lower the resolution below the maximum obtainable. That maximum may be much lower than we should like, but it is nevertheless high enough to make air photography a very valuable tool. With an average air camera, not of outstandingly good performance, we may expect to get a resolving power of some twelve lines per millimetre for detail of the contrast encountered in typical country seen from the air. This is equivalent to 2,700 lines in the 9-in. picture frame, or, putting the same facts in another way, we may say that details occupying as little as one seven-millionth of the area of the ground covered can be perceived in each of our photographs. To do this from a rapidly moving platform when the ground is some miles distant behind a veil of haze is perhaps, after all, no mean performance.

INDEX

CATALOGUE OF DOVER BOOKS

PHYSICS

General physics

FOUNDATIONS OF PHYSICS, R. B. Lindsay & H. Margenau. Excellent bridge between semi-popular works & technical treatises. A discussion of methods of physical description, construction of theory; valuable for physicist with elementary calculus who is interested in ideas that give meaning to data, tools of modern physics. Contents include symbolism, mathematical equations; space & time foundations of mechanics; probability; physics & · continua; electron theory; special & general relativity; quantum mechanics; causality. "Thorough and yet not overdetailed. Unreservedly recommended," NATURE (London). Unabridged, corrected edition. List of recommended readings. 35 illustrations. xi + 537pp. 5⅜ x 8.
S377 Paperbound **$3.00**

FUNDAMENTAL FORMULAS OF PHYSICS, ed. by D. H. Menzel. Highly useful, fully inexpensive reference and study text, ranging from simple to highly sophisticated operations. Mathematics integrated into text—each chapter stands as short textbook of field represented. Vol. 1: Statistics, Physical Constants, Special Theory of Relativity, Hydrodynamics, Aerodynamics, Boundary Value Problems in Math. Physics; Viscosity, Electromagnetic Theory, etc. Vol. 2: Sound, Acoustics, Geometrical Optics, Electron Optics, High-Energy Phenomena, Magnetism, Biophysics, much more. Index. Total of 800pp. 5⅜ x 8.
Vol. 1 S595 Paperbound **$2.25**
Vol. 2 S596 Paperbound **$2.25**

MATHEMATICAL PHYSICS, D. H. Menzel. Thorough one-volume treatment of the mathematical techniques vital for classic mechanics, electromagnetic theory, quantum theory, and relativity. Written by the Harvard Professor of Astrophysics for junior, senior, and graduate courses, it gives clear explanations of all those aspects of function theory, vectors, matrices, dyadics, tensors, partial differential equations, etc., necessary for the understanding of the various physical theories. Electron theory, relativity, and other topics seldom presented appear here in considerable detail. Scores of definitions, conversion factors, dimensional constants, etc. "More detailed than normal for an advanced text . . . excellent set of sections on Dyadics, Matrices, and Tensors," JOURNAL OF THE FRANKLIN INSTITUTE. Index. 193 problems, with answers. x + 412pp. 5⅜ x 8.
S56 Paperbound **$2.00**

THE SCIENTIFIC PAPERS OF J. WILLARD GIBBS. All the published papers of America's outstanding theoretical scientist (except for "Statistical Mechanics" and "Vector Analysis"). Vol I (thermodynamics) contains one of the most brilliant of all 19th-century scientific papers—the 300-page "On the Equilibrium of Heterogeneous Substances," which founded the science of physical chemistry, and clearly stated a number of highly important natural laws for the first time; 8 other papers complete the first volume. Vol II includes 2 papers on dynamics, 8 on vector analysis and multiple algebra, 5 on the electromagnetic theory of light, and 6 miscellaneous papers. Biographical sketch by H. A. Bumstead. Total of xxxvi + 718pp. 5⅝ x 8⅜.
S721 Vol I Paperbound **$2.50**
S722 Vol II Paperbound **$2.00**
The set **$4.50**

BASIC THEORIES OF PHYSICS, Peter Gabriel Bergmann. Two-volume set which presents a critical examination of important topics in the major subdivisions of classical and modern physics. The first volume is concerned with classical mechanics and electrodynamics: mechanics of mass points, analytical mechanics, matter in bulk, electrostatics and magnetostatics, electromagnetic interaction, the field waves, special relativity, and waves. The second volume (Heat and Quanta) contains discussions of the kinetic hypothesis, physics and statistics, stationary ensembles, laws of thermodynamics, early quantum theories, atomic spectra, probability waves, quantization in wave mechanics, approximation methods, and abstract quantum theory. A valuable supplement to any thorough course or text.
Heat and Quanta: Index. 8 figures. x + 300pp. 5⅜ x 8½. S968 Paperbound **$2.00**
Mechanics and Electrodynamics: Index. 14 figures. vii + 280pp. 5⅜ x 8½.
S969 Paperbound **$1.85**

THEORETICAL PHYSICS, A. S. Kompaneyets. One of the very few thorough studies of the subject in this price range. Provides advanced students with a comprehensive theoretical background. Especially strong on recent experimentation and developments in quantum theory. Contents: Mechanics (Generalized Coordinates, Lagrange's Equation, Collision of Particles, etc.), Electrodynamics (Vector Analysis, Maxwell's equations, Transmission of Signals, Theory of Relativity, etc.), Quantum Mechanics (the Inadequacy of Classical Mechanics, the Wave Equation, Motion in a Central Field, Quantum Theory of Radiation, Quantum Theories of Dispersion and Scattering, etc.), and Statistical Physics (Equilibrium Distribution of Molecules in an Ideal Gas, Boltzmann statistics, Bose and Fermi Distribution, Thermodynamic Quantities, etc.). Revised to 1961. Translated by George Yankovsky, authorized by Kompaneyets. 137 exercises. 56 figures. 529pp. 5⅜ x 8½. S972 Paperbound **$2.50**

ANALYTICAL AND CANONICAL FORMALISM IN PHYSICS, André Mercier. A survey, in one volume, of the variational principles (the key principles—in mathematical form—from which the basic laws of any one branch of physics can be derived) of the several branches of physical theory, together with an examination of the relationships among them. Contents: the Lagrangian Formalism, Lagrangian Densities, Canonical Formalism, Canonical Form of Electrodynamics, Hamiltonian Densities, Transformations, and Canonical Form with Vanishing Jacobian Determinant. Numerous examples and exercises. For advanced students, teachers, etc. 6 figures. Index. viii + 222pp. 5⅜ x 8½. S1077 Paperbound **$1.75**

Catalogue of Dover Books

Acoustics, optics, electricity and magnetism, electromagnetics, magneto-hydrodynamics

THE THEORY OF SOUND, Lord Rayleigh. Most vibrating systems likely to be encountered in practice can be tackled successfully by the methods set forth by the great Nobel laureate, Lord Rayleigh. Complete coverage of experimental, mathematical aspects of sound theory. Partial contents: Harmonic motions, vibrating systems in general, lateral vibrations of bars, curved plates or shells, applications of Laplace's functions to acoustical problems, fluid friction, plane vortex-sheet, vibrations of solid bodies, etc. This is the first inexpensive edition of this great reference and study work. Bibliography. Historical introduction by R. B. Lindsay. Total of 1040pp. 97 figures. 5⅜ x 8.
S292, S293, Two volume set, paperbound, **$4.70**

THE DYNAMICAL THEORY OF SOUND, H. Lamb. Comprehensive mathematical treatment of the physical aspects of sound, covering the theory of vibrations, the general theory of sound, and the equations of motion of strings, bars, membranes, pipes, and resonators. Includes chapters on plane, spherical, and simple harmonic waves, and the Helmholtz Theory of Audition. Complete and self-contained development for student and specialist; all fundamental differential equations solved completely. Specific mathematical details for such important phenomena as harmonics, normal modes, forced vibrations of strings, theory of reed pipes, etc. Index. Bibliography. 86 diagrams. viii + 307pp. 5⅜ x 8. **S655 Paperbound $2.00**

WAVE PROPAGATION IN PERIODIC STRUCTURES, L. Brillouin. A general method and application to different problems: pure physics, such as scattering of X-rays of crystals, thermal vibration in crystal lattices, electronic motion in metals; and also problems of electrical engineering. Partial contents: elastic waves in 1-dimensional lattices of point masses. Propagation of waves along 1-dimensional lattices. Energy flow. 2 dimensional, 3 dimensional lattices. Mathieu's equation. Matrices and propagation of waves along an electric line. Continuous electric lines. 131 illustrations. Bibliography. Index. xii + 253pp. 5⅜ x 8.
S34 Paperbound **$2.00**

THEORY OF VIBRATIONS, N. W. McLachlan. Based on an exceptionally successful graduate course given at Brown University, this discusses linear systems having 1 degree of freedom, forced vibrations of simple linear systems, vibration of flexible strings, transverse vibrations of bars and tubes, transverse vibration of circular plate, sound waves of finite amplitude, etc. Index. 99 diagrams. 160pp. 5⅜ x 8. **S190 Paperbound $1.50**

LIGHT: PRINCIPLES AND EXPERIMENTS, George S. Monk. Covers theory, experimentation, and research. Intended for students with some background in general physics and elementary calculus. Three main divisions: 1) Eight chapters on geometrical optics—fundamental concepts (the ray and its optical length, Fermat's principle, etc.), laws of image formation, apertures in optical systems, photometry, optical instruments etc.; 2) 9 chapters on physical optics—interference, diffraction, polarization, spectra, the Rayleigh refractometer, the wave theory of light, etc.; 3) 23 instructive experiments based directly on the theoretical text. "Probably the best intermediate textbook on light in the English language. Certainly, it is the best book which includes both geometrical and physical optics," J. Rud Nielson, PHYSICS FORUM. Revised edition. 102 problems and answers. 12 appendices. 6 tables. Index. 270 illustrations. xi +489pp. 5⅜ x 8½. **S341 Paperbound $2.50**

PHOTOMETRY, John W. T. Walsh. The best treatment of both "bench" and "illumination" photometry in English by one of Britain's foremost experts in the field (President of the International Commission on Illumination). Limited to those matters, theoretical and practical, which affect the measurement of light flux, candlepower, illumination, etc., and excludes treatment of the use to which such measurements may be put after they have been made. Chapters on Radiation, The Eye and Vision, Photo-Electric Cells, The Principles of Photometry, The Measurement of Luminous Intensity, Colorimetry, Spectrophotometry, Stellar Photometry, The Photometric Laboratory, etc. Third revised (1958) edition. 281 illustrations. 10 appendices. xxiv + 544pp. 5½ x 9¼. **S319 Paperbound $3.00**

EXPERIMENTAL SPECTROSCOPY, R. A. Sawyer. Clear discussion of prism and grating spectrographs and the techniques of their use in research, with emphasis on those principles and techniques that are fundamental to practically all uses of spectroscopic equipment. Beginning with a brief history of spectroscopy, the author covers such topics as light sources, spectroscopic apparatus, prism spectroscopes and graphs, diffraction grating, the photographic process, determination of wave length, spectral intensity, infrared spectroscopy, spectrochemical analysis, etc. This revised edition contains new material on the production of replica gratings, solar spectroscopy from rockets, new standard of wave length, etc. Index. Bibliography. 111 illustrations. x + 358pp. 5⅜ x 8½. **S1045 Paperbound $2.25**

FUNDAMENTALS OF ELECTRICITY AND MAGNETISM, L. B. Loeb. For students of physics, chemistry, or engineering who want an introduction to electricity and magnetism on a higher level and in more detail than general elementary physics texts provide. Only elementary differential and integral calculus is assumed. Physical laws developed logically, from magnetism to electric currents, Ohm's law, electrolysis, and on to static electricity, induction, etc. Covers an unusual amount of material; one third of book on modern material: solution of wave equation, photoelectric and thermionic effects, etc. Complete statement of the various electrical systems of units and interrelations. 2 Indexes. 75 pages of problems with answers stated Over 300 figures and diagrams. xix +669pp. 5⅜ x 8. **S745 Paperbound $3.50**

SUPERFLUIDS: MACROSCOPIC THEORY OF SUPERCONDUCTIVITY, Vol. I, Fritz London. The major work by one of the founders and great theoreticians of modern quantum physics. Consolidates the researches that led to the present understanding of the nature of super-conductivity. Prof. London here reveals that quantum mechanics is operative on the macro-scopic plane as well as the submolecular level. Contents: Properties of Superconductors and Their Thermodynamical Correlation; Electrodynamics of the Pure Superconducting State; Relation between Current and Field; Measurements of the Penetration Depth; Non-Viscous Flow vs. Superconductivity; Micro-waves in Superconductors; Reality of the Domain Structure; and many other related topics. A new epilogue by M. J. Buckingham discusses developments in the field up to 1960. Corrected and expanded edition. An appreciation of the author's life and work by L. W. Nordheim. Biography by Edith London. Bibliography of his publica-tions. 45 figures. 2 Indices. xviii + 173pp. 5⅝ x 8⅜. S44 Paperbound **$1.75**

SELECTED PAPERS ON PHYSICAL PROCESSES IN IONIZED PLASMAS, Edited by Donald H. Menzel, Director, Harvard College Observatory. 30 important papers relating to the study of highly ionized gases or plasmas selected by a foremost contributor in the field, with the assistance of Dr. L. H. Aller. The essays include 18 on the physical processes in gaseous nebulae, covering problems of radiation and radiative transfer, the Balmer decrement, electron temperatives, spectrophotometry, etc. 10 papers deal with the interpretation of nebular spectra, by Bohm, Van Vleck, Aller, Minkowski, etc. There is also a discussion of the intensities of "forbidden" spectral lines by George Shortley and a paper concern-ing the theory of hydrogenic spectra by Menzel and Pekeris. Other contributors: Goldberg, Hebb, Baker, Bowen, Ufford, Liller, etc. viii + 374pp. 6⅛ x 9¼. S60 Paperbound **$2.95**

THE ELECTROMAGNETIC FIELD, Max Mason & Warren Weaver. Used constantly by graduate engineers. Vector methods exclusively: detailed treatment of electrostatics, expansion meth-ods, with tables converting any quantity into absolute electromagnetic, absolute electrostatic, practical units. Discrete charges, ponderable bodies, Maxwell field equations, etc. Introduc-tion. Indexes. 416pp. 5⅜ x 8. S185 Paperbound **$2.25**

THEORY OF ELECTRONS AND ITS APPLICATION TO THE PHENOMENA OF LIGHT AND RADIANT HEAT, H. Lorentz. Lectures delivered at Columbia University by Nobel laureate Lorentz. Unabridged, they form a historical coverage of the theory of free electrons, motion, absorption of heat, Zeeman effect, propagation of light in molecular bodies, inverse Zeeman effect, optical phenomena in moving bodies, etc. 109 pages of notes explain the more advanced sections. Index. 9 figures. 352pp. 5⅜ x 8. S173 Paperbound **$2.00**

FUNDAMENTAL ELECTROMAGNETIC THEORY, Ronold P. King, Professor Applied Physics, Harvard University. Original and valuable introduction to electromagnetic theory and to circuit theory from the standpoint of electromagnetic theory. Contents: Mathematical Description of Matter—stationary and nonstationary states; Mathematical Description of Space and of Simple Media—Field Equations, Integral Forms of Field Equations, Electromagnetic Force, etc.; Transformation of Field and Force Equations; Electromagnetic Waves in Unbounded Regions; Skin Effect and Internal Impedance—in a solid cylindrical conductor, etc.; and Electrical Circuits—Analytical Foundations, Near-zone and quasi-near zone circuits, Balanced two-wire and four-wire transmission lines. Revised and enlarged version. New preface by the author. 5 appendices (Differential operators: Vector Formulas and Identities, etc.). Problems. Indexes. Bibliography. xvi + 580pp. 5⅜ x 8½. S1023 Paperbound **$3.00**

Hydrodynamics

A TREATISE ON HYDRODYNAMICS, A. B. Basset. Favorite text on hydrodynamics for 2 genera-tions of physicists, hydrodynamical engineers, oceanographers, ship designers, etc. Clear enough for the beginning student, and thorough source for graduate students and engineers on the work of d'Alembert, Euler, Laplace, Lagrange, Poisson, Green, Clebsch, Stokes, Cauchy, Helmholtz, J. J. Thomson, Love, Hicks, Greenhill, Besant, Lamb, etc. Great amount of docu-mentation on entire theory of classical hydrodynamics. Vol I: theory of motion of frictionless liquids, vortex, and cyclic irrotational motion, etc. 132 exercises. Bibliography. 3 Appendixes. xii + 264pp. Vol II: motion in viscous liquids, harmonic analysis, theory of tides, etc. 112 exercises. Bibliography. 4 Appendixes. xv + 328pp. Two volume set. 5⅜ x 8.
S724 Vol I Paperbound **$1.75**
S725 Vol II Paperbound **$1.75**
The set **$3.50**

HYDRODYNAMICS, Horace Lamb. Internationally famous complete coverage of standard refer-ence work on dynamics of liquids &. gases. Fundamental theorems, equations, methods, solutions, background, for classical hydrodynamics. Chapters include Equations of Motion, Integration of Equations in Special Gases, Irrotational Motion, Motion of Liquid in 2 Dimen-sions, Motion of Solids through Liquid-Dynamical Theory, Vortex Motion, Tidal Waves, Surface Waves, Waves of Expansion, Viscosity, Rotating Masses of liquids. Excellently planned, ar-ranged; clear, lucid presentation. 6th enlarged, revised edition. Index. Over 900 footnotes, mostly bibliographical. 119 figures. xv + 738pp. 6⅛ x 9¼. S256 Paperbound **$3.75**

HYDRODYNAMICS, H. Dryden, F. Murnaghan, Harry Bateman. Published by the National Research Council in 1932 this enormous volume offers a complete coverage of classical hydrodynamics. Encyclopedic in quality. Partial contents: physics of fluids, motion, turbulent flow, compressible fluids, motion in 1, 2, 3 dimensions; viscous fluids rotating, laminar motion, resistance of motion through viscous fluid, eddy viscosity, hydraulic flow in channels of various shapes, discharge of gases, flow past obstacles, etc. Bibliography of over 2,900 items. Indexes. 23 figures. 634pp. 5⅜ x 8.   S303 Paperbound **$2.75**

Mechanics, dynamics, thermodynamics, elasticity

MECHANICS, J. P. Den Hartog. Already a classic among introductory texts, the M.I.T. professor's lively and discursive presentation is equally valuable as a beginner's text, an engineering student's refresher, or a practicing engineer's reference. Emphasis in this highly readable text is on illuminating fundamental principles and showing how they are embodied in a great number of real engineering and design problems: trusses, loaded cables, beams, jacks, hoists, etc. Provides advanced material on relative motion and gyroscopes not usual in introductory texts. "Very thoroughly recommended to all those anxious to improve their real understanding of the principles of mechanics." MECHANICAL WORLD. Index. List of equations. 334 problems, all with answers. Over 550 diagrams and drawings. ix + 462pp. 5⅜ x 8.
S754 Paperbound **$2.00**

THEORETICAL MECHANICS: AN INTRODUCTION TO MATHEMATICAL PHYSICS, J. S. Ames, F. D. Murnaghan. A mathematically rigorous development of theoretical mechanics for the advanced student, with constant practical applications. Used in hundreds of advanced courses. An unusually thorough coverage of gyroscopic and baryscopic material, detailed analyses of the Coriolis acceleration, applications of Lagrange's equations, motion of the double pendulum, Hamilton-Jacobi partial differential equations, group velocity and dispersion, etc. Special relativity is also included. 159 problems. 44 figures. ix + 462pp. 5⅜ x 8.
S461 Paperbound **$2.25**

THEORETICAL MECHANICS: STATICS AND THE DYNAMICS OF A PARTICLE, W. D. MacMillan. Used for over 3 decades as a self-contained and extremely comprehensive advanced undergraduate text in mathematical physics, physics, astronomy, and deeper foundations of engineering. Early sections require only a knowledge of geometry; later, a working knowledge of calculus. Hundreds of basic problems, including projectiles to the moon, escape velocity, harmonic motion, ballistics, falling bodies, transmission of power, stress and strain, elasticity, astronomical problems. 340 practice problems plus many fully worked out examples make it possible to test and extend principles developed in the text. 200 figures. xvii + 430pp. 5⅜ x 8.   S467 Paperbound **$2.25**

THEORETICAL MECHANICS: THE THEORY OF THE POTENTIAL, W. D. MacMillan. A comprehensive, well balanced presentation of potential theory, serving both as an introduction and a reference work with regard to specific problems, for physicists and mathematicians. No prior knowledge of integral relations is assumed, and all mathematical material is developed as it becomes necessary. Includes: Attraction of Finite Bodies; Newtonian Potential Function; Vector Fields, Green and Gauss Theorems; Attractions of Surfaces and Lines; Surface Distribution of Matter; Two-Layer Surfaces; Spherical Harmonics; Ellipsoidal Harmonics; etc. "The great number of particular cases . . . should make the book valuable to geophysicists and others actively engaged in practical applications of the potential theory," Review of Scientific Instruments. Index. Bibliography. xiii + 469pp. 5⅜ x 8.   S486 Paperbound **$2.50**

THEORETICAL MECHANICS: DYNAMICS OF RIGID BODIES, W. D. MacMillan. Theory of dynamics of a rigid body is developed, using both the geometrical and analytical methods of instruction. Begins with exposition of algebra of vectors, it goes through momentum principles, motion in space, use of differential equations and infinite series to solve more sophisticated dynamics problems. Partial contents: moments of inertia, systems of free particles, motion parallel to a fixed plane, rolling motion, method of periodic solutions, much more. 82 figs. 199 problems. Bibliography. Indexes. xii + 476pp. 5⅜ x 8.   S641 Paperbound **$2.50**

MATHEMATICAL FOUNDATIONS OF STATISTICAL MECHANICS, A. I. Khinchin. Offering a precise and rigorous formulation of problems, this book supplies a thorough and up-to-date exposition. It provides analytical tools needed to replace cumbersome concepts, and furnishes for the first time a logical step-by-step introduction to the subject. Partial contents: geometry & kinematics of the phase space, ergodic problem, reduction to theory of probability, application of central limit problem, ideal monatomic gas, foundation of thermo-dynamics, dispersion and distribution of sum functions. Key to notations. Index. viii + 179pp. 5⅜ x 8.
S147 Paperbound **$1.50**

ELEMENTARY PRINCIPLES IN STATISTICAL MECHANICS, J. W. Gibbs. Last work of the great Yale mathematical physicist, still one of the most fundamental treatments available for advanced students and workers in the field. Covers the basic principle of conservation of probability of phase, theory of errors in the calculated phases of a system, the contributions of Clausius, Maxwell, Boltzmann, and Gibbs himself, and much more. Includes valuable comparison of statistical mechanics with thermodynamics: Carnot's cycle, mechanical definitions of entropy, etc. xvi + 208pp. 5⅜ x 8.   S707 Paperbound **$1.45**

Catalogue of Dover Books

FOUNDATIONS OF POTENTIAL THEORY, O. D. Kellogg. Based on courses given at Harvard this is suitable for both advanced and beginning mathematicians. Proofs are rigorous, and much material not generally avaliable elsewhere is included. Partial contents: forces of gravity, fields of force, divergence theorem, properties of Newtonian potentials at points of free space, potentials as solutions of Laplace's equations, harmonic functions, electrostatics, electric images, logarithmic potential, etc. One of Grundlehren Series. ix + 384pp. 5⅜ x 8.
S144 Paperbound **$2.00**

THERMODYNAMICS, Enrico Fermi. Unabridged reproduction of 1937 edition. Elementary in treatment; remarkable for clarity, organization. Requires no knowledge of advanced math beyond calculus, only familiarity with fundamentals of thermometry, calorimetry. Partial Contents: Thermodynamic systems; First & Second laws of thermodynamics; Entropy; Thermodynamic potentials: phase rule, reversible electric cell; Gaseous reactions: van't Hoff reaction box, principle of LeChatelier; Thermodynamics of dilute solutions: osmotic & vapor pressures, boiling & freezing points; Entropy constant. Index. 25 problems. 24 illustrations. x + 160pp. 5⅜ x 8.
S361 Paperbound **$1.75**

THE THERMODYNAMICS OF ELECTRICAL PHENOMENA IN METALS and A CONDENSED COLLECTION OF THERMODYNAMIC FORMULAS, P. W. Bridgman. Major work by the Nobel Prizewinner: stimulating conceptual introduction to aspects of the electron theory of metals, giving an intuitive understanding of fundamental relationships concealed by the formal systems of Onsager and others. Elementary mathematical formulations show clearly the fundamental thermodynamical relationships of the electric field, and a complete phenomenological theory of metals is created. This is the work in which Bridgman announced his famous "thermomotive force" and his distinction between "driving" and "working" electromotive force. We have added in this Dover edition the author's long unavailable tables of thermodynamic formulas, extremely valuable for the speed of reference they allow. Two works bound as one. Index. 33 figures. Bibliography. xviii + 256pp. 5⅜ x 8. S723 Paperbound **$1.75**

TREATISE ON THERMODYNAMICS, Max Planck. Based on Planck's original papers this offers a uniform point of view for the entire field and has been used as an introduction for students who have studied elementary chemistry, physics, and calculus. Rejecting the earlier approaches of Helmholtz and Maxwell, the author makes no assumptions regarding the nature of heat, but begins with a few empirical facts, and from these deduces new physical and chemical laws. 3rd English edition of this standard text by a Nobel laureate. xvi + 297pp. 5⅜ x 8.
S219 Paperbound **$1.85**

THE MATHEMATICAL THEORY OF ELASTICITY, A. E. H. Love. A wealth of practical illustration combined with thorough discussion of fundamentals—theory, application, special problems and solutions. Partial Contents: Analysis of Strain & Stress, Elasticity of Solid Bodies, Elasticity of Crystals, Vibration of Spheres, Cylinders, Propagation of Waves in Elastic Solid Media, Torsion, Theory of Continuous Beams, Plates. Rigorous treatment of Volterra's theory of dislocations, 2-dimensional elastic systems, other topics of modern interest. "For years the standard treatise on elasticity," AMERICAN MATHEMATICAL MONTHLY. 4th revised edition. Index. 76 figures. xviii + 643pp. 6⅛ x 9¼.
S174 Paperbound **$3.25**

STRESS WAVES IN SOLIDS, H. Kolsky, Professor of Applied Physics, Brown University. The most readable survey of the theoretical core of current knowledge about the propagation of waves in solids, fully correlated with experimental research. Contents: Part I—Elastic Waves: propagation in an extended plastic medium, propagation in bounded elastic media, experimental investigations with elastic materials. Part II—Stress Waves in Imperfectly Elastic Media: internal friction, experimental investigations of dynamic elastic properties, plastic waves and shock waves, fractures produced by stress waves. List of symbols. Appendix. Supplemented bibliography. 3 full-page plates. 46 figures. x + 213pp. 5⅜ x 8½.
S1098 Paperbound **$1.75**

Relativity, quantum theory, atomic and nuclear physics

SPACE TIME MATTER, Hermann Weyl. "The standard treatise on the general theory of relativity" (Nature), written by a world-renowned scientist, provides a deep clear discussion of the logical coherence of the general theory, with introduction to all the mathematical tools needed: Maxwell, analytical geometry, non-Euclidean geometry, tensor calculus, etc. Basis is classical space-time, before absorption of relativity. Partial contents: Euclidean space, mathematical form, metrical continuum, relativity of time and space, general theory. 15 diagrams. Bibliography. New preface for this edition. xviii + 330pp. 5⅜ x 8.
S267 Paperbound **$2.25**

ATOMIC SPECTRA AND ATOMIC STRUCTURE, G. Herzberg. Excellent general survey for chemists, physicists specializing in other fields. Partial contents: simplest line spectra and elements of atomic theory, building-up principle and periodic system of elements, hyperfine structure of spectral lines, some experiments and applications. Bibilography. 80 figures. Index. xii + 257pp. 5⅜ x 8.
S115 Paperbound **$2.00**

SELECTED PAPERS ON QUANTUM ELECTRODYNAMICS, edited by **J. Schwinger.** Facsimiles of papers which established quantum electrodynamics, from initial successes through today's position as part of the larger theory of elementary particles. First book publication in any language of these collected papers of Bethe, Bloch, Dirac, Dyson, Fermi, Feynman, Heisenberg, Kusch, Lamb, Oppenheimer, Pauli, Schwinger, Tomonoga, Weisskopf, Wigner, etc. **34** papers in all, 29 in English, 1 in French, 3 in German, 1 in Italian. Preface and historical commentary by the editor, xvii + 423pp. 6⅛ x 9¼. S444 Paperbound **$2.75**

THE FUNDAMENTAL PRINCIPLES OF QUANTUM MECHANICS, WITH ELEMENTARY APPLICATIONS, E. C. Kemble. An inductive presentation, for the graduate student or specialist in some other branch of physics. Assumes some acquaintance with advanced math; apparatus necessary beyond differential equations and advanced calculus is developed as needed. Although a general exposition of principles, hundreds of individual problems are fully treated, with applications of theory being interwoven with development of the mathematical structure. The author is the Professor of Physics at Harvard Univ. "This excellent book would be of great value to every student . . . a rigorous and detailed mathematical discussion of all of the principal quantum-mechanical methods . . . has succeeded in keeping his presentations clear and understandable," Dr. Linus Pauling, J. of the American Chemical Society. Appendices: calculus of variations, math. notes, etc. Indexes. 611pp. 5⅜ x 8. S472 Paperbound **$3.00**

QUANTUM MECHANICS, H. A. Kramers. A superb, up-to-date exposition, covering the most important concepts of quantum theory in exceptionally lucid fashion. 1st half of book shows how the classical mechanics of point particles can be generalized into a consistent quantum mechanics. These 5 chapters constitute a thorough introduction to the foundations of quantum theory. Part II deals with those extensions needed for the application of the theory to problems of atomic and molecular structure. Covers electron spin, the Exclusion Principle, electromagnetic radiation, etc. "This is a book that all who study quantum theory will want to read," J. Polkinghorne, PHYSICS TODAY. Translated by D. ter Haar. Prefaces, introduction. Glossary of symbols. 14 figures. Index. xvi + 496pp. 5⅜ x 8⅜. S1150 Paperbound **$2.75**

THE THEORY AND THE PROPERTIES OF METALS AND ALLOYS, N. F. Mott, H. Jones. Quantum methods used to develop mathematical models which show interrelationship of basic chemical phenomena with crystal structure, magnetic susceptibility, electrical, optical properties. Examines thermal properties of crystal lattice, electron motion in applied field, cohesion, electrical resistance, noble metals, para-, dia-, and ferromagnetism, etc. "Exposition . . . clear . . . mathematical treatment . . . simple," Nature. 138 figures. Bibliography. Index. xiii + 320pp. 5⅜ x 8. S456 Paperbound **$2.00**

FOUNDATIONS OF NUCLEAR PHYSICS, edited by **R. T. Beyer.** 13 of the most important papers on nuclear physics reproduced in facsimile in the original languages of their authors: the papers most often cited in footnotes, bibliographies. Anderson, Curie, Joliot, Chadwick, Fermi, Lawrence, Cockcroft, Hahn, Yukawa. UNPARALLELED BIBLIOGRAPHY. 122 double-columned pages, over 4,000 articles, books, classified. 57 figures. 288pp. 6⅛ x 9¼. S19 Paperbound **$2.00**

MESON PHYSICS, R. E. Marshak. Traces the basic theory, and explicitly presents results of experiments with particular emphasis on theoretical significance. Phenomena involving mesons as virtual transitions are avoided, eliminating some of the least satisfactory predictions of meson theory. Includes production and study of π mesons at nonrelativistic nucleon energies, contrasts between π and μ mesons, phenomena associated with nuclear interaction of π mesons, etc. Presents early evidence for new classes of particles and indicates theoretical difficulties created by discovery of heavy mesons and hyperons. Name and subject indices. Unabridged reprint. viii + 378pp. 5⅜ x 8. S500 Paperbound **$1.95**

Prices subject to change without notice.

Dover publishes books on art, music, philosophy, literature, languages, history, social sciences, psychology, handcrafts, orientalia, puzzles and entertainments, chess, pets and gardens, books explaining science, intermediate and higher mathematics, mathematical physics, engineering, biological sciences, earth sciences, classics of science, etc. Write to:

Dept. catrr.
Dover Publications, Inc.
180 Varick Street, N.Y. 14, N.Y.